...acted, that to facilitate the transportation of

...to prepare postage stamps, which, when attached

...yment of the postage chargeable on such letter....

Act of Congress, March 3, 1847.

Benjamin Franklin (1706 - 90)
JOSEPH SIFFRED DUPLESSIS
(Courtesy, Hirschl & Adler Galleries, New York, N.Y.)

Benjamin Franklin, the father of the U.S. postal system, appeared on one of our first stamps; George Washington on the other. The two patriots have traditionally been shown on regular stamps ever since.

PICTORIAL
TREASURY
OF
U.S.
STAMPS

PICTORIAL
TREASURY
OF
U.S.
STAMPS

Edited and Published by
Collectors Institute, Ltd.
Omaha, Nebraska

Editor
Elena Marzulla

Associate Editors
Richard Bouma
Duane Hillmer
Rita Lenczowski

Stamp Curator
Arnold H. Beerenstrauch

Art Director
Max E. Watson

Art Production
Larry D. Cahill
Joseph N. Schiro

Typography
Patricia M. Ockrassa

Consultants
Norman S. Hubbard, Ph.D.
Wm. W. Wylie

George Washington (Vaughan Portrait)
GILBERT STUART
National Gallery of Art, Washington, D.C.
Andrew W. Mellon Collection

Printed in the United States of America
by Hillmer Graphics Co., Omaha, Nebraska 68127

Library of Congress Catalogue Card Number 74-15228

TABLE OF CONTENTS

With Appreciation...

"The noblest question in the world is,
What Good may I do in it?"
Poor Richard's Almanack, December, 1737

The dedication applied to the creation of this book by our staff was outstanding. Numerous craftsmen also worked hard to attain their highest level of achievement.

Well-deserving of acknowledgment are the contributing writers, and the following organizations whose cooperation and assistance was significant.

Robert A. Siegel, Inc.
120 East 56th Street
New York, N.Y. 10022

Fidelity Trading Co.
P.O. Box 353
Cypress, Calif. 90630

Daniel F. Kelleher Co., Inc.
40 Court St.
Boston, Mass. 02108

Greg Manning, Inc.
76 So. Orange Ave.
South Orange, N.J. 07079

Palm Springs Stamp Co.
1566 No. Palm Canyon Drive
Palm Springs, Calif. 92262

Smithsonian Institution
Division of Postal History
National Museum of History
and Technology
Washington, D.C. 20560

The National Gallery of Art
Washington, D.C. 20565

Superior Stamp and Coin Co., Inc.
517 W. Seventh St.
Los Angeles, Calif. 90014

U.S. Postal Service
Office of Stamps
Washington, D.C. 20260

Raymond H. Weill Co.
407 Royal St.
New Orleans, La. 70130

Everyone who has a genuine fondness for the stamp hobby — or who is interested in stamps as symbols of our history and culture — would undoubtedly join in our sincere thanks to all who helped produce this volume.

PREFACE

"We will draw the curtain and show you the picture."
William Shakespeare, *Twelfth Night*

This book reveals the color, artistic beauty, and historical content of U.S. postage stamps in a new and exciting way. It is the first book ever published that shows all U.S. stamp designs in color at either 153% of actual size or 250% of actual size.

These enlarged illustrations depict a multitude of details in creative workmanship and design that are usually not perceptible. They also magnify the impact of the postage stamp as a form of graphic art that communicates aspects of our culture to everyone who sees them.

Stamps are diminutive masterpieces of design which depict a host of fascinating subjects. While most entrancing to collectors, they can also be enjoyed by others. As official government issues they are an authentic source of a large amount of knowledge. As a pictorial reference, they provide an amazingly comprehensive portrayal of American life, past and present.

Each design is accompanied by a capsule story that includes information about the subject of the stamp and, where appropriate, the famous work of art that it depicts. Together with the pictures, this text narrates the saga of the U.S. heritage, recalling for all of us the common threads of liberty, courage, and perseverance which wove the fabric of today's United States.

The book also includes a digest of stamp market values at ten-year intervals from 1925 to 1975. This digest — the first of its kind — shows the way in which the value of this art form has appreciated over the past fifty years.

Useful philatelic information includes cities of issue, quantities released or sold, and first days of issue. These notes are especially valuable to collectors.

One of the most significant features of the book is the inclusion of thirteen background articles that cover everything from U.S. postal history to the way in which the stamp illustrations in this book were produced. The first group of articles deals with the historical, cultural, and artistic aspects of stamps. The second group delves into the world of collecting, and the third covers the technical aspects of stamp production, especially those that relate to color and its perception.

Stained glass window, showing an early philatelist.
(Photograph courtesy of Raymond H. Weill Co.)

Color is an exciting phenomenon that adds immeasurably to anyone's appreciation of stamp art and simplifies identification for a collector. Purity of design, pleasing and intricate, may be achieved with the use of a single color, a fact which both early and later stamps exemplify. In addition to color, the art of calligraphy also adds to the charm of stamps.

In all, over 1,300 designs are shown in this array of profound beauty and stimulating color. Through formats of miniature magnificence these designs provide a vivid picture of the United States and its nearly 200-year-old history.

EXPLANATORY NOTES

Besides their obvious artistic elements, stamp designs are affected by shape, size, and their edges, which are usually perforated.

Perforations are small round holes punched in sheets of stamps to facilitate their separation. The stamp shown below is "perf. 11", meaning that 11 concave half-holes can be counted in a 20 millimeter length along each edge. The combination "perf. 10-1/2 x 11" means that 10-1/2 holes were punched horizontally and 11 holes vertically per 20 millimeters.

Sizes of U.S. postage stamps have varied from 15/16" square (page 32) to 2-3/16" x 3-15/16" (page 204). Note below the comparison of design elements, perforated edges, color intensities, and overall sizes of an actual stamp, its typical 153% enlargement, and a 250% enlargement. The actual-size stamp is shown cancelled because U.S. Treasury Department regulations specify that unused stamps be shown in color at 75% or less, or 150% or more, of actual size.

Each stamp subject, generally the first time it appears, is described by an explanatory paragraph. A typical listing includes:

N. George Rogers Clark, 150th anniversary of his victory at Vincennes, which won the Old Northwest for the United States.
Vincennes, Ind.   16,684,674

'35	.06	'55	.16	'75	.35
'45	.06	'65	.24		

The boldface letter keys the caption to a picture of the stamp. The caption includes historical, biographical, or design information. It also lists (in smaller type) the designated city, if any, where the stamp was issued first; the quantity sold; and the approximate market values of the stamp at ten-year intervals.

Some displays are arranged to help the reader identify or compare the many hues, values, and chroma of stamps. Charts on pages 23-25 should be useful, and pages 30, 31, 37, 41, and 202 show various nuances of reddish color.

Light sources are very important to accurate color recognition. Common light sources are sunny daylight, cloudy daylight, incandescent light bulb (yellowish cast), fluorescent warm tube (yellowish), and fluorescent cool tube (bluish). Each causes the same viewer to receive different color impressions.

An index of stamp subjects and other data begins on page 220. Some of the many worthwhile books on U.S. stamps are listed and briefly reviewed on pages 218-19. Additional reference material is indicated on page 15.

Caution About Values

Stamps are priced according to their condition and scarcity (supply and demand). The prices in this book are estimates for uncancelled stamps in "good to fine" condition.

"Very fine" or "superb" stamps include the more valuable specimens which are well-centered, untorn and unrepaired; are near to their original degree of color brightness; have full original gum and no missing perforations; or, if imperforate, have margins (the larger the better) on all four sides (see **F** on page 27). These specimens usually sell at considerably higher prices.

Conversely, market prices are lower when stamps are off-center (i.e., cancelled stamp at lower left), faded, stained, missing perforations, etc.

Actual size stamp, cancelled on first day of issue at a designated city.

Below: 250% enlargement.

Below: 153% enlargement.

N. *2/25/29*

N. *2/25/29*

The date below the illustration is the first day of issue. Regular style type indicates a 153% reproduction.

The use of italic type for the issue date indicates a 250% reproduction.

U.S. POSTAL HISTORY

By Carl H. Scheele

Curator of Postal History, National Museum of History and Technology, Smithsonian Institution

That colorful artifact, the postage stamp, is but one product of an extremely large and intricate organization created to facilitate the exchange of written communications. The postal service was so commonplace in America for two hundred years that until recently its story has been largely neglected. Happily, in the last few years there has been a

The world's first adhesive postage stamp, issued by Great Britain in conjunction with the postal reform of 1840. Queen Victoria is shown.

growing awareness by historians of the importance of the American postal service, and an increasing number of scholarly and well-written popular publications have appeared.

Transformation of the historically democratic American postal system to a buttoned-down business in 1970 was unique in the nation's experience. It instantly stimulated fresh curiosity about post office origins, growth, and character.

Since the first simple postal services were established by the more prosperous and populated colonies in the 17th century, Americans have enjoyed the benefits of a democratically operated mail system. Even during the period of direct Parliamentary control, from 1707 until the Revolutionary War, Americans themselves managed the daily post office business, served as postmasters and clerks, and carried the mails on horseback. Under the guiding hand of the occasionally brilliant but always shrewd native son, Benjamin Franklin, service in the colonies developed into a vital necessity for the conduct of commerce, the carriage of newspapers, and the exchange of correspondence.

Before the new U.S. Postal Service was created in 1970 the last sweeping organizational change occurred in 1775, when the Continental Congress assumed responsibility for postal communications in the Thirteen Colonies. This action supplanted the royal mails, which had virtually ceased to function. For nearly two centuries this postal organization continued with little basic change except its formalization by the Act of 1792.

This is not to say that American mail service was static. Beginning with President Andrew Jackson's administration, the organization became thoroughly responsive to the political needs of the party in power. In the long run this grass roots foundation made the post office more sensitive to the requirements of the

people than it would have been under more conservative arrangements.

But in many respects the most significant result was a sophisticated philosophical concept developed by the officials and politicians who charted the course of the old department; namely, the principle that the foremost goal of the postal system was to provide the public with the best possible service. Although difficult to attain and not shared by all officials or legislators, this ideal nevertheless dominated policy for nearly a century. Those who did not place this idea in the first rank at least advanced the reasonable hope that the mails should pay their own way, with revenues equaling or surpassing expenditures whenever possible.

The fruits of the service-first leaders who implemented this policy are seen in the postal rate reforms of 1845, 1851, 1863, and 1883. The reform of 1845 — inspired largely by the British postal reform of 1840 — is perhaps the most significant. It drastically reduced the cost of sending a letter, and laid the groundwork for subsequent rate reductions, a pattern so firmly fixed that it was not reversed until the second quarter of the 20th century.

Mailed pieces showing three types of mail service: Blood's Penny Post, local delivery to the post office; the Pony Express; illustrated mining cover (Smithsonian Institution, Washington, D.C.).

The high cost of sending letters before 1845 — as high as 25c for a single sheet traveling more than 400 miles — is sharply emphasized by noting that letters eventually could be sent anywhere in the U.S. for 3c per half ounce in 1863, and for 2c in 1883.

These rock-bottom rates made it difficult to achieve a balanced postal budget, and following the first reform in 1845, postal deficits were reported in all but 16 years of the ensuing century.

Nevertheless, the service-first philosophy retained its vigor. In the 19th century the expense of providing mail service to the Old South and the newly developing western states and territories was enormous. Heavy newspaper mails, transported partly free and partly under token rates, imposed a further financial drain. Postal officials generally placed mail transport contracts with the most efficient but highest priced carriers — the railroads — over routes connecting principal population centers.

The service-first philosophy is also evident in the numerous innovations attempted in the hundred years following 1845. Major improvements were introduced, and a record of public service probably unmatched by any other Federal agency was compiled. The list is impressive: domestic registry service (1855), uniform nationwide 3c letter postage (1863), free city delivery (1863), domestic money order service (1864), 1c postal cards (1873), 2c letter postage (1883), special delivery (1885), rural free delivery (1896), a postal savings banking system (1911), and parcel post (1913). Each of these innovations created a profound impact which

Upper left: The Meeting of the Ways, *color drawing by Stanley M. Arthurs.*

Center left: Specialized self-propelled vehicle for early parcel post delivery. It could be loaded from the top, the sides, and the front (Smithsonian Institution, Washington, D.C.).

Lower left: Fast mail train with typical railway post office of the 1870s. (Library of Congress, Washington, D.C.).

Right: 1861 Wells Fargo broadside advertising the services of the Pony Express to New York residents.

PONY EXPRESS !

CHANGE OF TIME!   REDUCED RATES!

10 Days to San Francisco!

LETTERS

WILL BE RECEIVED AT THE

OFFICE, 84 BROADWAY,

NEW YORK,

Up to **4** P. M. every TUESDAY,

AND

Up to **2½** P. M. every SATURDAY,

Which will be forwarded to connect with the PONY EXPRESS leaving ST. JOSEPH, Missouri,

Every WEDNESDAY and SATURDAY at 11 P. M.

TELEGRAMS

Sent to Fort Kearney on the mornings of MONDAY and FRIDAY, will connect with **PONY** leaving St. Joseph, WEDNESDAYS and SATURDAYS.

EXPRESS CHARGES.

LETTERS weighing half ounce or under $1 00
For every additional half ounce or fraction of an ounce   1 00
In all cases to be enclosed in 10 cent Government Stamped Envelopes,
And all Express CHARGES Pre-paid.

☞ PONY EXPRESS ENVELOPES For Sale at our Office.

WELLS, FARGO & CO., Ag'ts.

New York, July 1, 1861.

was keenly felt at the time but is now perhaps accepted as the ordinary, the expected, the mundane.

For example, around 1911 the postal savings system stimulated as much debate in print as did the introduction of bobbed hair and short skirts a decade later. Established in a period of national financial instability and bank failures, it created a steadying influence on the country's banking practices. It provided millions of immigrants and native poor with a reliable means of securing the precious personal savings which stood between these citizens and the poorhouse or the gutter. When postal savings were ended in 1966 there was hardly a ripple in the public media.

In addition to the special services, the post office made every effort to reduce the time of delivery and to improve the security of the mails. The nation's steamboat lines were pressed into mail service, as were the railroads, which rapidly became the dominant method of moving long-distance mails. In 1918 the department inaugurated the first public-service air mail system on a regularly scheduled basis. Since there were no adequately equipped commercial airlines at that time, the post office developed special aircraft, plus an elaborate system of airways and airports across the country to insure the most efficient service possible.

Although top-level management remained in the grip of political fortune until 1970, the large supervisory work force was gradually placed on a competitive foundation. This provided the system with stability and the beneficial influence of an experienced, professional staff; i.e., the important position of General Superintendent of the Railway Mail Service. This office came to control the movement of most mail in the years following the Civil War, and was invariably filled by a postal veteran with a broad knowledge of both post office practice and the national transportation system.

The tasks confronting America's postal work force were profoundly difficult. The population increased dramatically with every decade, the nation's settled territory expanded rapidly in irregular geographic patterns, and there was steady growth and increasing complexity in urban areas. Probably no other nation faced these problems on the dimensions present in America. Few if any solved the resulting postal problems as well. The highly political and basically democratic postal service of the U.S. had provided its citizens with a dependable and efficient system of communications for their commercial, public, and personal requirements for nearly two hundred years.

At right, various unusual post office facilities.
Top: *Anaktuvuk Post Office, Alaska*
Center: *Cedar Stump Post Office, Washington*
Bottom: *Ladies Only Section of New York City Post Office, 1827*
(Smithsonian Institution, Washington, D.C.)

STAMPS SEEN AS A CULTURAL EXCHANGE PROGRAM

By Norman Hirschl
Director, Hirschl & Adler Galleries

One stamp, journeying within a country or beyond its borders on an envelope, provides one of the world's most effective mediums of cultural exchange.

Almost every country in the world has used the postage stamp as a form of visual communication. Stamps depicting the fine arts — chiefly painting — make it possible for both the student and the layman to enrich their understanding of the culture of the world.

Belgium, for example, has issued stamps which portray the paintings of the Flemish masters. Spain has shown us works by Goya and El Greco. France has issued stamps that honor Renoir, Monet, and other impressionists. In the United States, stamps depicting works by Gilbert Stuart, Charles Willson Peale, and John Trumbull recall the early years of American history and art — an era in which the nation's first great artists painted its first great heroes.

Today the fine arts are so international that great works are often shown by the country that owns them, or by any country. One example would be a 1967 U.S. stamp which depicts *Madonna and Child* by Memling, an artist of German origin (see p. 146). The original is in the National Gallery of Art. Another would be a stamp issued by Czechoslovakia in 1966 that portrays *Guernica*, a work by Spanish artist Pablo Picasso that hangs in The Museum of Modern Art in New York.

Through stamps such as these and others we can reconstruct each era in European art since the 13th and 14th century frescoes of Giotto. A mini-exhibition of such stamps might include Fra Angelico's *Archangel Gabriel,* painted c. 1425 and shown on a stamp issued by Spain in 1956; Albrecht Dürer's *Praying Hands,* created c. 1500 and shown on a stamp issued by Canada in 1966; Rubens' *Children* and Van Dyck's *Daughter of Charles I,* painted in the 17th century and shown on stamps issued by Belgium in 1964; many Rembrandt portraits shown on stamps of the Netherlands, and Watteau's *Gillis,* an 18th century work shown on a stamp of Monaco.

The fruitful 19th century has yielded works by the early English impressionists Constable and Turner, the French impressionists, and the post-impressionists Cézanne, Van Gogh, and Gauguin. In the 20th century, every major artist from Picasso to Chagall has left an indelible imprint on the stamps of the world. A modest collection of such stamps would afford anyone a comprehensive art course and a cultural exchange of ideas.

Raphael's School of Athens, *shown above, was painted in 1509. It is part of the Stanza della Segnatura in the Vatican. In 1974 a detail from this work was reproduced on the U.S. stamp shown at left.*

Letters mingle souls
Donne
Raphael
10c US

SELECTING STAMP SUBJECTS

By Gordon C. Morison
Director, Office of Stamps, U. S. Postal Service

Depending on where you sit, stamp subject selection American-style is either a curse or a blessing. In this Republic of ours, anybody can suggest a stamp subject, and the volume of our mail sometimes makes us wonder if everyone isn't.

There are, among philatelists and other critics of stamp art, those who would have a select design group do the choosing. Some, in fact, would rather that outstanding art be acquired first, then find a way to justify putting it on a stamp.

Fortunately, that isn't the way it is done in our country. The subject comes first. Everyone can suggest a subject for a stamp simply by writing a letter to the Postmaster General, Washington, D.C. 20260.

The U.S. grass roots approach was refined significantly in 1957 with the establishment of the Citizens' Stamp Advisory Committee, whose members include historians, artists, businessmen, stamp collectors, and others who have a deep interest in the American heritage. It is the responsibility of this committee to recommend stamp issuances to the Postmaster General, and it is he who makes the final decision on each stamp.

In order to make recommendations, however, the committee must evaluate literally thousands of suggestions from the public each year. There are a number of rules that the committee follows as it goes about its task. A few of these are:

— No living person shall be honored by portrayal on any United States postage stamp.
— All postage stamps, including commemoratives honoring individuals, will be issued preferably on significant anniversaries of their births and not before ten years after their deaths. Exceptions are memorial issues honoring recently deceased Presidents of the United States.
— Commemorative postage stamps of historical significance shall be considered for issuance on even-date anniversaries, preferably starting with the 50th year and continuing at 50-year intervals.
— Only themes and events of widespread national appeal will be considered as subjects for postage stamps.

Not all finished designs are approved by the Postmaster General, but it is a tribute to the conscientiousness of the committee and the quality of the artists who receive commissions that relatively few recommended stamps are turned down.

Each commemorative is produced in quantities of at least 140 million stamps. As a communicating vehicle, they have considerable impact. Following the issuance of the "Donate Blood" stamp (see p. 164), the president of the American Association of Blood Banks attributed to this stamp the fact that there was no major blood shortage for six months, despite the fact two holidays occurred during this period.

We go to considerable lengths to promote stamp collecting as a hobby, and, in fact, the U.S. Postal Service is the world's largest producer of hobby goods. This benefits not only the Postal Service — for sales to collectors provide significant revenues to offset costs of operating the Postal Service — but the whole of the hobby industry.

But we never lose sight of the fact that the purpose of the stamp is prepayment of postage. It must serve this function as well. It must be coated with a luminescent tagging that will activate our mail processing equipment, and, for special services, it must be of a distinctive design or color.

Another distinctly American factor in our stamp subject selection process is that our stamps are produced with all postal customers in mind — not just the philatelists. We are just as concerned about the customer who simply wants to dress up envelopes as we are about philatelists finding favor with stamps purchased for their collections.

The stamp that accomplishes its key role in the moving of the mails while managing to educate, to commemorate, and to focus attention on national concerns with attractive artwork and design is a good stamp.

STAMP SUBJECTS	QUANTITY OF STAMP ISSUES				
	25	50	75	100	
Agriculture					
Architecture					
Arts					134
Communication					
Conservation - Nature					
Exploration					
Famous People					290
Flags					
Historical					213
Industry - Labor					
Military					
Organizations					
Postal History					
Professions					
Science					
Scenic Views					
Space - Aviation					
Special Events - Topics					
Sports					
Transportation					

The above chart groups U.S. stamps according to their subject matter. Stamps were counted twice when they relate to more than one topic (i.e., a historical commemorative depicted by a work of art).

POSTAGE STAMP DESIGN

By Stevan Dohanos
Chairman, Citizens' Stamp Advisory Committee, U.S. Postal Service

The next time you use a United States postage stamp on a letter or package look at it closely. An American artist of recognized ability has spent many hours and days of effort transforming that small oblong of paper into an eye-catching design. He has solved a design problem featuring the price of the stamp, its title, and the name of the issuing country. He has rendered the pictorial theme as strongly and as tastefully as he can in the smallest area in which he has ever worked. In some cases all of these ingredients are arranged in an area of less than one square inch. It is truly Art in Miniature. It is an extremely difficult task, but artists love the challenge and rise to it.

Designers are selected from an up-to-date nationwide talent file. The U.S. Postal Service prides itself in the fact that several hundred free-lance artists have performed well as designers since the program of buying art from the professional art world began in 1957. Prior to that time the visual treatment was executed by the staff of the Bureau of Engraving and Printing.

Designed by John Carter Jones, this 1965 commemorative portrays a detail from The Copley Family *by John Singleton Copley. The detail shows the artist's daughter, Elizabeth Clarke Copley.*

Robert J. Jones designed this commemorative, which portrays The Boating Party *by Mary Cassatt.*

Let's follow a new stamp proposal from the moment its theme has been approved by the Postmaster General. This stamp issue will be one of about twenty released in a twelve-month period. Art members of the Stamp Advisory Committee are generally delegated to seek the artist best suited to design the subject. For example, one artist may be skilled in painting wildlife, another may execute architectural subjects with ease and authority. In some cases the subject matter is not literal. Many stamps simply require a knowledge of typography and the skillful use of graphics and color.

It is generally a great surprise and pleasure when an artist is invited to do his first design. Even though he has had wide exposure in the national print media, a postage stamp represents a new challenge. The client is the U.S.A., and an artist is invariably proud to use his talent to reach this huge new audience.

Months in advance of the issuance of a new stamp, an art member of the Citizens' Stamp Advisory Committee confers in person with the selected designer, who is given the requirements and job specifics for the stamp he is designing. From preliminary sketches he begins to plan his design in the designated color or colors. Several sketches are developed, each about five times the size of the final stamp. After the sketches are reviewed by the stamp committee a final design is selected and rendered by the artist at about ten times actual size. All historical detail is carefully checked, for the public responds to the slightest error.

In many cases existing art from our great art museums is available to the Postal Service, as well as archive material from special national or private collections. In these cases a designer who is an expert on typography is selected. He reduces the art to stamp size and adds the proper typography, creating a harmonious arrangement.

Fortunately, we do not pay by the square inch. All artists are paid the same fair fee regardless of their professional status or reputation.

In addition to the satisfaction he receives from seeing his design appear in stamp form, the artist is honored at the issuing ceremonies, where he receives a leather bound album. Only a few of these are presented and the first one is always designated for the President of the United States.

After a stamp is in daily use the artist receives mail from a new segment of people. There are now an estimated 20 million stamp collectors and they are an appreciative audience. They are also ardent letter writers. The broad public, too, is becoming increasingly aware that the small adhesive stamp is not only moving the mail but is also a showcase that communicates our noblest aims and goals. Stamps tell the story of America to ourselves and the world. The purchase of a stamp is also the purchase of a work of art.

Note: The six paintings on these pages are reproduced courtesy of the National Gallery of Art, Washington, D.C.

George Washington. Designed by Bill Hyde, from a portrait by Rembrandt Peale.

John Jay. Designed by C. R. Chickering and V. S. McCloskey, Jr., from a portrait by Gilbert Stuart.

Alexander Hamilton. Designed by Chickering and McCloskey from a portrait by John Trumbull.

Andrew Jackson. Designed by Lester Beal from a portrait by Thomas Sully.

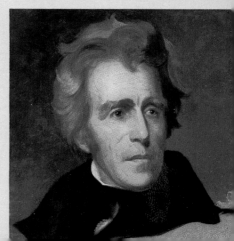

STAMPS: A MIRROR OF HISTORY

By Elena Marzulla

The relationship between our history and stamps is intimate, interesting, and in many ways unique.

The United States was the first nation in the world to show pictures of historical personages of the past upon its postage stamps. The first stamps issued by the United States government in 1847 depicted two great figures of the Revolutionary era, Benjamin Franklin and George Washington.

These two stamps, issued in a year that also marked the sixtieth anniversary of the signing of our Constitution, set two precedents which paved the way for future stamps depicting pages of our history. They were the first adhesives in the world to portray anybody other than a living monarch (in 1840 Queen Victoria was shown on the world's first stamp). They established a tradition that is now a law, whereby: "No portrait shall be placed upon any...postal currency of the United States, while the original of such portrait is living." (U.S. Postal Laws, Act of April 7, 1866.)

From 1847 until the Civil War only Franklin, Washington, and another architect of American democracy, Thomas Jefferson, were shown on our stamps. But in the wake of the War Between the States and its aftermath new subjects were added. In 1863, one of our most popular early presidents, Andrew Jackson, first appeared on a stamp, and in 1866 a simple black adhesive was released which portrayed Abraham Lincoln, our sixteenth president. Lincoln died one year prior to the issue of this stamp, and because of this many people think the stamp was a memorial, though it was not classified as such.

If the Lincoln stamp was a forerunner of memorial issues, the pictorials of 1869 were the forerunners of modern stamps depicting everything from historic sites and monuments to the lunar rover. The pictorials, issued in the same year that our first transcontinental railroad was completed, were the first to use anything but portraiture to dramatize our history on stamps. Among other things, the designs portrayed a locomotive, an ocean steamship, a postrider, the flag, the landing of Columbus, and John Trumbull's celebrated painting, *The Declaration of Independence.*

In 1893, when the Columbian Exposition Issue was released, another milestone was achieved. These sixteen stamps, the first official United States commemoratives, paid homage to Christopher Columbus in connection with the 400th anniversary of his discovery of North America in 1492. They also set the stage for hundreds of future stamps related to our history.

Today, United States stamps are truly touchstones to our nation's past. For Americans and non-Americans alike, they reflect the hopes and dreams, the struggles and the aspirations which have helped produce our way of life. From familiar figures and events to more obscure occurrences, they provide a wealth of material which mirrors our history.

Note: Ms. Marzulla edited the first editions of *United States Stamps and Stories* and *Canada Stamps and Stories,* published for the U.S. Postal Service and the Canada Post, respectively.

Above: A 1968 commemorative recreates a portion of The Battle of Bunker's Hill *by John Trumbull. The original is reproduced at left (Yale University Art Gallery).*

COLLECTING INSTINCTS AND THEIR FULFILLMENT

By Duane Hillmer
President of Collectors Institute, Ltd.

Personal satisfaction, achieved in one's own way, is a result often obtained by people who form collections. They begin and continue for many diverse reasons. Popularity of collecting has been evident for centuries; activities of millions involve their particular quests.

Acquirement is related to self - preservation, a prime instinct in nearly everyone. Thrift has been extolled throughout time as a virtue, and "saving things" is a long - standing practice. This doesn't explain the affinity — much less the affection — for collecting.

Accumulation may be classed as collecting in a semantic sense, but as a hobby or occupation collecting includes more than gathering objects. There is the important added element of logical arrangement or grouping, varied by wishes or whims of the individual. Creativity is prominent in this phase of the activity.

Ready availability is one advantage enjoyed by the many people who collect rocks, coins, glass, books — or stamps. The beauty of things in each of these groups is more important to collectors than their comparatively large supply. Mere ease of acquisition doesn't explain why affluent persons or prominent leaders of many countries have collected stamps. It is a hobby with recreational aspects for all, but at the same time productive enough to satisfy the many people who dislike wasting time even in an avocation.

Collectors look for the interesting, the unusual, the beautiful, and from the results of their finds they get knowledge and a feeling of accomplishment. Inner satisfaction stems from all of these, plus the joy of creativity, and another sensation — thinking to one's self: "I've finished the work!" (The collection is completed.) This conclusion in stamp collecting is rather as rare as some of the stamps.

Young people collect when their curiosity is aroused; collecting and its activities of hunting and discovery are good outlets for energetic exuberance. In later years a return to collecting recalls bygone pleasures, and youthful frustrations are supplanted with new satisfactions. Dollars spent on a classic rare stamp are especially gratifying to one who recalls a boyhood limit of thirty cents a week for the stamp hobby.

Nostalgia may be a significant factor to a collector. Love of history, reverence for the past, the desire to learn and become better educated — these associated motives bring many to collecting hobbies. Stamps are one of the most readily and cheaply available of a multitude of historically related articles to collect. One of the nicest stamp collections I ever saw was formed for far less than a hundred dollars. It combined a beautiful stamp, depicting the landing of Columbus (see pp. 22, 38), with about 80 cancellations. It's possible to find this Columbian Exposition stamp with different

Collectibles above reveal beauty from various cultural heritages. Two artifacts (c. 100 B.C.) are shown at right rear. Paintings, books, coins, stamps, glass, and china have many devotees. Also popular are many items collected from nature, such as rocks, leaves, butterflies, etc.

postmarks from places whose names relate to Columbus. Such a collection would be an unusual, inexpensive, interesting, attractive, and satisfying creation.

Perhaps of all the motives ascribed to collecting, the prospect of financial gain is the most involved. Collectors often disdain this as a reason for collecting, and many are sincere when they scoff at increasing values of collections. Most are pleased with ascending values, but dislike appearing concerned about them. That seems as illogical as believing it is wrong to enjoy one's work; because one is paid to do something doesn't preclude the service from being pleasurable.

It is inaccurate to categorize collectors as loners or companion seekers; there are ample opportunities for either. Many collectors describe eloquently their collections and their work upon them as fulfilling otherwise lonely times. Some extoll the personal associations and cooperative activities derived from stamp clubs, meetings, exhibitions, pen pals, etc.

Goethe (1749 - 1832), a famous German philosopher, was asked in one of his later years to estimate how much total time in his long life he thought he had known happiness. He replied that it was perhaps only about forty hours. Then he discerned between happiness and contentment, a more readily attainable condition.

Whatever the original motivation, a collector soon probes for more knowledge of his chosen items. Learning becomes fun, which doesn't make it less valuable. During the progression of an individual's search there are many chances for satisfaction, pleasure, contentment — and even occasional moments of happiness.

THE NAME OF A HOBBY — STAMPS OR RARE STAMPS

By Raymond Weill
Specialist in Rare Stamps

If every collectible postage stamp were issued in large quantities, and all of them, even the oldest ones, were easily and cheaply available, philately might not be either the "king of hobbies" or the "hobby of kings".

Indeed there are many purists in our ranks, who tell us they collect in the abstract — stamps for the sake of the stamp alone, its beauty or lack of it, to the exclusion of scarcity or value. Most aficionados, by choice or not, limit their expenditures, thereby excluding valuable specimens from their holdings. But it is the rare individual whose eyes do not glow when he reads the magic words "rare stamps", whose heart does not skip a beat when his mediocre stamp suddenly appears to be unusual — possibly of great value.

We love all stamps. The philatelist aims at completeness, which means he wants the "commoners" along with the noblest varieties. We would like to lend special attention to limited issues, called "rarities", and those of extra appeal in that area — errors. Errors are "slips". Stamps are intended to be made as planned — perfect examples. If by production deviations the center of a two-color stamp were inverted, we might have an airplane doing stunt-flying, upside-down, as happened with our own United States 24c stamp of the 1918 issue. Just one sheet of 100 subjects was issued with the Jenny doing upside-down antics. Thus we have an error, a rarity, and an item of great value.

The most valuable stamps are not solely the errors. Perhaps more important are the limited issues. Some earlier varieties were printed in small numbers; even fewer exist today. In some instances only one or two examples are known to exist. The famous "Penny Magenta" of British Guiana is a one-cent stamp released in 1856 of which but a single specimen is known. In 1969 at a New York auction this stamp realized $280,000.00, the highest price a single stamp has ever brought. *The Guinness Book of Records* cites this and also tells us that the record for a single philatelic item was the sum of $380,000.00 paid in 1968 for an envelope bearing two examples of the one penny stamp issued in 1847 by the British colony of Mauritius.

In recent years many rare stamps have realized up to $100,000.00 or more. The 2c Hawaiian "Missionary" of 1851 has exceeded that figure at least twice. The previously mentioned United States airmail of 1918 with inverted center in perfect condition sells for $40,000.00 or more, even though one hundred specimens are believed to exist.

Collect stamps. Love and cherish stamps. Your budget need not be unlimited, for there is always the joy of collecting for fun, knowledge, and enlightenment, with that little extra — the possibility of discovering another Penny Magenta or a previously unrecorded 2c Hawaiian "Missionary".

The unique 1c British Guiana sold for $280,000 in 1969.

The $47,000 inverted airplane.

This philatelic gem brought $380,000 in 1968.

Another rare U.S. invert.

These Swiss 1845 Geneva stamps, transposed from their usual positions, sold recently for $36,000.00. A normal "Double Geneva" commands $18,000.

The famous 2c Hawaiian "Missionary" has realized over $100,000 twice.

THE ECONOMIC POTENTIAL OF POSTAGE STAMPS

By Norman S. Hubbard, Ph.D.
Professor of Economics, Brooklyn College

In addition to educational, artistic, and recreational aspects, postage stamps have a significant economic character; some are important financial assets.

Stamps reflect accurate values with attributes of international mediums of exchange. They are traded on markets where worldwide buyers and sellers compete. They can be converted at will into almost any currency to retain their value in terms of foreign exchange, a protection against devaluation of money.

Stamps are easily stored, transportable, and negotiable. These convenient qualities are ideal for holding wealth in a form quickly movable if necessary, with little chance of discovery and theft. In the 1930s fleeing refugees frequently lost all their wealth except what they had with them. Stamps served their owners well then, and still provide such emergency insurance.

When prices rise, quality stamps increase with everything else; they are a hedge against inflation when assets such as bank accounts and bonds with fixed dollar terms have diminished purchasing power. Price increases at least comparable with general increases have made stamps retain their real value.

In addition to underlying advantages, stamps must be evaluated from the two fundamental dimensions of all assets — the rate of return and the risk.

Price trends with an impressive pattern of individual increases can be seen in the pictorial section of this book. An average annual rate of return of eight to ten percent is attainable on fine postage stamps. This return is capital gain when stamps are sold; no taxes are paid until gains by sale are realized. Stamps do not produce income during ownership, but can yield great pleasure and other nonpecuniary rewards.

The demand for fine stamps grows as the number of collectors increases. More leisure time encourages hobbies, and higher incomes provide necessary funds. An added demand comes from investors who are becoming more aware of the potential of stamps.

With more demand there is a diminishing supply of fine stamps, producing price increases. When printing is completed stamps become nonreproducible objects.

Each year some are lost through neglect, carelessness, or disasters. Some are permanently removed from sale by placement in museums and libraries.

Large numbers of common stamps have little or no price rises, and many decrease in recovery value. Much of their price is labor cost of handling. They are a recreational expense; their recovery value is a bonus beyond the pleasure received. Manipulated stamps, created and promoted by opportunists for short-term gain, seldom achieve permanent recognition.

Established stamps in limited quantity and top condition are blue chip investment assets. Their labor cost is insignificant, and any minus gap between buying and selling prices will be relatively small. High quality assures demand at the time of sale. Poor-quality stamps are difficult to sell even at discounts. A well-formed quality collection will show a substantial rate of return.

The other major dimension of assets is risk, i.e., the likelihood of having to sell at less than cost. This risk is large for common stamps where labor costs may swamp other considerations. Scarce quality stamps have not had great downside risk. In the depression of the '30s stamps retained more value than most assets.

Market stability is enhanced by the infrequency of fads in philately. Most stamps are desired to attain certain objectives in collections. There is usually not a tremendous surge for one particular stamp at any given moment followed by the inevitable collapse. Stamps keep approximately the same relative standing within their areas so prices are internally consistent. Some collectibles have a style, period, or artist in vogue at one moment, but are discarded and forgotten the next.

Added strength in the market is provided by professionals with faith in the future of stamps, who will purchase virtually any good stamps. Like specialists in the stock market, they buy in areas of temporary excess and sell in areas of heavy demand. The moderate volume of fine stamps sold each year helps to maintain an orderly market.

Postage stamps of high caliber and quality offer the prospect of a substantial rate of return with little risk of capital loss. They qualify for serious consideration as a type of asset to be held by investors.

Adjoining stamps as shown above are called tête-bêche. *This rare pair of France is valued in excess of $50,000.*

Actual stamp size is less than one square inch. Sold for over $17,000.

5c U.S. stamp issued in 1925. Value now about $8.00.

THE EVOLUTION OF U.S. STAMP COLLECTING

By David Lidman

Chairman, Philatelic Advisory Panel, American Revolution Bicentennial Administration

There's a tradition that Great Britain's release of the world's first postage stamp in 1840 inspired a young woman to accumulate some 16,000 used copies of the Penny Black and Two Pence Blue and cover the walls of her dressing room with them. She's been called the world's first stamp collector.

Certainly, the acquisitive urge is innate, and when adhesive stamps were introduced there must have been many who "saved" them because they were something new and different or were released with governmental authority. Inevitably this artless accumulation of interesting bits of printed paper became what we know today as stamp collecting.

From its simple beginnings over 130 years ago stamp collecting has now assumed mature stature as an avocation the world over, with millions of enthusiastic devotees, a well organized commercial structure, and an extensive literature. Though conceived for the utilitarian purpose of indicating prepayment of postage, the adhesive stamp has become a recognized medium for publicity, and production of stamps for sale to collectors is an accepted element of postal routine in nearly all the world's countries.

When relatively few stamps existed, little more than simple accumulation was possible. But by 1860 something like 2,000 different postal adhesives had been issued by 85 postal administrations, and classification by country of origin, physical differences, and colors superseded casual "stamp saving".

Those who were studying stamps instead of simply accumulating them felt that this activity ought to have a distinctive name. Late in 1863 Georges Herpin of Paris proposed *philately* as a suitable name for the study of postage stamps. He coined the word by combining Greek words implying an affection for things on which taxes had been paid. Although his etymology is considered rather fanciful in many ways, *philately* caught on and is today universally recognized as the formal name for all avocational activity involving stamps.

The pronunciation of the "highbrow" name for the hobby has often perplexed newcomers in stamp collecting, but it's essentially simple. "Phil" is always pronounced with a short "i" as in Philadelphia. "Lat" is pronounced as the "lat" in latter. When used as a noun the accent is on the second syllable, but when used as an adjective (philatelic) the accent is on the third syllable.

At about the same time stamp collecting acquired a formal name, Dr. J. A. Legrand of Paris proposed a system for classifying the perforations along which single stamps are separated from the printed sheets. He suggested that perforations be classified by the number of "teeth" in the space of two centimeters. To eliminate the chore of measuring and counting, Doctor Legrand suggested use of a card with rows of dots in different spacings which the collector could match with the perforations on a stamp he was

Examples of popular philatelic items commonly collected in addition to single stamps appear below. Pictured (clockwise from upper right): a block of four, an American commemorative stamp panel, a souvenir card, and three first day covers.

Postal stationery includes a broad spectrum of interesting varieties of postal cards, envelopes collected as entires or cut squares, air letter sheets (aerogrammes), and covers with cancelled stamps, addressee and sender usually shown (see p. 1).

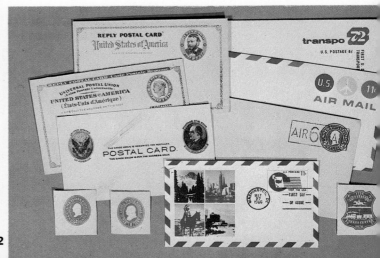

measuring. Perforations are still classified by the system proposed by Doctor Legrand in 1866, and they are still measured by some form of the perforation gauge he invented (see p. 24).

The world's first stamp album appeared in 1862, published by Justin Lallier of Paris in editions sold in England as well as in France. In 1863 a stamp album was published by D. Appleton & Co. in New York City.

Stamp dealers appeared on the philatelic scene as systematic collecting replaced casual accumulation. In Belgium, 19-year-old Jean B. Moens began collecting stamps in 1848, and in 1852, he was selling stamps to his fellow collectors. In England in 1856 young E. Stanley Gibbons set up shop as a stamp dealer in his father's pharmacy in Plymouth.

Since individuals seek the company of those who share their interests, organizations of stamp collectors came into being promptly. There was one in Paris as early as 1865, and stamp collectors in New York City formed a club in 1867. In England the London Philatelic Society was formally organized in 1869. Today, it's the prestigious Royal Philatelic Society of London, enjoying royal patronage because of the interest the late King George V took in its affairs.

During the 1870s clubs of stamp collectors were organized in Boston, Chicago, Providence, and other large cities. On September 14, 1886, what is now the American Philatelic Society was organized, with John K. Tiffany of St. Louis as its first president. It has more than 30,000 members on its roster today.

The Collectors Club of New York came into being in 1896. Since 1937 it has occupied its own clubhouse in New York City. The Society of Philatelic Americans, another prominent organization, was founded around 1890. It was originally called the Southern Philatelic Association.

Today, clubs of stamp collectors flourish in all sections of the country. There are no less than a dozen state and regional federations of stamp clubs, and scores of organizations of collectors with specialized philatelic interests.

William P. Brown seems to have been the first stamp dealer in the United States, first doing business in City Hall Park, New York City, where he displayed boards on which the stamps he had for sale were pinned.

In 1861 John Walter Scott came to the United States, bringing with him the stamp collection he had formed in England. Brown suggested he go into the stamp business. Within a decade young Scott was one of this country's most active dealers.

In 1867 he began issuing the monthly price lists which became the *Scott Standard Postage Stamp Catalogue*. The first of some 30 different albums to bear his imprint was published in 1868. In 1870 Scott held the world's first auction sale of stamps in New York City, and in 1872 he took stock to England where it was sold at the first stamp auction in London. He was one of the founders of the Collectors Club and was its librarian when he died in 1919.

Scott, who has been called the Father of American Philately, was a prime mover in the organization of this country's first exhibition, staged in 1889 in the Eden Musee, New York City, by members of the

Printed albums for U.S. stamps range from introductory kits to comprehensive volumes with spaces for every recognized variety of U.S. postal paper. A selection of popular stamp albums and kits is shown below.

Exhibitions, whether local or international, competitive or not, enable hobbyists to share the fruits of their avocation. Shown below is a typical page that might be shown at an exhibition, along with an overall view of the noncompetitive Anphilex exhibition, held in New York City in 1971.

Brooklyn Philatelic Club, the National Philatelic Society, and the Staten Island Philatelic Society. One of the exhibitors in this show was Charles B. Corwin, who in 1851 had paid $1,010.00 for a 2c British Guiana "Cotton Reel" in the DeCoppet Collection. This was the world's first sale of a single stamp for more than $1,000.00.

In subsequent years, several almost legendary collections have been formed and dispersed. Philippe de la Renotière von Ferrari of Paris was the world's most famous collector during the decades before World War I. His fabulous collection realized $1,636,524.00 when it was dispersed during the 1920s in a series of 21 auction sales. Philatelic holdings of Col. E. H. R. Green brought nearly $3 million when sold at auction in the 1930s. Collections formed by Alfred H. Caspary, a New York stockbroker, brought $2,895,146.00 when dispersed in 16 auction sales in the late 1950s.

The first competitive exhibition of international caliber was held in New York City in 1913. Most of the great philatelic names of that era participated, with the major award going to George Worthington.

Some of the more popular accessories developed during a century of stamp collecting are depicted in the six panels below.
Upper left: a perforation gauge in use.
Upper right: two common styles of magnifiers.
Center left: tray used with bottle of fluid to detect watermarks. Special lamps are also available for this purpose.
Center right: gummed stamp hinges, used to attach stamps to album pages.
Lower left: cutter with millimeter scale to trim plastic mounting enclosures.
Lower right: tongs being used to insert a stamp in a plastic mount on an album page. A good set of tongs is essential to collecting.

Similar exhibitions were held in New York in 1926, 1937, 1947, and 1956. The star of the 1926 exhibition was Alfred F. Lichtenstein, whose Uruguay collection won the Grand Award. In 1947 the Grand Award went to Saul Newbury for his outstanding collection of 19th century United States, and in 1956 Robert Hoffman won this prize for his Uruguay collection.

In 1966 and 1971 Washington, D.C. and New York City were the scenes of major international exhibitions. The 1966 show was competitive with Robert J. Gill receiving the Grand Award; the 1971 display, Anphilex, was not. The next international exhibition, Interphil, will take place in Philadelphia, Pennsylvania, in 1976. It will commemorate the nation's bicentennial and 200 years of American postal progress.

In 1921 the U.S. Post Office Department formally recognized the existence of the stamp collector market by establishing the Philatelic Agency in Washington, D.C. It provided a place where collectors could obtain stamps of selected philatelic quality as well as items sought by collectors but not available in many post offices.

In 1922, when it launched a new regular postage series, the Post Office Department adopted the policy of placing new stamps on sale on specified dates at designated post offices. This was the beginning of the first day service which means so much to those who collect U.S. stamps.

There was tremendous expansion of the air mail service in the 1920s and the Post Office Department not only gave advance notice of first flights over new routes, but provided special cachets which were applied to covers mailed on those flights.

The election of President Franklin D. Roosevelt in 1932 gave stamp collecting a tremendous boost in this country, for he had been a collector since his boyhood, made no secret of his enthusiasm for stamp collecting, and saw to it that the postal service catered to its stamp collecting patrons.

Scene below shows a New York auction, typical of many held each month. Auctions enable collectors to buy or sell particular items of philatelic character, including rarities, complete specialized collections, and unique covers.

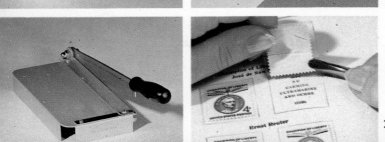

14

During the Roosevelt era commemorative issues appeared frequently and stamp collecting boomed as Presidential interest in the avocation stimulated stamp collecting activity.

A development of the 1930s was the release of a new U.S. regular postage series, adding likenesses of all the Presidents of the United States to philately's portrait gallery. A distinctive first day of issue postmark was provided for use at first day sales, and many of these first day sales were scheduled during exhibitions and other philatelic events.

It was to please its stamp collecting patrons that the postal service persuaded the Bureau of Engraving and Printing to install equipment for efficient production of stamps printed in two or more colors.

A Citizens' Stamp Advisory Committee was named in 1957 to help postal service personnel select subjects for commemorative issues. Automatic distribution of supplies of commemorative stamps to all post offices was inaugurated. Postmasters were encouraged to provide special windows for stamp collecting patrons.

In recent years postal service philatelic activity has expanded greatly, and a variety of products have been created for stamp collectors. These include annual sets of mint commemoratives, souvenir pages with first - day cancellations for each issue, attractive presentation sheets of stamp panels, and souvenir cards issued in connection with major nonstamp shows and international philatelic exhibitions. Many of these items, including starter kits and informative books on U.S. stamps, are designed to attract new collectors to the hobby. They may be purchased at local post offices or from the Philatelic Sales Division of the U.S. Postal Service in Washington, D.C.

Long ago stamp collecting ceased to be simply the mounting of tiny pieces of printed paper in an album. This is still a part of philately and it is eminently satisfying to thousands of the avocation's devotees. But philately has many other pathways, and the individual elects to follow the one he finds most satisfying. It's been said that there are as many approaches to stamp collecting as there are collectors, and each one of them is justified by the pleasure it gives the individual.

More than 60 years ago, during the 1913 International Stamp Exhibition in New York City, the late George Worthington, who was one of the leading collectors of that era, observed that philately is the greatest democracy known to man.

"Stamps are collected," he pointed out, "in every civilized nation and in some that can scarcely be called civilized. Men of opposite tastes, politically, religiously, and in every way that differentiates the tastes of mankind, come together and enjoy each other because they are philatelists."

CATALOGUES, PRICE LISTS, AND GUIDEBOOKS

Shown above are some of the most widely used U.S. stamp catalogues, along with examples of dealers' price lists and guidebooks for new collectors.

PERIODICALS

For information on new stamps, coming issues, and contemporary philatelic activity, the collector finds current stamp papers indispensable. They also carry advertising that is helpful to collectors seeking stamps, accessories, and services. Shown below are some of the best known periodicals and newspapers.

Western Stamp Collector
(weekly)
P.O. Box 10
Albany, Oregon 97321

Mekeel's Weekly Stamp News
P.O. Box 1660
Portland, Maine 04104

Linn's Stamp News *(weekly)*
Amos Press Building
Sidney, Ohio 45365

Stamps *(weekly)*
153 Waverly Place
New York, New York 10014

Minkus Stamp Journal
(quarterly)
116 West 32nd Street
New York, New York 10001

The American Philatelist
(monthly)
P.O. Box 800
State College,
   Pennsylvania 16801

Topical Time
(bi-monthly)
3306 North 50th Street
Milwaukee, Wisconsin 53216

The Collectors Club Philatelist
(bi-monthly)
22 East 35th Street
New York, New York 10016

The United States Specialist
(monthly)
19 Maple Street
Arlington, Massachusetts 02174

Scott Monthly Journal
604 Fifth Avenue
New York, New York 10020

S.P.A. Journal *(monthly)*
P.O. Box 9086
Cincinnati, Ohio 45209

PRINCIPLES OF COLOR PERCEPTION AND PRINTING

By Ed Brown
Director of Color Research, Hillmer Graphics Co.

A certain aura of mystery and romance attaches itself to using only three colors of ink to print reproductions of objects which have many colors. One way to describe the sight of a colorful object is to call it an "illusionary phenomenon".

Color can be beautiful, exciting, and dramatic; it also enables us to see differences in otherwise identical objects. When we look outside in the sunlight the colors of the sky, the trees, and the grass are all sharply defined. On a rainy day the same landscape may seem gray; by moonlight it is almost black. This is not because the objects have changed, but because color is a phenomenon of light.

To put it another way, color is the physical and psychological result of a stimulus produced by the

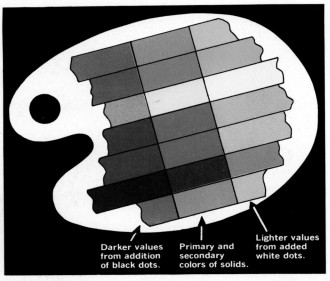

Darker values from addition of black dots.

Primary and secondary colors of solids.

Lighter values from added white dots.

The artist's palette has three primary colors of solids — yellow, red, and blue. Green, red orange, and purple are secondary colors obtained from mixing their adjoining primaries. Darker and lighter values are at left and right of the basic colors.

visible light portion of the electromagnetic spectrum. The physical stimulus takes place in the eye due to the reaction of light rays striking the rods and cones of the retina. The psychological effect takes place in the brain. Light emitted from the sun is made up of all the colors of the rainbow, but there are only three primary colors of light: red, green, and blue. They are called primary colors because all other visible colors emanate from mixtures of them. One of the things that helps us to understand light is that it is energy in the form of waves. The only difference between the sensations of red light and blue light is in the size of the wavelengths, which are measured in millimicrons (one-billionth of a meter).

Color can be described as having three qualities: hue, value, and chroma. Hue is the name of the color, the difference between yellow and red. Value is the degree of brightness, i.e., dark red as distinct from light red. Chroma is the strength or purity of a color at a given level of brightness, i.e., the difference between a grayish "dirty" light red and a pure or vivid light red.

Repeated views entrench remembered impressions of color. If a carpet is seen as blue in daylight, the same observer would be most likely to say it appeared blue in candlelight. Viewed by someone else for the first time in candlelight, it would probably be termed black.

Some colors in solids such as paints and inks are created differently than when formed by light. In printing three basic ink colors — yellow, magenta (red), and cyan (blue) — are commonly used to reproduce paintings, stamps, photographs, and other subjects on paper. Black is a fourth ink used to atone for the shortcomings of the other three.

Many color differences that we perceive in printed matter result from the size and placement of an immense number of dots on paper. When a press is printing "red", the magenta dots are large in area. When

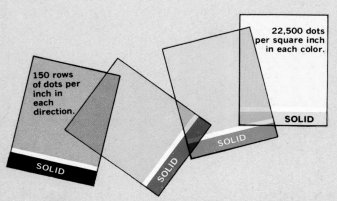

150 rows of dots per inch in each direction.

22,500 dots per square inch in each color.

SOLID

SOLID

SOLID

SOLID

The four dotted squares contain a total of 90,000 dots. The illusion of a color difference appears where the dots overlap.

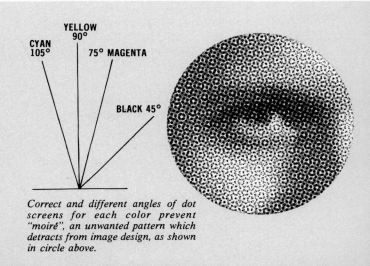

CYAN 105° YELLOW 90° 75° MAGENTA

BLACK 45°

Correct and different angles of dot screens for each color prevent "moiré", an unwanted pattern which detracts from image design, as shown in circle above.

what appears to be "pink" is printed, each dot covers a lesser area, and more white paper shows through. Because the eye cannot focus upon each of 22,500 dots per square inch, an illusion of pink is created. Similar phenomena occur to produce other colors.

Color Separations

The color printing process involves a number of different steps. The flat subject to be reproduced is photographed or electronically scanned, and separations are made, one for each color. Film halftone screened positives are made from the separations, and printing plates are made from these positives.

In a conventional color reproduction department, continuous tone negatives are made. They are similar to those produced from a common camera such as a "Baby Brownie". One negative is made for each color by photographing the image several times, using different filters which permit only the desired light waves to pass for each color negative. These negatives are converted to halftone positives by dividing the continuous tone image into dots of various sizes. Less color may be wanted, i.e., cyan in flesh tones, or more color may be needed, i.e., magenta in lips. The size of the area of the dot is modulated to fulfill the required need.

Reproducing Stamp Designs for This Book

The color separations in this book were produced by an electronic scanner, a highly sophisticated combination of an analog and a digital computerized machine, with the combination achieving a remarkably consistent level of color fidelity.

Four pages of mounted stamps were wrapped around a cylinder which revolved before an intense light source at 1,200 revolutions per minute while they were scanned for an extraction of colors. Each primary color plus the black received a separate scan. The color signals were translated into electronic factors for computation in the analog section by devices which calculate over 1.5 million factors per minute. At the same time, with even greater speeds, digital computers in the machine were

Above: DC - 300 scanner developed by Dr. - Ing. Rudolf Hell and associates of Kiel, Germany.

(Cabinets containing computer panels and power sources omitted.)

Gray scale shows varying densities of black dots to form different degrees of gray tones.

Below: Copy mounted on cylinder is to be scanned for color separation. After scanning, small size word copy is added to film with black tone separation.

1
2
3
4
5
6

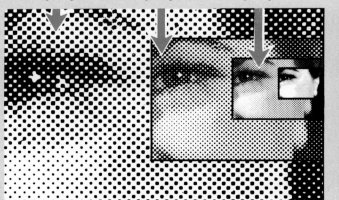

Dot structure magnification.
400 dots per sq. in. 1600 dots per sq. in. 6400 dots per sq. in.

This highly magnified dot pattern from a full-color reproduction shows the basic printing colors of magenta, cyan, and yellow. By varying each color dot size, an infinite variety of additional hues can be shown.

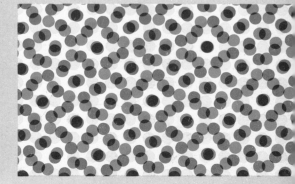

able to calculate any desired size variation between one - tenth and 27 times copy size. For this book four pages of stamps were mounted on a 10" x 13" paste - up to make up one flat, and all were enlarged 153%.

The dot - screening of film positives also occurred simultaneously as signals were transmitted through contact screens. The scanning head moved one inch horizontally in 38 seconds, so in about six minutes per color the separations were made, the dot structure impulses were relayed to film, and all selected color alterations were made in the subject matter.

As indicated on page viii, some of the stamps shown in this book are reproduced at 250%, rather than at 153% as mentioned above. These stamps were scanned separately in groups of 15 to 20. Individual film positives of each stamp were then hand - stripped into their proper positions on the four - page layouts. Seven inverted center stamps were scanned independently from transparencies (see pp. 33, 47, 184).

Color Controls and Light Source

Each color channel in the DC - 300 scanner has fine correction controls for the white and black, six controls for selective correction of the three primary colors and the three secondary colors of the first degree, and a control for correction of both light red and dark brown tones, as encountered in flesh, wood, and earth colors.

High - speed scanning requires the brightest known light sources, of which the xenon lamp is one. Powerful radiation of white light is produced by arc discharge between the electrodes in the spherical section of the quartz bulb.

Printing Methods

Three methods of printing are commonly used to yield tone values. The size of the dots is critical in all three, but the application of ink to the paper differs.

1) Letterpress. This method uses raised image areas to receive the ink, which is transferred to paper or other material. Being the oldest of the three processes, it is still widely used, especially for newspaper printing.

2) Gravure. This method uses ink troughs in which revolve etched cylinders whose surfaces contain millions of tiny concave indentures in which ink is deposited. "Doctor" blades remove excess ink, leaving thin residues to be transferred to paper. Gravure requires the most expensive preparation costs, but will maintain high - quality output on large quantities. More than 90% of the world's postage stamps are produced by gravure.

3) Lithography (or photo - offset). In this process, the image is photo - mechanically transferred, in the form of various sized dots, from the film positives to four press plates. These plates have qualities which allow them to accept the oily printing ink on the image areas and repel the ink from the nonprinting areas, which are coated with a mixture of water and alcohol, a hygroscopic agent. These wrap around and bolt to cylinders in the printing units, each with its own inking system and water - alcohol system. Rollers transmit fluids to the plates, the image area receiving ink, the nonimage area getting the water mix.

Each cylinder comes into intimate but light contact with another of like diameter, covered with a rubber blanket, to which the inked image is transferred or "offset". The paper now passes between the blanket and

Short - arc xenon lamp provides intensive light source vital to accurate color recognition.

THREE PRINTING METHODS

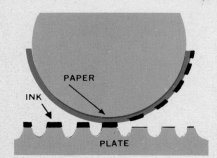

Letterpress principle.

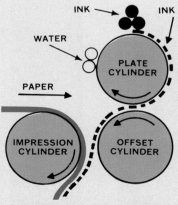

Lithography (offset) process.

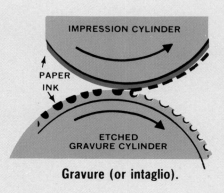

Gravure (or intaglio).

a steel impression cylinder, and with a gentle squeeze the inked image transfers to the paper. Lithography is advantageous on multi-color work and faster because it combines photo-mechanical and chemical processes.

How This Book Was Printed

This book was printed eight pages at a time by the lithographic process on a Harris-Aurelia press manufactured recently in Milan, Italy. Running at 6,000 sheets per hour (considerably below its maximum speed), the press printed sheets of paper up to 26"x40". This smaller paper size produced more consistent registration because paper distortion was reduced, and variations were more readily seen.

When four colors are laid on in rapid succession the finished appearance is obvious at once. Lack of this feature is a handicap to speed when printing each color separately with a single-color press. Another prevalent hazard is that sheets with billions of dots do shrink or stretch from humidity variations which may occur in the time elapsed between color applications. Dots then would be variably and improperly positioned with misregister one unsatisfactory result.

Any short synopsis omits much vital detail; our brief résumé highlights only a few of the many key facets of the graphic arts. Perhaps a glimmer of light has been cast to help you understand some mysteries of color and its reproduction.

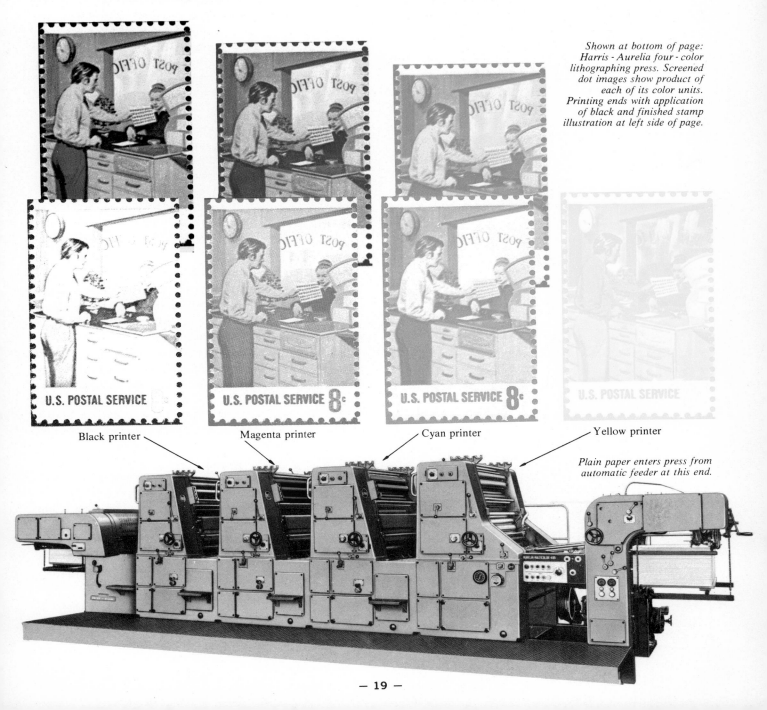

Shown at bottom of page: Harris-Aurelia four-color lithographing press. Screened dot images show product of each of its color units. Printing ends with application of black and finished stamp illustration at left side of page.

Black printer   Magenta printer   Cyan printer   Yellow printer

Plain paper enters press from automatic feeder at this end.

HOW U.S. STAMPS ARE PRODUCED

By Everett J. Prescott

Chief of Currency and Stamp Printing, U.S. Bureau of Engraving and Printing

The Bureau of Engraving and Printing has been producing U.S. postage stamps for eighty years. During this time printing methods have expanded from line engraving (intaglio), which produces single-color stamps, to a combination of multiple offset lithography and intaglio, which produces multicolor stamps.

Over half of all U.S. stamps are still printed in one color from line-engraved plates. This does not indicate a lack of "progress", but rather the intrinsic beauty of this type of stamp.

After the original stamp designs are received in the Bureau, models are prepared for submission to the Postal Service. Printers, engravers, and technicians responsible for paper and inks confer, and a final determination is made as to colors and their placement, with allowances made for design limitations due to inherent printing specifications. Production plates or cylinders are manufactured, and proof sheets are printed for final approval by the Postal Service prior to production runs. These can vary from about 150 million commemorative stamps to two billion Christmas stamps or unlimited quantities of ordinary issues, which are printed on a continuing basis.

Table shows the various sheet and web-fed presses in the Bureau of Engraving and Printing and the types of stamps they produce.

PRESS	YEAR INSTALLED	PRINTING PROCESS	TYPES OF STAMPS
Cottrell	1955	Web-fed intaglio	Line-engraved, single-color. Also, in precancelled form.
Giori	1957	Sheet-fed intaglio	Line-engraved, multicolor.
Harris	1964	Sheet-fed offset	Partial designs prior to final printing by Giori press.
Huck 9-Color	1968	Web-fed intaglio	Line-engraved in up to six colors with three additional colors by indirect intaglio.
Andreotti	1971	Web-fed gravure	Photoengraved.
Giori	1975	Web-fed intaglio	Line-engraved, multicolor. For production of coil stamps.
Giori Rotocolor	1975	Web-fed intaglio and gravure	Combination line-engraved and photoengraved.

The six-color Horse Racing stamp was produced on the Andreotti press. The single-color line-engraved Eisenhower coil is a product of the Cottrell press.

Types of Printing Presses

Stamps are printed in two basic forms, sheet and roll. Sheet stamps have been printed on hand-operated and power-driven flat-bed presses in the past, but they are presently printed on multicolor Giori presses.

The old presses utilized a heavy iron plate, approximately 1/4" thick, while the newer Giori presses use a thin .030" nickel plate. To extend their life, all intaglio printing plates are chromium plated before being placed in use.

Roll stamps are printed on web presses. The first web press in the Bureau was designed by an employee, Benjamin Stickney, and these presses were in use from the early 1900s until the mid-1950s. Since then, more sophisticated machines have been developed — the single-color Cottrells, the nine-color Huck, the Andreotti gravure, and two new multicolor intaglio web presses.

Gumming of Stamps

Postage stamps are gummed either before or after printing. Stamps printed on the Giori and Andreotti presses require that the paper be pregummed. Cottrell presses and the Huck nine-color apply gum manufactured in the Bureau to the printed web of paper. Quality control procedures insure fulfillment of the strict requirements for providing acceptably pure adhesives on U.S. stamps.

Perforation Methods

Stamps are perforated in several ways. Sheets printed on the Giori sheet-fed presses go through what is known as an L-perforator, which has two sets of perforating wheels and pins set at right angles to each other. The sheet is fed through the first set of wheels and pins to perforate in one direction; it then moves laterally through the second set to be perforated in the cross direction. This machine also trims excess paper from the sides of the sheet. These wheels can be easily adjusted to accommodate any size stamp — ordinary, commemorative, jumbo, or special purpose.

Rolls of postage stamps are placed in a machine called an electric eye perforator which unwinds the printed roll. An electric eye device, following a printed line on the roll of stamps, guides the web through a unit that perforates crosswise and lengthwise, and then cuts the web into individual sheets. After the defective sheets are sorted out, the perfect ones are stapled into units of 100 sheets and cut into four quarters. These quarter-sheets, the size sold at post offices, contain 50 stamps in the commemorative size, 100 stamps in the regular size, or varying quantities in the jumbo or special sizes.

Phosphor Application

The Huck nine-color press, after printing the stamps on the moving web, applies phosphor to each stamp. To produce sheet stamps, it then perforates and cuts the web into full-size press sheets. To produce coils, the press does not perforate or cut the web into sheets, but rewinds it into a continuous roll. This finished roll of stamps is then placed in an examining machine where the web is unwound, inspected, and rewound after defective portions have been removed. This roll of perfect stamps proceeds to another machine which again unwinds it, perforates the web in the cross direction, and slits it into a series of 18 ribbons each one stamp wide. These ribbons are then wound into coils of 100, 500, or 3,000 stamps, wrapped in plastic, and labeled by the same machine. Operators place the finished coils in boxes for subsequent delivery.

Paper and Ink Research

This is a continuing activity of the Bureau. Relatively inexpensive wood sulphite papers are used for postage stamps printed on the intaglio presses. The gravure process requires a smoother surface, so the Bureau has developed superior paper for use on the gravure presses.

Paper for postage stamps must be able to receive and hold the ink printed on it without undue penetra-tion. The ink and paper must remain stable to minimize the deterioration of stamps over a long period of time. The inks must also be resistant to sunlight and chemicals.

Output and Capacity

During an average month the Bureau produces about 27 different stamps, including repeat runs of current issues. In 1973 total stamp output exceeded 26 billion.

To accomplish this (in addition to printing our country's paper money) requires 3,200 employees who work in shifts 24 hours a day, over 125 printing presses and associated machines, and buildings with over 25 acres of floor space — the largest plant of its kind in the world.

*Main building,
Bureau of Engraving
and Printing,
Washington, D.C.*

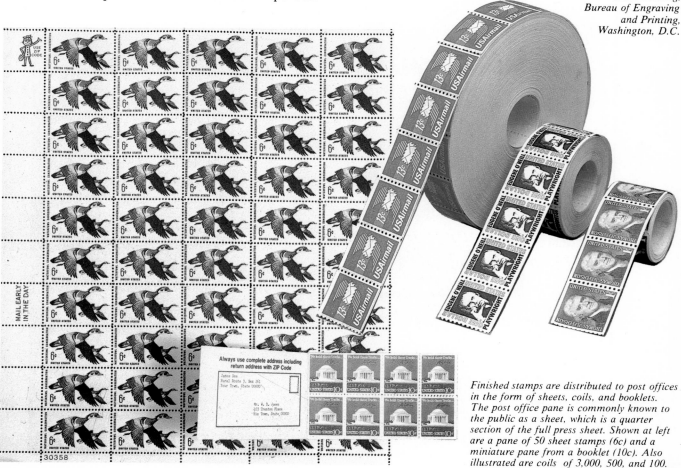

Finished stamps are distributed to post offices in the form of sheets, coils, and booklets. The post office pane is commonly known to the public as a sheet, which is a quarter section of the full press sheet. Shown at left are a pane of 50 sheet stamps (6c) and a miniature pane from a booklet (10c). Also illustrated are coils of 3,000, 500, and 100.

COLORS AND COLLECTORS — A RAINBOW WORLD

By Franklin R. Bruns, Jr.

Associate Curator of Postal History, National Museum of History and Technology, Smithsonian Institution

Stamp collecting is a pleasant hobby, and for the majority of devotees it should be permitted to remain so, uncluttered by detail and technicalities.

Color is one area in which generalities exist knowingly, to eliminate confusion. Gradations in color and the side effects of handling, climate, paper, and storage are best left to the specialist.

Present-day technology permits stamp printers to blend inks according to minutely detailed formulas, under virtually identical conditions, and perfect matching of colors a week, month, or year apart is a rule rather than an exception. This was not, of course, true in 1840 or 1847, or in 1869, 1902, or 1922. Controlled temperature and humidity were unattainable in those years. And, in the earlier years, the mixing of inks had the individual touch.

Even now there are elements which affect color which are beyond the mixing and blending. One is the paper on which stamps are printed.

Rolls or sheets of paper may have been produced according to strict formula. Yet certain rolls or lots of paper may have been held over from a previous job, or may have been stored or shipped under what can best be described as different conditions. As a result, perfectly matched inks may be applied to papers with varying degrees of absorption.

A group of cancelled actual-size 2c Columbian stamps. Time has eroded the paper and faded the original ink colors.

Students of philatelic detail find each instance of variation interesting, and much can be learned of the development of a stamp from the earliest to the latest impression — particularly in the mid-19th century.

The "beginner" and the "average" collector are content with a generalized color identification. Red and carmine are essentially synonymous, as are purple and violet, and brown and chocolate.

It is therefore mutually convenient to a writer, publisher, or a collector to generalize a color identification. This has become the rule, except in those instances where color difference has a specific relationship to the proper collecting of stamps. However, those acquiring two or more examples of a specific stamp are generally struck by the difference, and mount one shade under or beside another.

And, in a natural progression, individuals endeavor to give a more specific designation to a stamp or stamps. Is a stamp carmine, deep red, or dark red?

Over the years color guides have been developed for stamp collectors. Some have served only to confuse collectors. Others have been produced by firms having no relation to stamp printers.

One of the largest stamp firms, Stanley Gibbons, Ltd., of London, has endeavored to provide hobbyists with quality color guides over a seventy-five-year period. One such aid, *A Colour Dictionary*, appeared in 1899 (2 shillings, sixpence), giving about 200 names of colors used in printing, with impressions showing some of the colors more frequently encountered. More recently that firm has made available a "Stamp Colour Key" with 200 gradations specified in its catalogues. Its selections were based on the British Colour Council's *Dictionary of Colour*, but the descriptions were those thought to be most familiar to collectors.

The *Munsell Book of Color* is, of course, a standard guide, but it is rather expensive; variances are identified by number. The *Pictorial Treasury of U.S. Stamps* offers a happy combination of identifying numbers and color gradations as used for stamps.

C-I-L COLOR COMPARISON CHART

The stamps shown on pages 23-25 were printed in various hues, values, and chroma of seven common colors. Each stamp is described by a number which corresponds to one of the numbered color blocks above or below the illustrations.

The same number appears in a caption below the stamp, where it is keyed to the different color names by which the stamp has been described over the years.

By comparing actual stamps to the numbered color blocks it is possible to establish a standard reference, based on colorful graphics, that is more precise than is possible with words. Always compare the darkest shade on a stamp with the corresponding color block. (Note that R-17 appears pink because of finely engraved background lines. The solid color relates to color block R-17).

1 2 3 4 5 6 7 8 9 10 12 14 16 18 20 22 24 26 28 30 32 34 36 38 40 42

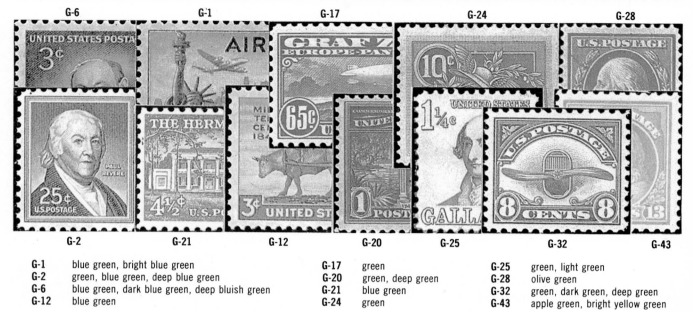

G-6   G-1   G-17   G-24   G-28

G-2   G-21   G-12   G-20   G-25   G-32   G-43

G-1	blue green, bright blue green		G-17	green	G-25	green, light green
G-2	green, blue green, deep blue green		G-20	green, deep green	G-28	olive green
G-6	blue green, dark blue green, deep bluish green		G-21	blue green	G-32	green, dark green, deep green
G-12	blue green		G-24	green	G-43	apple green, bright yellow green

HOW TO USE THESE PAGES TO IDENTIFY STAMP COLORS

The color blocks are positioned along the edges of these pages so that they may be used to identify actual stamp colors. Grasp a stamp with tongs and slip it under the page, as shown. Move the stamp along the edge of the page to find the block that corresponds to the darkest shade of color on the stamp. The number of this block is the C-I-L color code for the stamp.

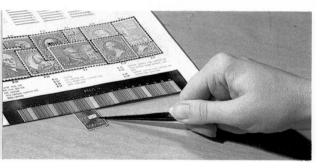

O-1   O-2   O-6   K-1   K-3

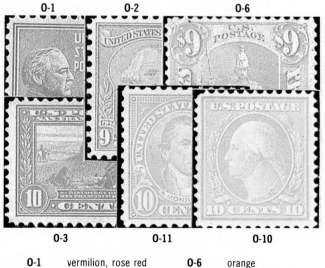

O-3   O-11   O-10   K-2   K-4   K-13

O-1	vermilion, rose red	O-6	orange	K-1	black	K-3	black, gray black
O-2	vermilion, pale red, salmon	O-10	yellow	K-2	purple black, black brown, deep purple brown	K-4	black
O-3	orange	O-11	orange, orange yellow			K-13	gray, gray black

1 2 3 4 5 6 7 8 9 10 12 14   1 2 3 4 5 6 7 8 9 10 12 14

B-8   B-22   B-10   B-17   B-41

B-1   B-4   B-15   B-13   B-2   B-30   B-6

B-1	blue, deep blue	
B-2	blue, dull blue	
B-4	blue, ultramarine, bright blue	
B-6	ultramarine, pale ultramarine	

B-8	indigo, dark blue, deep blue
B-10	ultramarine, gray blue, bright blue
B-13	ultramarine, bright blue
B-15	indigo

B-17	ultramarine, blue
B-22	blue, dark blue
B-30	blue, Prussian blue
B-41	light blue, gray blue, light slate blue

PERFORATION GAUGE

The perforation of loose stamps may be checked against the gauge at right. Stamps may be aligned against the scale so that the black dots fill the perforation holes. The number at the right end of the best fitting scale indicates the perforation of the stamp.

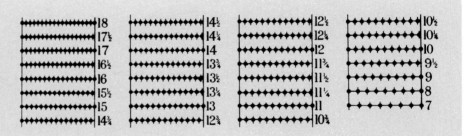

R-24   R-20   R-15   R-9   R-16   R-17

R-15*   R-14   R-19   R-4   R-24*   R-9*

R-4	scarlet, rose, red	
R-9	dull rose, dull red	
R-9*	red, carmine	
R-14	rose carmine, carmine red, deep carmine	

R-15	carmine
R-15*	red, carmine red
R-16	rose, bright rose, carmine rose
R-17	pink, rose pink

R-19	carmine, carmine rose, carmine red
R-20	rose carmine, bright carmine, rose pink
R-24	carmine, carmine rose, carmine red
R-24*	carmine lake, deep lake

P-1   P-12   P-15   P-36   P-23   P-28*

P-2   P-3   P-11   P-28   P-40   P-41

P-1	violet, dark red violet	P-12	violet, deep violet	
P-2	bright violet, dark red violet	P-15	lilac, purple brown, dull purple	
P-3	violet	P-23	purple, dark lilac, reddish violet	
P-11	violet	P-28	purple, dark violet, reddish purple	

P-28*   bright violet, reddish violet, light reddish violet
P-36   red violet, bright purple
P-40   magenta, red violet, bright purple
P-41   mauve, light red violet, bright purple

WATERMARKS

Stamps issued between 1895 and 1916 were printed on sheets of paper that were watermarked double- or single-line USPS. As the diagrams indicate, many stamps contained only partial letters.

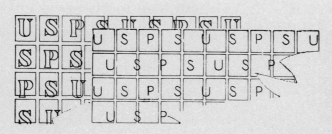

A few of the 6c and 8c stamps of 1895 and the $1 regular stamp of 1951 were accidentally printed on paper that was watermarked double-line USIR.

USIR

Br-17   Br-7   Br-11   Br-8   Br-25   Br-18

Br-1   Br-6   Br-10   Br-15   Br-25*   Br-31

Br-1	brown, dark brown	Br-10	dark brown, sepia	Br-18	orange brown, yellow brown
Br-6	violet brown, purple black	Br-11	claret, brown red, deep lake	Br-25	brown, yellow brown
Br-7	violet brown, brown purple	Br-15	chocolate, dark brown, red brown	Br-25*	brown, pale red brown
Br-8	brown, deep brown	Br-17	brown	Br-31	bistre, olive bistre, yellow olive

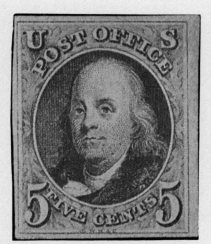

A. *7/1/47*

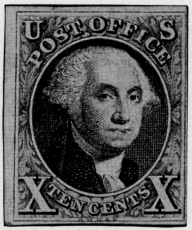

B. *7/1/47*

REGULAR ISSUE OF 1847

The first stamps issued by the U.S. government were released on July 1, 1847. Their appearance followed seven years of important events in postal history.

In 1840 Great Britain lowered its postage rates and introduced adhesive stamps to prepay postage. Prior to this time the person who received mail generally paid this fee instead of the sender.

In 1842 postage stamps were introduced to the United States by a private mail delivery firm, Greig's Despatch Post of New York City. Three years later, when U.S. postage rates were lowered, local postmasters began to issue provisional stamps for use on mail in their locales. During this period pen and ink or handstamped "paid" markings were also used.

On March 3, 1847, Congress passed the historic legislation that resulted in the first general issue of 1847. Two denominations were produced by Rawdon, Wright, Hatch & Edson of New York. The earliest known use of the stamps was July 7 for the 5c denomination and July 9 for the 10c.

The new stamps were released in imperforate sheets from which individual stamps were cut by postal clerks. As soon as they went on sale provisional stamps became invalid. In 1856 the use of stamps on U.S. mail became mandatory.

A. Benjamin Franklin (1706-90), the father of the U.S. postal system, after a painting by John Longacre. A versatile and productive genius, Franklin invented bifocal glasses, the lightning rod, and the Franklin stove, wrote *Poor Richard's Almanack* and his famous *Autobiography.* He also served as the deputy postmaster general of the American colonies, as a member of the committee that drafted the Declaration of Independence, and as an envoy to France during the Revolution. When he was 81 he played a role in the framing of the Constitution.

Any post office 3,700,000
'25	11.00	'45	22.00	'65	57.50
'35	15.00	'55	37.50	'75	295.00

B. George Washington (1732-99), 1st president (1789-97), after the Athenaeum portrait by Gilbert Stuart (Boston Museum of Fine Arts). Although he was the wealthy owner of a large estate in Virginia, he served as a frontier surveyor, an officer of the Virginia militia, and a public office holder. Washington first won recognition as a military leader in the French and Indian War. In 1775 he accepted the post of commander-in-chief of the Continental Army. He brought to this position courage, strength of purpose, and executive ability, three qualities that enabled him to lead the Americans to victory in the Revolution. After the war the same qualities helped him to guide the nation through its early years of constitutional democracy (see p. 64).

Any post office 865,000
'25	55.00	'55	130.00
'35	80.00	'65	160.00
'45	85.00	'75	1,500.00

Note: In 1875 official reproductions of the first two U.S. stamps were made for the Centennial Exposition at Philadelphia. The reproductions are in the same colors as the originals, but slight engraving differences may be detected in the designs. They were not valid for postage.

REGULAR ISSUE OF 1851

C. *7/1/51*

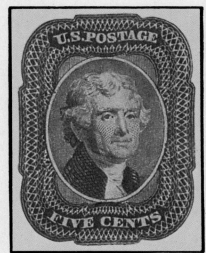

D. *3/24/56*

E. 1853

F. *5/12/55*

G. 8/4/51

The issue of 1851 was a milestone in U.S. postal history and philately. It resulted from a new schedule of rates which lowered domestic postage and encouraged the use of stamps by prescribing lower rates for prepaid mail than for letters sent collect. The imperforate stamps in this issue, together with the perforate issue of 1857, are all highly prized. Some of them exist in a variety of types which resulted from the way in which the printing plates were engraved. These types, seen as slight variations in the borders or the frames of the designs, are often difficult to identify.

C. Benjamin Franklin. Eight major types exist, one of which is found only on perforated stamps. Shown: type I (used).

Any post office	30,000		
'25	150.00	'55	700.00
'35	400.00	'65	1,100.00
'45	700.00	'75	4,500.00

D. Thomas Jefferson. Two major types exist, one of which appears only on perforated stamps. Shown: type I.

Any post office	150,000		
'25	50.00	'45	90.00	'65	120.00
'35	80.00	'55	100.00	'75	750.00

E. George Washington. Two major types exist, one of which appears only on perforated stamps. Color varieties also exist. Shown: type I.

Any post office

'25	1.25	'45	1.75	'65	4.95
'35	1.50	'55	2.95	'75	16.00

F. Washington. Five major types exist, one of which is found only on perforated stamps. Shown: type I.

Any post office	500,000		
'25	40.00	'55	225.00
'35	200.00	'65	225.00
'45	250.00	'75	1,100.00

G. Washington, by Stuart.

Any post office	2,500,000		
'25	14.00	'45	27.50	'65	42.00
'35	22.50	'55	33.50	'75	225.00

In 1857 perforated stamps were introduced to the United States by the postal service. The designs of the new stamps were reproduced from the imperforate stamps of 1851 and three new denominations were added to the set.

A. George Washington, after a detail from *Washington at Trenton* by John Trumbull (Yale University Art Gallery, New Haven, Connecticut). This is one of the very few U.S. stamps that is generally more valuable used than unused. It was available only for one year.

Any post office 29,000
'25 25.00 '45 42.00 '65 100.00
'35 28.00 '55 65.00 '75 250.00

B. Benjamin Franklin, type V.
Any post office
'25 1.00 '45 1.50 '65 4.75
'35 1.25 '55 1.90 '75 13.50

C. Washington, type I.
Any post office 38,750,000
'25 5.00 '45 7.25 '65 19.00
'35 5.00 '55 10.00 '75 77.50

D. Washington, type II. This stamp may also be identified by its color, which is slightly different from the type I variety.
Any post office 620,000,000
'25 .12 '45 .35 '65 1.75
'35 .20 '55 .95 '75 5.35

E. Thomas Jefferson, after a copy of a portrait by Gilbert Stuart, type I. This stamp was printed in a variety of shades ranging from brown to red brown. The highly prized Indian red (shown) is valued at $2,900.00.

F. Jefferson, type II. This variety was printed in brown (shown) and orange brown.
Any post office 825,000
'25 7.75 '45 10.00 '65 22.50
'35 8.50 '55 13.00 '75 55.00

G. Washington, type V.
Any post office
'25 3.50 '45 4.25 '65 10.00
'35 3.50 '55 5.50 '75 22.00

H. Washington, by Stuart.
Any post office 5,800,000
'25 3.00 '45 5.00 '65 17.50
'35 4.00 '55 11.50 '75 40.00

A. *8/13/60*

B. 11/17/57

C. 2/28/57

D. 7/13/57

G. 5/9/59

E. 3/31/58

F. 3/4/60

Thomas Jefferson (1743-1826), 3rd president (1801-09), was one of the most complex and versatile of the Founding Fathers. He was an aristocrat who believed that virtue and talent are more important than wealth and birth. He was a statesman who also excelled in science, music, architecture, and other fields. Although he was a rather poor public speaker, his political philosophy helped to shape the fabric of our nation. He died on the 50th anniversary of the adoption of the Declaration of Independence, of which he was the main author.

H. 7/30/57

I. 6/15/60

J. 8/8/60

REGULAR ISSUE OF 1861 - 67

K. 8/17/61

L. 8/19/61

M. 8/20/61

N. 8/30/61

O. 8/20/61

P. 8/ - /61

I. Washington, by Stuart.
Any post office 750,000
'25 6.00 '45 7.75 '65 22.50
'35 6.25 '55 13.00 '75 75.00

J. Benjamin Franklin.
Any post office 357,000
'25 8.00 '45 12.00 '65 28.00
'35 9.00 '55 19.00 '75 80.00

Regular Issue of 1861 - 67.
After the outbreak of the
Civil War in 1861 all U.S.
stamps were demonetized
to prevent the Confederates
from using them (see p. 208).
Prior to August 1 of that
year new designs were
prepared by the National
Bank Note Company of New
York. Samples of the designs
were submitted to the postal
service for approval.
Although not regularly
issued, these first designs
are rare and very valuable.
They are almost identical to
the regularly issued stamps
(shown) but minute
differences may be detected
in most of the denominations.

**K. Benjamin Franklin, after
a bust by John Dixey.**
Any post office 138,000,000
'25 .50 '45 1.50 '65 5.75
'35 .85 '55 2.85 '75 17.50

L. Thomas Jefferson.
Originally printed in buff
(shown), this stamp was
reprinted in brown in 1862.
A red brown variety
also exists.
Any post office 175,000
'25 65.00 '45 85.00 '65 100.00
'35 85.00 '55 87.50 '75 425.00

M. Washington, by Stuart.
Any post office 27,300,000
'25 2.50 '45 3.25 '65 7.25
'35 2.75 '55 4.65 '75 25.00

N. Washington, by Stuart.
Any post office 7,314,000
'25 2.50 '45 5.75 '65 13.50
'35 4.50 '55 7.00 '75 45.00

O. Franklin, by Dixey.
Any post office 3,300,000
'25 3.75 '45 10.50 '65 21.00
'35 5.00 '55 11.75 '75 65.00

P. Washington, by Trumbull.
Any post office 388,700
'25 16.00 '45 23.00 '65 47.50
'35 23.00 '55 26.50 '75 165.00

A-E. George Washington, after a bust by Jean Antoine Houdon. Five color varieties of this design are shown on this page. Ranging from the shades of the trial colors to those of the regularly issued stamp and an 1875 reissue, they provide a graphic illustration of the way in which color differentiates recognized philatelic varieties of a single stamp design.

A. Washington, August design (brown rose).

'25	12.00	'45	17.50	'65	42.00
'35	15.00	'55	22.50	'75	185.00

B. Washington (pink).
Any post office   100,000

'25	30.00	'45	100.00	'65	150.00
'35	85.00	'55	120.00	'75	500.00

C. Washington (rose).
Any post office   1,782,000,000

'25	.45	'45	.70	'65	2.25
'35	.70	'55	1.25	'75	6.50

D. Washington, trial color proof (lake).

E. Washington, 1875 reprint (brown red).

F-J. Cancellations are intended to make it impossible to reuse stamps. Many of them are so unusual and interesting that stories of their uses and varieties are a study in themselves.
In the 19th century, post offices used cancellers cut from cork or wood blocks which produced fanciful or geometric cancellations.
Also in the 19th century an effort was made to make it impractical to wash and reuse cancelled stamps. From 1867 to 1875 U.S. stamps were embossed with rectangular patterns called grills, which were designed to break the paper fibre so that cancellation ink would soak in more thoroughly. A number of grill patterns exist.
Some created raised impressions on the face of the stamps, others on the back. A few are extremely faint. All stamps issued in this period were released with and without grills. Some of the grilled varieties are extremely rare.

A. 1861

B. 8/18/61

C. 8/19/61

D. 1861

E. 1875

F. 8/19/61

G. 8/19/61

K. *1/7/62*

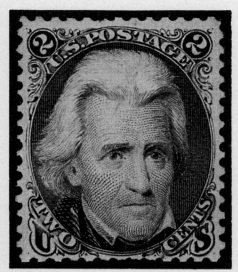

L. *7/1/63*

M. *1866*

H. 8/18/61

I. 8/18/61

J. 8/19/61

K. Washington, after a portrait by Gilbert Stuart. The color varieties of this stamp range from red lilac, brownish lilac, and steel blue (1861) to lilac and gray shades (1862).

Any post office	400,000	
'25 17.00	'45 24.00	'65 30.00
'35 20.00	'55 18.00	'75 100.00

L. Andrew Jackson (1767 - 1845), 7th president (1829 - 37). Born in the backwoods of South Carolina and orphaned at the age of fourteen, Andrew Jackson rose to become a self-made president who ushered in an era of popular democracy. A strong - willed firebrand, "Old Hickory" was swept to fame by his victories at Horseshoe Bend and New Orleans in the War of 1812. During his administrations the executive branch of government became more powerful. This stamp, nicknamed the "Black Jack", is one of the most popular of all U.S. issues. It depicts the last likeness made of Jackson before he died.

Any post office	256,566,000	
'25 .50	'45 1.25	'65 5.75
'35 .70	'55 2.85	'75 21.00

M. Abraham Lincoln (1809 - 65), 16th president (1861 - 65), was a tall and lanky man who often kept memos in his stovepipe hat. He had the eloquence of a statesman, the mettle of a hero, the strength of a great leader, and the objectivity of a lawyer. Tested and trained by life on the frontier, he is respected throughout the world as the "Great Emancipator" (see p. 120).

Any post office	2,139,000	
'25 4.00	'45 9.75	'65 15.75
'35 7.50	'55 10.85	'75 85.00

Note: In 1875 all regular stamps issued from 1857 to 1867 were reprinted in limited quantities for the Centennial Exposition at Philadelphia. The reproductions of the issue of 1861 - 67 were valid for postage.

The appearance of a horse, a flag, a locomotive, a steamship, and two famous paintings on the stamps of 1869 marked an innovation in U.S. stamp design. For the first time in American postal history something other than a portrait was shown on a stamp.

The first bicolor U.S. stamps and a portent of commemoratives to come, the new adhesives were reported to be unpopular with the public. Produced with grills by the American Bank Note Company, they were withdrawn from sale within a year of their release. In 1875 a limited number were reissued without grills.

Today the stamps are highly esteemed and copies are becoming increasingly hard to find. The celebrated rarities of the set are the three inverted center varieties, the first stamps of this type to appear in the United States. Shown:

A. Benjamin Franklin, after a bust by John Dixey.
Any post office 16,605,150
'25 1.50	'45 3.75	'65 11.25
'35 2.50	'55 7.95	'75 45.00

B. Post rider and horse.
Any post office 57,387,500
'25 1.15	'45 2.25	'65 8.25
'35 1.35	'55 4.60	'75 25.00

C. Locomotive.
Any post office 386,475,900
'25 .85	'45 1.40	'65 4.75
'35 .85	'55 2.50	'75 13.50

D. George Washington, painted by Gilbert Stuart.
Any post office 4,882,750
'25 4.50	'45 9.00	'65 21.00
'35 5.00	'55 14.00	'75 87.50

E. Eagle and shield.
Any post office 3,299,700
'25 2.75	'45 8.75	'65 25.00
'35 3.50	'55 16.50	'75 95.00

F. Ocean steamship S.S. *Adriatic,* the finest wooden paddle liner of the day.
Any post office 3,012,950
'25 2.00	'45 7.75	'65 17.50
'35 3.50	'55 13.50	'75 85.00

A. 3/27/69

B. *3/27/69*

C. *3/27/69*

D. 4/26/69

E. 4/1/69

F. *4/5/69*

G. 4/2/69

H. 5/23/69

J. 4/7/69

L. 5/15/69

N. 9/9/69

I. *1869*

K. *1869*

M. *1869*

G. Landing of Columbus, after a painting by John Vanderlyn.

Any post office   200,000
| '25 | 8.75 | '45 | 32.00 | '65 | 85.00 |
| '35 | 19.00 | '55 | 62.50 | '75 | 275.00 |

H. Landing of Columbus, a revised design with an extra frame line around the painting.

Any post office   1,238,940
| '25 | 5.25 | '45 | 11.00 | '65 | 20.00 |
| '35 | 6.50 | '55 | 13.50 | '75 | 100.00 |

I. Landing of Columbus, center inverted. Two-color printing required two press impressions. Carelessness in correlating the two impressions produced this famous mistake, in which the vignette is upside down in relation to the frame. Inverted varieties of eight U.S. postage stamps have reached the public. Three of them are shown on this page (see pp. 47, 134, 184).

'25	5,000.00	'55	10,000.00
'35	8,000.00	'65	17,500.00
'45	10,000.00	'75	40,000.00

J. The Declaration of Independence, after the painting by John Trumbull (Yale University Art Gallery, New Haven, Connecticut).

Any post office   235,350
| '25 | 6.50 | '45 | 21.50 | '65 | 52.00 |
| '35 | 10.00 | '55 | 38.50 | '75 | 250.00 |

K. Declaration of Independence, center inverted.

'25	3,500.00	'55	6,000.00
'35	4,250.00	'65	9,500.00
'45	6,000.00	'75	25,000.00

L. Shield, eagle, and flags.

Any post office   244,110
| '25 | 6.50 | '45 | 20.00 | '65 | 65.00 |
| '35 | 9.50 | '55 | 47.50 | '75 | 265.00 |

M. Shield, eagle, and flags; flags inverted. This is the rarest of the 1869 inverts, the least obvious, and the last to be discovered.

'25	4,000.00	'55	8,000.00
'35	5,000.00	'65	10,000.00
'45	8,000.00	'75	35,000.00

N. Abraham Lincoln.

Any post office   47,460
| '25 | 32.00 | '45 | 75.00 | '65 | 150.00 |
| '35 | 65.00 | '55 | 110.00 | '75 | 650.00 |

Challenging, complex, and classic — these words describe the regular issues of 1870-89. Nicknamed the "Bank Note" issues by collectors, they are a single series of stamps which were printed by three different firms: the National Bank Note Company (1870-71), the Continental Bank Note Company (1873-75), and the American Bank Note Company (1879-88). Each company produced the stamps in a slightly different fashion, so the designs exist in many philatelic varieties. The National Bank Note Company produced the stamps with and without grills. The Continental Bank Note Company added so-called "secret marks" to distinguish their plates from earlier ones. This firm also issued all the stamps except the 90c denomination with and without grills. The American Bank Note Company used different paper than the other printers and reengraved the 1c, 3c, 6c, and 10c denominations. In addition, four special printings were issued in limited quantities for collectors. On these pages every major design issued from 1870 to 1889 is shown.

A. Benjamin Franklin, after a bust by John Dixey.
Any post office   140,000,000
'25 1.25   '45 1.40   '65 6.00
'35 1.40   '55 3.75   '75 14.00

B. Andrew Jackson, after a bust by Hiram Powers.
Any post office   250,000,000
'25 .45   '45 .70   '65 3.00
'35 .50   '55 1.25   '75 8.00

C. George Washington, after a bust by Jean Antoine Houdon.
Any post office   1,200,000,000
'25 .90   '45 1.10   '65 1.95
'35 .90   '55 1.15   '75 7.25

D. Abraham Lincoln, after a bust by Thomas D. Jones.
Any post office   27,600,000
'25 1.50   '45 3.25   '65 9.50
'35 2.00   '55 6.95   '75 37.50

A. 4/ - /70

B. 4/ - /70

C. 3/13/70

D. 4/ - /70

F. 4/ - /70

H. 4/-/70

E. *3/6/71*

G. *4/-/70*

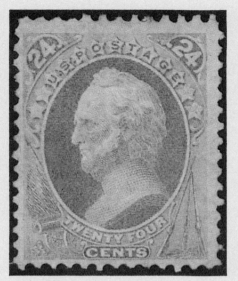

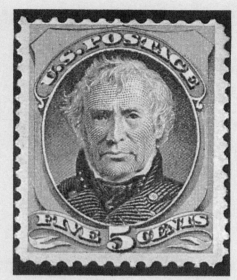

I. 4/ - /70

M. 6/21/75

J. 4/ - /70

K. 4/ - /70

L. 6/21/75

N. 4/10/82

O. 10/1/83

P. 10/1/83

E. Edwin M. Stanton (1814 - 69), attorney general for President Buchanan and secretary of war for Presidents Lincoln and Johnson.
Any post office   2,825,000
'25 2.75   '45 4.75   '65 13.50
'35 3.75   '55 7.75   '75 48.50

F. Thomas Jefferson, after a bust by Hiram Powers.
Any post office   10,920,000
'25 3.50   '45 5.25   '65 11.75
'35 4.75   '55 7.95   '75 40.00

G. Henry Clay (see p. 43).
Any post office   3,890,000
'25 5.00   '45 8.25   '65 16.00
'35 8.25   '55 9.00   '75 77.50

H. Daniel Webster, after a bust by S. V. Clevenger.
Any post office   5,500,000
'25 1.75   '45 6.75   '65 16.50
'35 2.75   '55 12.00   '75 60.00

I. Winfield Scott (1786 - 1866), general who was a national military hero from the War of 1812 to the Civil War.
Any post office   1,148,000
'25 6.50   '45 12.00   '65 22.50
'35 10.00   '55 17.00   '75 55.00

J. Alexander Hamilton, after a bust by Giuseppe Ceracchi.
Any post office   893,000
'25 7.00   '45 17.50   '65 32.50
'35 14.00   '55 21.00   '75 140.00

K. Commodore Oliver H. Perry, after a bust from a statue by William Walcutt.
Any post office   185,000
'25 8.00   '45 23.50   '65 57.50
'35 18.00   '55 45.00   '75 175.00

L. Andrew Jackson, new color.
Any post office   279,000,000
'25 .75   '45 2.10   '65 7.50
'35 .80   '55 4.45   '75 27.00

M. Zachary Taylor (1784 - 1850), 12th president (1849 - 50) and hero of the Mexican War. After a daguerreotype attributed to Matthew Brady.
Any post office   38,000,000
'25 1.60   '45 2.75   '65 6.00
'35 2.50   '55 4.45   '75 24.00

N. James A. Garfield.
Any post office   167,351,000
'25 .90   '45 1.25   '65 4.25
'35 1.50   '55 2.75   '75 13.00

O. George Washington, new design.
Any post office   4,320,000,000
'25 .15   '45 .20   '65 .75
'35 .30   '55 .50   '75 2.50

P. Andrew Jackson, new design.
Any post office   78,500,000
'25 .70   '45 1.00   '65 3.85
'35 1.80   '55 2.35   '75 12.00

A. 6/11/87

B. 9/10/87

C. 9/23/87

D. 11/21/88

F. *1/3/88*

Commodore Oliver Hazard Perry (1785 - 1819), shown below, fought against the Barbary pirates before becoming a naval hero in the War of 1812. On September 10, 1813, he defeated the British fleet on Lake Erie and secured the Northwest for the United States. "We have met the enemy and they are ours," was his dispatch to General William H. Harrison.

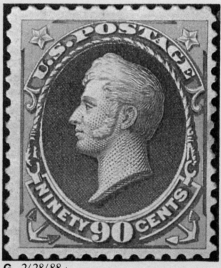

G. *2/28/88*

Alexander Hamilton (1757 - 1804), shown above, served in the Revolutionary War and as a delegate to the Constitutional Convention before becoming the first secretary of the treasury. A believer in a strong central government, he was the leader of the Federalists, one of America's first political parties. His illustrious career ended when he was killed in a duel with Aaron Burr.

E. 2/18/88

A-G. In 1887 and 1888 some of the stamps in the regular issue of 1870-89 were produced in new colors and the 1c denominaton was redesigned.

A. Benjamin Franklin, after a bust by Jean Antoine Houdon.

Any post office	1,325,000,000		
'25	.13	'45 .55	'65 1.60
'35	.40	'55 .80	'75 6.75

B. George Washington, new color.

Any post office	3,580,000,000		
'25	.13	'45 .10	'65 .50
'35	.25	'55 .25	'75 1.85

C. Washington, new color.

Any post office	15,000,000		
'25	.50	'45 1.00	'65 3.25
'35	1.20	'55 1.80	'75 6.50

D. Andrew Jackson, new color.

Any post office	24,500,000		
'25	.40	'45 .75	'65 3.25
'35	1.00	'55 1.50	'75 10.00

E. James A. Garfield (1831-81), 20th president (1881). A dedicated and effective Union Army officer in the Civil War, Garfield served nine terms in the House of Representatives before becoming president. Four months after his inauguration he was assassinated by a disappointed office seeker. New color.

Any post office	85,000,000		
'25	.50	'45 1.00	'65 3.00
'35	1.10	'55 1.40	'75 9.00

F. Alexander Hamilton, new color.

Any post office	915,000		
'25	1.35	'45 4.25	'65 11.00
'35	4.00	'55 7.50	'75 32.50

G. Commodore Oliver H. Perry, new color.

Any post office	135,000		
'25	4.50	'45 20.00	'65 38.50
'35	10.00	'55 25.00	'75 100.00

Regular Issue of 1890, printed by the American Bank Note Company.

H. Benjamin Franklin, after a bust by Jean Antoine Houdon.

Any post office	2,206,093,450		
'25	.05	'45 .20	'65 .90
'35	.15	'55 .32	'75 2.50

H. 2/22/90

I. 2/22/90

J. 6/3/90

K. 2/22/90

L. 6/2/90

M. 6/2/90

N. 2/22/90

O. 3/21/93

P. *2/22/90*

Q. 2/22/90

R. 2/22/90

S. 2/22/90

I. George Washington, after a bust by Jean Antoine Houdon (lake or purplish red).

Any post office   100,000,000
'25 .40   '45 1.00   '65 1.75
'35 1.15   '55 1.20   '75 7.50

J. Washington (carmine).

Any post office   6,244,719,500
'25 .07   '45 .20   '65 .75
'35 .15   '55 .22   '75 1.95

K. Andrew Jackson, after a bust by Hiram Powers.

Any post office   46,877,250
'25 .15   '45 .85   '65 2.35
'35 .60   '55 1.50   '75 7.00

L. Abraham Lincoln, after a daguerreotype by Matthew Brady.

Any post office   66,759,475
'25 .30   '45 1.00   '65 3.00
'35 .65   '55 1.80   '75 8.75

M. U.S. Grant (see p. 42), after a photograph by William Kurtz.

Any post office   152,236,530
'25 .30   '45 .95   '65 3.75
'35 .80   '55 2.20   '75 8.75

N. James A. Garfield.

Any post office   9,253,400
'25 .55   '45 .70   '65 2.40
'35 1.00   '55 1.60   '75 7.25

O. General William T. Sherman (see p.42), after a photograph by Napoleon B. Sarony.

Any post office   12,087,800
'25 .30   '45 .65   '65 2.20
'35 .50   '55 1.55   '75 6.00

P. Daniel Webster (see p. 66), after a daguerreotype by Marcus Root.

Any post office   70,591,710
'25 .50   '45 1.75   '65 6.50
'35 1.00   '55 4.10   '75 15.00

Q. Henry Clay, after a daguerreotype by

Marcus Root.

Any post office   5,548,710
'25 .65   '45 3.00   '65 7.25
'35 2.00   '55 4.50   '75 22.50

R. Thomas Jefferson, after a bust by Giuseppe Ceracchi.

Any post office   1,735,018
'25 1.30   '45 2.75   '65 10.50
'35 2.75   '55 7.25   '75 29.50

S. Commodore Oliver H. Perry, from a statue by William Walcutt.

Any post office   219,721
'25 2.25   '45 6.00   '65 16.50
'35 4.50   '55 10.50   '75 47.50

COLUMBIAN EXPOSITION ISSUE OF 1893

A. *1/2/93*

C. 1/2/93

F. 1/2/93

G. 1/2/93

B. *1/2/93*

Columbian Exposition Issue.

These sixteen stamps, the first U.S. commemoratives and the first large stamps issued by the Post Office, were a magnificent salute to Christopher Columbus (c. 1451 - 1506) and the 400th anniversary of his discovery of North America. Issued during the World's Columbian Exposition held in Chicago in 1893, they depict many events in the life of the great explorer. Shown:

A. Columbus in Sight of Land during his historic voyage of discovery. After a painting by William H. Powell.

Any post office		440,195,550	
'25	.05	'55	.55
'35	.15	'65	.95
'45	.20	'75	4.00

B. Landing of Columbus on Guanahani (San Salvador), October 12, 1492. After a painting by John Vanderlyn in the Rotunda of the Capitol.

Any post office		1,464,588,750	
'25	.06	'55	.35
'35	.18	'65	.84
'45	.20	'75	3.65

C. Flagship of Columbus, after a Spanish engraving of the *Santa Maria*.

Any post office		11,501,250	
'25	.10	'55	1.15
'35	.45	'65	2.50
'45	.80	'75	9.00

D. Fleet of Columbus, after a Spanish engraving of the caravels *Santa Maria, Nina,* and *Pinta*. Normal color: ultramarine or gray blue.

Any post office		19,181,550	
'25	.10	'55	2.00
'35	.30	'65	3.20
'45	.90	'75	10.50

E. Error of color or shade in **D**. The stamps are a strong blue in contrast to the soft, almost pastel coloring of the ordinary stamp. One unused pane of 50 of this variety has been identified. Since the stamps were printed in sheets of 100, another pane is believed to have existed.

'25	125.00	'55	1,000.00
'35	800.00	'65	2,100.00
'45	1,000.00	'75	4,650.00

D. 1/2/93

E. *1/2/93*

H. 3/3/93

I. 1/2/93

K. 1/2/93

J. 1/2/93

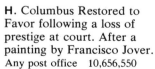

L. 1/2/93

F. Columbus Soliciting Aid of Isabella, after a painting by Vaczlav Brozik.

Any post office	35,248,250		
'25	.15	'55	2.10
'35	.60	'65	4.00
'45	1.20	'75	11.75

G. Columbus Welcomed at Barcelona following his voyage. After a bronze door by Randolph Rogers in the Capitol.

Any post office	4,707,550		
'25	.25	'55	2.50
'35	.90	'65	4.00
'45	1.00	'75	12.50

H. Columbus Restored to Favor following a loss of prestige at court. After a painting by Francisco Jover.

Any post office	10,656,550		
'25	.25	'55	1.90
'35	.55	'65	2.50
'45	.75	'75	9.50

I. Columbus Presenting Natives, after a painting by Luigi Gregori at the University of Notre Dame in South Bend, Indiana.

Any post office	16,516,950		
'25	.25	'55	4.00
'35	1.15	'65	4.75
'45	1.20	'75	17.50

J. Columbus Announcing His Discovery of the land he believed to be the Asian Indies. After a painting by R. Baloca in Madrid.

Any post office	1,576,950		
'25	.90	'55	5.75
'35	2.50	'65	7.50
'45	4.00	'75	32.50

K. Columbus at La Rabida, a convent of Franciscan friars where Columbus rested after failing in his first attempt to receive Spanish aid for his expedition. After a painting by R. Maso.

Any post office	617,250		
'25	1.25	'55	7.00
'35	2.75	'65	10.50
'45	4.50	'75	45.00

L. Recall of Columbus to Spain, where he finally won support from Queen Isabella. After a painting by A. G. Heaton in the Capitol.

Any post office	243,750		
'25	1.75	'55	12.50
'35	4.00	'65	16.50
'45	5.75	'75	60.00

D. *1/2/93*

A. 1/2/93

B. 1/2/93

C. 1/2/93

E. 1/2/93

A. Isabella Pledging Her Jewels, after a painting by Munoz Degrain in Madrid. Although the Queen was apparently willing to pawn her jewels to finance Columbus, she was never forced to do so.

Any post office	55,050		
'25	4.00	'55	31.00
'35	8.75	'65	48.50
'45	21.00	'75	175.00

B. Columbus in Chains on his return to Spain from the third of his four voyages to the New World. After a painting by Emanuel Leutze in Germantown, Pennsylvania.

Any post office	45,550		
'25	4.50	'55	33.50
'35	11.50	'65	55.00
'45	24.00	'75	200.00

C. Columbus Describing His Third Voyage after being released from imprisonment by Ferdinand and Isabella. After a painting by Francisco Jover.

Any post office	27,650		
'25	7.00	'55	52.50
'35	17.00	'65	109.00
'45	34.00	'75	320.00

D. Isabella and Columbus. The painting of Queen Isabella is by Bartolome Bermejo; that of Columbus is by Lorenzo Lotto.

Any post office	26,350		
'25	8.50	'55	58.50
'35	21.50	'65	120.00
'45	44.00	'75	420.00

E. Columbus. After a Spanish medal. Columbus made his first voyage to prove that the Orient could be reached by sailing west from Europe. After landing in the Bahamas in 1492, he returned to Spain in triumph, convinced that he had achieved his goal. During three later voyages he reached mainland South America, but fell into disgrace when his expeditions failed to yield anticipated wealth. One year following his final voyage he died in neglect, unaware that he had found a New World.

Any post office	27,350		
'25	10.00	'55	67.50
'35	23.50	'65	135.00
'45	45.00	'75	580.00

FIRST BUREAU ISSUE 1894

Since 1894 all U.S. postage stamps except a few multicolored issues have been produced by the Bureau of Engraving and Printing. The first Bureau issue of 1894 was produced from engraving dies supplied by the American Bank Note Company. The stamps are similar to those of 1890, but triangles were added to the upper corners to distinguish them from the earlier issue. In 1895 the same designs were printed on paper watermarked double-line USPS.

A. 10/10/94

B. 1894

G. 9/24/94

C. 10/5/94

D. 1894

E. 1894

F. 1898

All designs in the first Bureau issue are shown on these pages. In addition, examples of the shades in which the 1c and 2c designs appeared are also shown. Most of these color variations resulted from production experiments and efforts to improve the appearance of the stamps.

A. Benjamin Franklin (ultramarine).

Any post office	100,000,000		
'25	.12	'45 .25	'65 .80
'35	.25	'55 .48	'75 2.85

B. Franklin (blue).

Any post office	305,000,000		
'25	.06	'45 .35	'65 .95
'35	.30	'55 .55	'75 3.90

C. George Washington (pink).

Any post office	40,000,000		
'25	.12	'45 .26	'65 .48
'35	.20	'55 .40	'75 2.25

D. Washington (carmine lake).

Any post office	100,000,000		
'25	.40	'45 1.35	'65 2.00
'35	1.00	'55 1.45	'75 11.00

E. Washington (carmine).

Any post office	910,000,000		
'25	.08	'45 .40	'65 .75
'35	.12	'55 .45	'75 2.65

F. Washington (red) watermarked double-line USPS. Also issued in booklets in 1900. These booklets, the first ever released by the postal service, contained miniature panes of six stamps each. Because of their convenient size they became very popular.

Any post office	12,000,000		
'25	.20	'45 .38	'65 .30
'35	.40	'55 .38	'75 .80

Note: Three engravings of the triangle design of the 2c stamp exist. The earliest of these, shown above on the stamps of 1894, has lines of equal thickness running through the triangles. On later printings the lines are thinner inside the triangles and on the 1898 variety shown above there are no lines within the frame lines of the triangles.

G. Andrew Jackson.

Any post office	20,214,300		
'25	.15	'45 .65	'65 1.85
'35	.45	'55 1.10	'75 6.25

A. 9/11/94

B. *9/28/94*

C. 7/18/94

D. 3/25/95

Ulysses S. Grant (1822 - 85),
18th president (1869 - 77), volunteered
to serve in the Union Army when the
Civil War began. After engaging the
Confederates at Shiloh he moved to
Vicksburg, where his brilliant strategy
won for him the command of the
western armies. As Lincoln's
commanding general he directed the
campaign to Richmond that resulted in
Lee's surrender. After the war he
became a popular hero and was
twice elected president.

E. 9/17/94

G. 11/1/94

F. 10/15/94

H. 11/15/94

A. Abraham Lincoln.
Any post office   16,718,150
'25 .30   '45 1.10   '65 2.60
'35 1.00   '55 1.60   '75 7.75

B. Ulysses S. Grant.
Any post office   30,688,840
'25 .30   '45 1.20   '65 1.70
'35 .60   '55 1.05   '75 5.75

C. James A. Garfield.
Any post office   5,120,800
'25 .55   '45 1.25   '65 2.75
'35 1.25   '55 2.10   '75 8.00

**D. General William T.
Sherman** (1820 - 91), military
commander most

remembered for his Civil
War campaign from
Atlanta to the sea. He once
said, "War is hell."
Any post office   2,426,100
'25 .45   '45 1.00   '65 2.30
'35 1.25   '55 1.65   '75 6.50

E. Daniel Webster.
Any post office   12,263,180
'25 .50   '45 2.50   '65 4.50
'35 2.40   '55 3.50   '75 15.00

F. Henry Clay.
Any post office   1,583,920
'25 .95   '45 5.75   '65 9.25
'35 3.00   '55 6.00   '75 29.00

G. Thomas Jefferson, design
of 1890, new denomination.
Any post office   175,330
'25 1.85   '45 4.50   '65 11.00
'35 4.50   '55 5.50   '75 35.00

**H. Commodore Oliver H.
Perry,** design of 1890,
new denomination.
Any post office   26,284
'25 3.60   '45 21.25   '65 33.50
'35 12.00 '55 24.00   '75 100.00

I. James Madison (1751 -
1836), 4th president (1809 -
17), after a painting by

Gilbert Stuart. Known as the
"Father of the Constitution",
Madison drew up the
Virginia Plan, which is the
basis of the Constitution, and
dominated the debates at the
Constitutional Convention of
1787. One of the authors of
the *Federalist* papers, he also
proposed nine of the ten
amendments in the Bill
of Rights.
Any post office   10,027
'25 8.00   '45 30.00   '65 52.00
'35 27.50   '55 32.50   '75 160.00

I. *12/10/94*

J. *12/10/94*

REGULAR ISSUE OF 1898

K. 1/17/98

In 1898 new colors were introduced for many denominations of regular stamps. The changes in the 1c and 5c stamps were made to conform to a Universal Postal Union system of color-coding international and domestic postage throughout the world. Also in 1898, U.S. postage stamps were overprinted for specialized use as revenue stamps and as postage in the nation's territories overseas (see p. 211).

L. 10/7/98

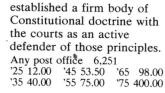

M. 3/8/98

N. 12/31/98

O. 1898

P. 11/30/98

J. John Marshall (1755 - 1835), after a painting by Henry Inman. A native of the Virginia frontier, Marshall served in the Revolution and then practiced law in Richmond. In 1801 he became chief justice of the Supreme Court, a position he held until his death. Through his opinion in *Marbury* vs. *Madison* he established the Supreme Court as the final interpreter of the Constitution. In subsequent decisions he

established a firm body of Constitutional doctrine with the courts as an active defender of those principles.

Any post office   6,251
'25 12.00   '45 53.50   '65 98.00
'35 40.00   '55 75.00   '75 400.00

K. Benjamin Franklin, new color.

Any post office   5,216,159,932
'25 .04   '45 .15   '65 .40
'35 .06   '55 .22   '75 1.00

L. Abraham Lincoln, new color.

Any post office   153,499,379
'25 .45   '45 .70   '65 1.40
'35 .60   '55 1.10   '75 3.35

M. Ulysses S. Grant, new color.

Any post office   279,622,170
'25 .18   '45 .50   '65 1.00
'35 .35   '55 .70   '75 2.65

N. James A. Garfield, new color.

Any post office   46,457,540
'25 .60   '45 2.00   '65 2.10
'35 1.20   '55 1.60   '75 5.50

O. Daniel Webster, new color.

Any post office   65,000,000
'25 .95   '45 3.50   '65 5.50
'35 3.00   '55 4.00   '75 14.00

P. Henry Clay (1777 - 1852), orator, lawyer, U.S. Senator and Congressman. His Compromise of 1850 helped to delay the Civil War for ten years. New color.

Any post office   15,993,313
'25 .80   '45 2.80   '65 6.00
'35 2.25   '55 4.25   '75 17.50

In 1898 the western part of the United States was beginning to reach maturity. Thousands of wagon trains had passed over its mountains, deserts, and Great Plains; wars had been fought with the Indians, and many new states had been admitted to the Union. To call attention to developments in the land west of the Mississippi River, an international exposition was held in Omaha, Nebraska, from June 1 to November 1 of that year. It featured central displays on art, agriculture, mining, machinery, and manufacturing. In conjunction with this exposition the postmaster general authorized the issuance of nine stamps which were later nicknamed "Omahas". The stamps were supposed to be produced in two colors, but because of the demand for revenues during the Spanish-American War the Bureau of Engraving and Printing was obliged to print them in one color only. Even so, many collectors prize them for their beauty. Shown:

A. Marquette on the Mississippi, after a painting by William Lamprecht. Father Marquette, a French Jesuit, explored the Mississippi as far as the Gulf of Mexico with Louis Jolliet.

Any post office	70,993,400		
'25 .07	'45 .40	'65 1.60	
'35 .22	'55 .85	'75 5.75	

B. Farming in the West, based upon a photograph taken in Cass County, North Dakota, where farmers were plowing out a wheat field damaged by hail.

Any post office	159,720,800		
'25 .07	'45 .32	'65 1.20	
'35 .15	'55 .42	'75 4.00	

C. Indian Hunting Buffalo, after an engraving by Seth Eastman in H.R. Schoolcraft's *History of the Indian Tribes* (1854).

Any post office	4,924,500		
'25 .25	'45 2.00	'65 5.85	
'35 1.00	'55 3.60	'75 18.50	

A. *6/17/98*

B. 6/17/98

D. 6/17/98

C. *6/17/98*

E. 6/17/98

F. 6/17/98

G. 6/17/98

H. *6/17/98*

I. 6/17/98

D. Frémont on Rocky Mountains, after a woodcut attributed to John W. Orr. Known as the "pathmarker", Capt. John Charles Frémont mapped and surveyed the Oregon Trail in the 1840's for future pioneers.

Any post office   7,694,180
'25   .30   '45 2.00   '65   5.50
'35 1.25   '55 3.10   '75 17.50

E. Troops Guarding Train, after a drawing by western artist Frederic Remington.

Any post office   2,927,200
'25   .55   '45 3.25   '65   7.50
'35 2.00   '55 4.50   '75 23.50

F. Hardships of Emigration, after a painting by Augustus Goodyear Heaton. It depicts a crisis scene for a lone family of pioneers.

Any post office   4,629,760
'25   .50   '45 3.35   '65   9.50
'35 2.00   '55 5.95   '75 31.50

G. Western Mining Prospector, after *The Gold Bug* by Frederic Remington.

Any post office   530,400
'25   3.00   '55   19.50
'35   7.00   '65   30.00
'45   12.00   '75 115.00

H. Western Cattle in Storm, after *The Vanguard* by J. A. MacWhirter. Despite its title this stamp depicts a group of cattle in the West Highlands of Scotland. It was designed from a reproduction of a painting that was used by an American cattle firm as a trademark.

Any post office   56,900
'25   4.50   '55   54.00
'35   12.50   '65   65.00
'45   35.00   '75 250.00

I. Mississippi River Bridge, after a photograph supplied by the Illinois and St. Louis Bridge Company of St. Louis. The picture depicts the Eads Bridge at St. Louis, which was built in the 19th century.

Any post office   56,200
'25   11.00   '55   69.50
'35   20.00   '65   85.00
'45   37.50   '75 350.00

A. Fast Lake Navigation, after a photograph of the Great Lakes steamer S.S. *City of Alpena.*

Any post office   91,401,500
'25 .06   '45 .26   '65 1.00
'35 .18   '55 .45   '75 4.50

B. Fast Express, after a photograph of the "Empire State Express". The photograph was taken while the train was speeding along at 60 miles an hour.

Any post office   209,759,700
'25 .07   '45 .32   '65 .90
'35 .18   '55 .43   '75 4.50

C. Automobile, after a photograph of one of the first electric models ever produced. The closed-coach vehicle was used by the Baltimore and Ohio Railroad to carry passengers from the Washington railroad station to all parts of the city.

Any post office   5,737,100
'25 .16   '45 1.50   '65 5.25
'35 1.00   '55 3.90   '75 18.50

D. Bridge at Niagara Falls, after a photograph of the largest single-span steel bridge in the world at that time. The bridge collapsed in 1938 under pressure from a 65-foot ice jam.

Any post office   7,201,300
'25 .30   '45 1.50   '65 5.20
'35 1.10   '55 3.60   '75 18.50

E. Canal Locks at Sault de Ste. Marie, after a photograph. Two ore boats and a tug are shown in the locks.

Any post office   4,921,700
'25 .35   '45 2.65   '65 5.75
'35 1.50   '55 3.75   '75 21.00

F. Fast Ocean Navigation, after a photograph of the S.S. *St. Paul.* This vessel was the first to be commissioned as an auxiliary cruiser of the navy in the Spanish-American War.

Any post office   5,043,700
'25 .35   '45 3.20   '65 8.00
'35 1.75   '55 5.25   '75 29.75

PAN-AMERICAN EXPOSITION
ISSUE OF 1901

The Pan-American Exposition, a salute to engineering achievements in the western hemisphere, was held in 1901 at Buffalo, New York. Six stamps honored the event. They were placed on sale on May 1 and withdrawn from sale on October 31, the opening and closing dates of the exposition. The first bicolor stamps since 1869, they were also the first stamps to be issued in the 20th century.

A. 5/1/01

B. 5/1/01

C. 5/1/01

D. 5/1/01

E. 5/1/01

F. 5/1/01

G. *1901*

H. *1901*

I. *1901*

G-I. Human error played a role in the creation of some of the most celebrated rarities of the 20th century. The small size Pan-American Exposition stamps were printed by hand on small presses, one sheet at a time. Despite all precautions a few of them were produced with inverted centers. Like their predecessors, the inverted stamps of 1869, they have become very famous and command premium prices.

G. Fast Lake Navigation, inverted center. It is estimated that about 1,000 of these stamps were printed. A few of them were used on mail before they were discovered.

'25	80.00	'55	500.00
'35	300.00	'65	1,600.00
'45	375.00	'75	3,750.00

H. Fast Express, inverted center. Only 158 copies of this stamp are known to exist. It is the rarest of the Pan-American inverts.

'25	750.00	'55	2,750.00
'35	2,700.00	'65	6,000.00
'45	2,500.00	'75	19,000.00

I. Automobile, inverted center. It is generally accepted that these stamps were deliberately produced after rumors of a 4c error reached Washington. The rumors were erroneous. Of the 400 so created, all but 206 were destroyed. Many of the copies which reached the public are overprinted "specimen".

'25	150.00	'55	1,000.00
'35	1,200.00	'65	2,500.00
'45	1,000.00	'75	6,500.00

A. Benjamin Franklin, painted by J. B. Longacre. Also issued imperforate, in coils, and in booklets.

Any post office	11,174,161,974				
'25	.04	'45	.15	'65	.33
'35	.10	'55	.18	'75	.90

B. George Washington, painted by Gilbert Stuart. Also issued in booklets.

Any post office	3,416,651,906				
'25	.20	'45	.20	'65	.45
'35	.20	'55	.25	'75	1.10

C. Andrew Jackson, painted by Thomas Sully.

Any post office	276,212,074				
'25	.20	'45	.80	'65	1.70
'35	.75	'55	1.00	'75	5.25

D. Ulysses S. Grant, from a ferrotype by Kurtz. Also issued imperforate.

Any post office	346,666,374				
'25	.20	'45	.65	'65	1.50
'35	.50	'55	.95	'75	5.25

E. Abraham Lincoln, from a Brady photograph. Also issued imperforate and in coils **(P)**.

Any post office	550,326,574				
'25	.25	'45	.60	'65	1.50
'35	.55	'55	1.10	'75	5.25

F. James A. Garfield, from a photograph.

Any post office	117,567,474				
'25	.30	'45	1.00	'65	2.10
'35	.95	'55	1.45	'75	6.25

G. Martha Washington.

Any post office	176,841,474				
'25	.30	'45	.55	'65	1.40
'35	.40	'55	1.00	'75	4.25

H. Daniel Webster, after a daguerreotype by Whipple.

Any post office	260,010,574				
'25	.40	'45	1.20	'65	2.25
'35	.90	'55	1.65	'75	7.50

I. Benjamin Harrison, from a photograph supplied by Mrs. Harrison.

Any post office	31,290,174				
'25	.40	'45	.80	'65	1.50
'35	.75	'55	1.00	'75	5.25

J. Henry Clay.

Any post office	41,205,754				
'25	.60	'45	3.00	'65	6.75
'35	2.00	'55	4.35	'75	20.00

K. Thomas Jefferson, painted by Gilbert Stuart.

Any post office	2,651,774				
'25	1.30	'45	7.50	'65	17.50
'35	4.50	'55	12.85	'75	55.00

A. 2/3/03

B. 1/17/03

C. 2/11/03

D. 2/10/03

E. 1/20/03

F. 2/20/03

G. *12/6/02*

H. 2/5/03

This stamp, the first to show an American woman, was designed from a Gilbert Stuart portrait of Martha Washington (1732 - 1802). It was regarded as the most beautiful stamp in the issue of 1902, which was the first set of U.S. stamps to be completely designed by the Bureau of Engraving and Printing.

I. 11/18/02

J. 5/27/03

K. 3/23/03

L. 6/5/03

M. 6/5/03

N. 6/5/03

THE EVOLUTION OF COILS

O. 10/2/06

Q. 7/31/08

P. 2/24/08

L. David Farragut, after an engraving by Charles Schlecht (see p. 73).

Any post office   504,374

'25	3.50	'55	24.00
'35	7.50	'65	32.00
'45	21.50	'75	100.00

M. James Madison, painted by Gilbert Stuart.

Any post office   37,872

'25	5.00	'55	37.00
'35	11.00	'65	48.00
'45	27.50	'75	140.00

N. John Marshall, after an engraving by Charles Schlecht.

Any post office   49,211

'25	10.00	'55	72.50
'35	22.00	'65	88.00
'45	55.00	'75	250.00

The Evolution of Coils. When the now familiar stamp dispensing machine was developed a need was created for stamps in rolls — or coils — to use in them. Beginning in 1906, non-government firms such as the Schermack Company made privately perforated coils from imperforate sheets of stamps issued by the postal service. Two years later, in 1908, the U.S. government became the first one in the world to issue coils. Values which follow are for coil pairs. Shown:

O. Imperforate issue with Schermack private perforation.

'25	.20	'45	3.00	'65	2.50
'35	.50	'55	2.50	'75	3.75

P. Abraham Lincoln coil, perforated horizontally. This stamp and the 1c value of the 1902 series were the first adhesives issued by the postal service in coil form. Copies are very rare and collectors are warned that forgeries exist.

'25	12.50	'55	125.00
'35		'65	500.00
'45		'75	1,450.00

Q. George Washington coil, perforated vertically. The design was also used on stamps issued in sheets and booklets. The stamp replaced the 2c design of the 1902 series **(B)**, which was unpopular.

'25	8.50	'55	125.00
'35		'65	600.00
'45		'75	1,350.00

LOUISIANA PURCHASE EXPOSITION ISSUE

A. 4/30/04

B. 4/30/04

C. 4/30/04

D. 4/30/04

E. 4/30/04

JAMESTOWN EXPOSITION ISSUE

F. 4/25/07

G. 4/25/07

H. 5/3/07

Louisiana Purchase Exposition Issue. Five stamps, issued for the St. Louis fair of 1904, celebrate the 100th anniversary of the Louisiana Purchase (see p. 107). The acquisition of this land from Napoleon of France added over 500,000,000 acres to the U.S. Shown:

A. Robert Livingston, minister to France during the negotiations.

Any post office   79,779,200
'25   .08   '45   .37   '65 2.35
'35   .45   '55 1.40   '75 7.00

B. Thomas Jefferson, president at the time of the purchase.

Any post office   192,732,400
'25   .09   '45   .35   '65 1.90
'35   .35   '55 1.05   '75 5.25

C. James Monroe, special ambassador to France who assisted in the negotiations.

Any post office   4,542,600
'25   .25   '45 2.50   '65 5.50
'35 1.60   '55 4.00   '75 16.50

D. William McKinley, president who authorized the St. Louis exposition.

Any post office   6,926,700
'25   .60   '45 2.75   '65 6.50
'35 1.65   '55 4.50   '75 19.75

E. U.S. map showing the Louisiana Territory.

Any post office   4,011,200
'25   .70   '45 5.00   '65 17.00
'35 3.50   '55 11.50   '75 50.00

Jamestown Exposition Issue. 300th anniversary of the founding of the first permanent English settlement in America. Shown:

F. John Smith, whose leadership helped the colony survive after famine and disease claimed over half of the original population.

Any post office   77,728,794
'25   .05   '45   .25   '65   .85
'35   .20   '55   .50   '75 3.25

G. The Founding of Jamestown by about 100 colonists on May 14, 1607.

Any post office   149,497,994
'25   .07   '45   .30   '65 1.00
'35   .30   '55   .55   '75 3.85

I. *9/25/09*

PANAMA-PACIFIC EXPOSITION ISSUE

J. *12/26/12*

K. *1/18/13*

L. *12/13/12*

M. *12/26/12*

N. *8/25/13*

H. Pocahontas, daughter of the chief Powhatan, who befriended the settlers.

Any post office   7,980,594

'25	.17	'45	2.50	'65	7.00
'35	1.50	'55	4.35	'75	24.50

I. Hudson - Fulton Exposition Issue. Also issued imperforate. In 1609 Henry Hudson discovered the Hudson River. In 1807 Robert Fulton's steamboat made its maiden voyage from New York to Albany along the same waterway. Shown: Hudson's ship, the *Half-Moon*, and Fulton's *Clermont*.

Any post office   72,634,631

'25	.08	'45	.26	'65	.85
'35	.20	'55	.35	'75	3.50

Panama-Pacific Exposition Issue, honoring the discovery of the Pacific Ocean by Balboa in 1513, the opening of the Panama Canal in 1914, and the San Francisco exposition of 1915. Stamps shown are perf. 12 and are not as valuable as the perf. 10 varieties which were issued in 1915. Quantities listed include both varieties. Shown:

J. Vasco Nuñez de Balboa.

Any post office   334,796,926

'25	.04	'45	.25	'65	.90
'35	.25	'55	.50	'75	4.50

K. Pedro Miguel Locks of the Panama Canal.

Any post office   503,713,086

'25	.05	'45	.25	'65	.90
'35	.25	'55	.50	'75	4.65

L. The Golden Gate.

San Francisco, Calif.
29,088,726

'25	.17	'45	2.65	'65	6.15
'35	1.50	'55	4.75	'75	17.50

M. The Discovery of San Francisco Bay.

San Francisco, Calif.
16,968,365 **(M & N)**

'25	.50	'45	5.00	'65	10.00
'35	2.50	'55	7.65	'75	35.00

N. Discovery of San Francisco Bay, new color to make the stamp design more prominent.

Any post office

'25	.50	'45	5.50	'65	13.00
'35	3.50	'55	8.00	'75	52.50

A. *12/2/08*

B. *11/16/08*

C. 12/24/08

D. 12/19/08

E. 12/31/08

F. 1/7/09

G. 1/11/09

H. 1/19/09

I. 1/13/09

J. 1/29/09

The regular issues of 1908-21 bring to mind the saying "looks can be deceiving." During this period the postal service standardized regular stamp design. All the values depict either Washington or Franklin after busts by Jean Antoine Houdon. At the same time postage stamp production nearly tripled, expanding from something close to seven billion in 1907 to just over 20 billion in 1920. Because of this the Bureau of Engraving and Printing tried to find new means of efficiently producing stamps in astronomical quantities. During their experiments new equipment was introduced, and the stamps were printed on two types of watermarked paper or on unwatermarked paper, on different presses and with different perforations. A few were also printed on experimental "bluish" paper. Imperforate stamps as well as coils and booklets were also released. The result was a group of stamps which are remarkably similar in design but are extremely varied in their perforations and their watermarks. These differences, while not regarded as significant by the postal service, are treated as major varieties by philatelists. Many of them are difficult to identify and require detailed study. The illustrations on these pages show examples of every denomination and color in which the stamps were printed. Unless otherwise indicated, stamps shown are perforated 12 and watermarked double-line USPS.

A. Benjamin Franklin.

| '25 | .03 | '45 | .11 | '65 | .36 |
| '35 | .04 | '55 | .22 | '75 | 1.50 |

B. George Washington.

| '25 | .04 | '45 | .05 | '65 | .20 |
| '35 | .06 | '55 | .08 | '75 | 1.25 |

C. Washington.

| '25 | .16 | '45 | .65 | '65 | 1.40 |
| '35 | .40 | '55 | .90 | '75 | 4.50 |

Several engravings, known as types, exist of **C & T**.

K. 12/24/08

L. 6/ - /09

M. 12/12/08

N. 6/ - /09

The blue paper stamps **(L,N,P)** shown on this page are relatively valuable and scarce. The bluish or grayish rag content paper was used in an unsuccessful effort to overcome problems caused by the uneven shrinkage of ordinary paper after stamps were printed.

O. 4/29/14

P. 2/ - /09

Q. 2/12/09

R. 6/1/09

S. 2/12/12

T. 2/12/12

D. Washington.

| '25 | .15 | '45 | .65 | '65 | 2.40 |
| '35 | .45 | '55 | 1.55 | '75 | 5.25 |

E. Washington.

| '25 | .25 | '45 | 1.10 | '65 | 2.60 |
| '35 | 1.00 | '55 | 1.60 | '75 | 6.25 |

F. Washington.

| '25 | .45 | '45 | 1.50 | '65 | 3.35 |
| '35 | .95 | '55 | 2.35 | '75 | 8.50 |

G. Washington.

| '25 | .60 | '45 | 1.20 | '65 | 2.75 |
| '35 | 1.00 | '55 | 1.90 | '75 | 5.75 |

H. Washington.

| '25 | .45 | '45 | 1.35 | '65 | 2.75 |
| '35 | 1.00 | '55 | 2.00 | '75 | 8.00 |

I. Washington.

| '25 | 1.15 | '45 | 6.60 | '65 | 15.00 |
| '35 | 4.00 | '55 | 11.75 | '75 | 42.50 |

J. Washington.

| '25 | 3.50 | '45 | 10.50 | '65 | 24.00 |
| '35 | 7.75 | '55 | 18.50 | '75 | 75.00 |

K. Washington.

| '25 | .13 | '45 | .55 | '65 | 1.70 |
| '35 | .35 | '55 | .94 | '75 | 5.25 |

L. Washington, blue paper.
Washington, D.C.

'25	125.00	'55	750.00
'35	1,000.00	'65	1,800.00
'45	750.00	'75	6,500.00

M. Washington.

| '25 | .40 | '45 | .60 | '65 | 1.60 |
| '35 | .60 | '55 | 1.05 | '75 | 3.95 |

N. Washington, blue paper.

Washington, D.C.

'25	125.00	'55	750.00
'35	1,000.00	'65	1,700.00
'45	750.00	'75	6,500.00

O. Washington, perf. 12, single-line USPS watermark.

| '25 | .20 | '45 | 1.95 | '65 | 5.00 |
| '35 | 1.75 | '55 | 3.75 | '75 | 12.50 |

P. Lincoln Centennial Issue, blue paper. Shown: statue by Saint - Gaudens.
Any post office.   637,000

| '25 | .50 | '45 | 6.50 | '65 | 18.50 |
| '35 | 4.00 | '55 | 11.50 | '75 | 49.75 |

Q. Lincoln Centennial Issue, ordinary paper. Also issued imperforate.

Any post office   148,387,191

| '25 | .08 | '45 | .16 | '65 | .70 |
| '35 | .20 | '55 | .28 | '75 | 2.75 |

R. Alaska - Yukon - Pacific Exposition Issue. Also issued imperforate. Shown: William H. Seward, who arranged the purchase of Alaska.
Seattle, Wash.   152,990,051

| '25 | .08 | '45 | .55 | '65 | .90 |
| '35 | .25 | '55 | .55 | '75 | 3.50 |

S. Washington, with numerals.

| '25 | .03 | '45 | .11 | '65 | .26 |
| '35 | .07 | '55 | .10 | '75 | 1.50 |

T. Washington, with numerals.

| '25 | .04 | '45 | .07 | '65 | .21 |
| '35 | .06 | '55 | .07 | '75 | 1.15 |

A-N. Regular issues of 1908 - 21, continued. Unless otherwise indicated, stamps shown are perforated 10 and watermarked single - line USPS.

A. Benjamin Franklin.

| '25 | .20 | '45 | .95 | '65 | 2.40 |
| '35 | .30 | '55 | 1.70 | '75 | 5.50 |

B. Franklin.

| '25 | .35 | '45 | 1.10 | '65 | 2.65 |
| '35 | .80 | '55 | 1.65 | '75 | 6.50 |

C. Franklin.

| '25 | .20 | '45 | .90 | '65 | 1.80 |
| '35 | .50 | '55 | 1.25 | '75 | 4.95 |

D. Franklin.

| '25 | .25 | '45 | .42 | '65 | 1.20 |
| '35 | .50 | '55 | .60 | '75 | 3.50 |

E. Franklin.

| '25 | .35 | '45 | 1.05 | '65 | 1.50 |
| '35 | .75 | '55 | 1.25 | '75 | 3.25 |

F. Franklin, perf. 11, unwatermarked.

| '25 | | '45 | .45 | '65 | .88 |
| '35 | .30 | '55 | .67 | '75 | 2.25 |

G. Franklin.

| '25 | .42 | '45 | 4.00 | '65 | 8.25 |
| '35 | 1.60 | '55 | 6.35 | '75 | 17.50 |

H. Franklin.

| '25 | .48 | '45 | 4.00 | '65 | 10.00 |
| '35 | 1.75 | '55 | 7.00 | '75 | 23.50 |

I. Franklin.

| '25 | 1.10 | '45 | 7.25 | '65 | 13.50 |
| '35 | 4.30 | '55 | 9.25 | '75 | 32.50 |

J. Franklin.

| '25 | 1.90 | '45 | 26.00 | '65 | 45.00 |
| '35 | 13.00 | '55 | 36.50 | '75 | 115.00 |

K. Franklin, perf. 12, watermarked double - line USPS.

| '25 | 2.75 | '45 | 16.00 | '65 | 31.00 |
| '35 | 10.00 | '55 | 22.50 | '75 | 80.00 |

L. Franklin, perf. 11.

| '25 | 3.50 | '45 | 27.50 | '65 | 47.50 |
| '35 | 10.00 | '55 | 39.50 | '75 | 100.00 |

M. Franklin, perf. 11.
296,653

| '25 | 6.00 | '45 | 10.75 | '65 | 15.50 |
| '35 | 6.75 | '55 | 12.50 | '75 | 47.50 |

N. Franklin, new color, perf. 11.
791,380 **(L & N)**

| '25 | 2.50 | '45 | 6.00 | '65 | 14.50 |
| '35 | 3.50 | '55 | 11.25 | '75 | 42.50 |

A. 9/26/14

B. 10/6/14

C. 9/9/14

D. 8/9/15

E. 9/10/14

F. 1/10/19

G. 9/16/14

H. 9/19/14

I. 9/19/14

J. 12/10/15

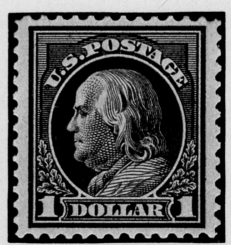

K. *2/12/12*

L. 8/19/18

M. 8/19/18

N. 11/1/20

Issued to celebrate victory in World War I, the stamp shown at right portrays Liberty Victorious holding the scales of justice and in the background the flags of the United States and its allies, Great Britain, Belgium, Italy, and France.

O. *3/3/19*

PILGRIM TERCENTENARY ISSUE

On a cold and rainy day in December 1620 the Pilgrims landed at Plymouth, Massachusetts. After giving thanks for their safe journey they began to build the colony that established liberty and independent worship in America.

Q. *12/21/20*

P. 12/21/20

R. 12/21/20

O. Victory Issue. World War I (1914-18), which claimed over 10,000,000 lives and brought the world great suffering and hardship, came to an end on November 11, 1918, when an armistice was signed at Compiègne, France. Washington, D.C. 99,585,200

| '25 | .05 | '45 | .30 | '65 | 1.10 |
| '35 | .35 | '55 | .75 | '75 | 3.75 |

Pilgrim Tercentenary Issue. The 101 colonists who settled the Plymouth Colony in 1620 included 35 Separatists from the Church of England who are known as Pilgrims. Denied the right to worship as they chose in England, they had lived in Holland for ten years before deciding to resettle in the New World. After 65 days at sea their 180-ton ship, the *Mayflower,* reached Cape Cod where they drew up America's first written constitution, the Mayflower Compact. With this historic document the men of the company pledged to "enacte, constitute, and frame such just & equall lawes . . . as shall be thought most meete & convenient for ye generall good of ye colonie . . ." Afterwards, the Pilgrims explored the coast of Massachusetts, looking for a favorable site for their colony. They finally chose Plymouth. Shown:

P. *The Mayflower,* watercolor by Harrison Eastman (Smithsonian Institution, Washington, D.C.).
Plymouth and Provincetown, Mass. 137,978,207

| '25 | .03 | '45 | .12 | '65 | .52 |
| '35 | .12 | '55 | .22 | '75 | 1.75 |

Q. *Landing of the Pilgrims,* after an 1846 Burt engraving of a sketch by Edwin White.
Plymouth and Provincetown, Mass. 196,037,327

| '25 | .05 | '45 | .27 | '65 | 1.00 |
| '35 | .20 | '55 | .42 | '75 | 3.25 |

R. *The Signing of the Compact,* painting by Edwin White.
Plymouth and Provincetown, Mass. 11,321,607

| '25 | .12 | '45 | 1.50 | '65 | 4.75 |
| '35 | 1.00 | '55 | 2.60 | '75 | 12.50 |

The regular issue of 1922-23 introduced a multiplicity of portraits to replace the Washington and Franklin designs of 1908-21. Originally issued perf. 11, many of the denominations were later issued perf. 10 and perf. 11 by 10½ or 10½ by 11.

A. Benjamin Franklin. Also issued imperforate, in coils, and in booklets.
Washington, D.C. and Philadelphia, Pa.

'25	.01	'45	.05	'65	.12
'35	.03	'55	.10	'75	.35

B. George Washington. Also issued imperforate, in coils, and in booklets. Two engravings of this stamp exist. They are classified as different types.
Washington, D.C.

'25	.02	'45	.06	'65	.17
'35	.06	'55	.08	'75	.38

C. Abraham Lincoln. Also issued in coils.
Washington, D.C. and Hodgenville, Ky.

'25	.05	'45	.75	'65	1.65
'35	.45	'55	1.30	'75	5.00

D. Martha Washington, painted by Gilbert Stuart. Also issued in coils.
Washington, D.C.

'25	.05	'45	.45	'65	.90
'35	.25	'55	.50	'75	4.50

E. Theodore Roosevelt. Also issued in coils.
Washington, D.C.; New York, N.Y.; Oyster Bay, N.Y.

'25	.07	'45	.40	'65	1.00
'35	.35	'55	.65	'75	4.00

F. James A. Garfield. Also issued in coils.
Washington, D.C.

'25	.08	'45	.95	'65	2.70
'35	.30	'55	1.85	'75	9.75

G. William McKinley (1843-1901), 25th president (1897-1901). An advocate of the gold standard and tariff protection for "infant industries", he led the nation during the Spanish-American War.
Washington, D.C.; Niles, Ohio

'25	.09	'45	.15	'65	.35
'35	.15	'55	.18	'75	1.75

H. Ulysses S. Grant.
Washington, D.C.

'25	.10	'45	.90	'65	2.90
'35	.30	'55	2.25	'75	11.00

A. 1/17/23

B. 1/15/23

C. 2/12/23

D. 1/15/23

E. *10/27/22*

Theodore Roosevelt (1858-1919). The 26th president (1901-09) was a spirited leader, a naturalist, and a writer. During his administrations work was started on the Panama Canal, the U.S. became a major naval power, and many conservation measures were enacted.

F. 11/20/22

G. 5/1/23

H. 5/1/23

I. 1/15/23

J. 1/15/23

K. 10/4/22

L. 3/20/23

M. 5/1/23

N. 11/11/22

O. 5/1/23

P. 11/11/22

Q. 3/20/23

I. Thomas Jefferson, painted by Gilbert Stuart.
Washington, D.C.

'25	.12	'45	.23	'65	.70
'35	.20	'55	.50	'75	2.50

J. James Monroe. Also issued in coils.
Washington, D.C.

'25	.12	'45	.43	'65	.80
'35	.30	'55	.50	'75	3.50

K. Rutherford B. Hayes (1822 - 93), 19th president (1877 - 81). He was a staunch supporter of merit appointment to the civil service, prison reform, and sound currency.
Washington, D.C. and
Fremont, Ohio

'25	.14	'45	.20	'65	.27
'35	.25	'55	.22	'75	.45

L. Grover Cleveland (1837 - 1908), 22nd and 24th president (1885 - 89 and 1893 - 97). An independent administrator who fought against political corruption, he opposed Congress on many issues and was nominated for president despite the opposition of Democratic party stalwarts.
Washington, D.C.;
Boston, Mass.; Caldwell, N.J.

'25	.15	'45	.28	'65	.54
'35	.20	'55	.40	'75	1.65

M. American Indian, Brule Sioux Chief Hollow Horn Bear.
Washington, D.C. and
Muskogee, Okla.

'25	.18	'45	.25	'65	.40
'35	.30	'55	.26	'75	1.25

N. Statue of Liberty (see p. 108).
Washington, D.C.

'25	.18	'45	.50	'65	1.20
'35	.25	'55	.90	'75	3.75

O. Golden Gate.
Washington, D.C. and
San Francisco, Calif.

'25	.25	'45	.75	'65	1.25
'35	.35	'55	.95	'75	4.95

P. Niagara Falls, New York.
Washington, D.C.

'25	.30	'45	.45	'65	1.25
'35	.50	'55	.80	'75	4.00

Q. Buffalo.
Washington, D.C.

'25	.36	'45	.75	'65	1.35
'35	.45	'55	.75	'75	6.50

A. 11/11/22

F. 5/1/24

B. 2/12/23

C. 3/20/23

G. 5/1/24

E. 9/1/23

D. 3/20/23

H. 5/1/24

A. Arlington National Cemetery Amphitheatre and the Tomb of the Unknown Soldier (World War I).
Washington, D.C.

| '25 | .56 | '45 | 1.25 | '65 | 2.50 |
| '35 | .70 | '55 | 1.65 | '75 | 11.50 |

B. The Lincoln Memorial.
Washington, D.C. and Springfield, Ill.

| '25 | 1.10 | '45 | 1.75 | '65 | 2.40 |
| '35 | 1.25 | '55 | 1.75 | '75 | 8.75 |

C. United States Capitol.
Washington, D.C.

| '25 | 2.25 | '45 | 3.50 | '65 | 7.00 |
| '35 | 2.50 | '55 | 4.50 | '75 | 22.50 |

D. America, after a statue on the Capitol dome (see p. 205).
Washington, D.C.

| '25 | 5.50 | '45 | 6.50 | '65 | 14.00 |
| '35 | 6.00 | '55 | 7.50 | '75 | 55.00 |

E. Warren G. Harding (1865 - 1923), 29th president (1921 - 23). Elected on his appeal to return to "normalcy", he died in mid-term. The memorial stamp was issued imperforate, perf. 10, and perf. 11 (shown). A scarce rotary press variety is now valued at $6,000.00, used.

Marion, Ohio   1,459,487,085

| '25 | .03 | '45 | .06 | '65 | .12 |
| '35 | .08 | '55 | .08 | '75 | .25 |

Huguenot - Walloon Issue, 300th anniversary of the settlement of New York by the Walloons, French - speaking Protestants (or Huguenots) from the southern Netherlands. The stamps also recalled an earlier Huguenot settlement in Florida where all the colonists were massacred by the Spanish. Shown:

F. The *New Netherland,* the Walloons' sailing ship.
Albany, New Rochelle, and New York, N.Y.; Allentown, Lancaster, Philadelphia, and Reading, Pa.; Charleston, S.C.; Jacksonville and Mayport, Fla.   51,378,023

| '25 | .02 | '45 | .12 | '65 | .50 |
| '35 | .09 | '55 | .24 | '75 | 1.50 |

G. The Landing of the Walloons at Fort Orange, now Albany, New York.
Same cities as **F**   77,753,423

| '25 | .03 | '45 | .22 | '65 | .65 |
| '35 | .15 | '55 | .36 | '75 | 2.00 |

I. 3/19/25

J. 4/4/25

K. 12/28/25

L. 1/11/26

LEXINGTON - CONCORD ISSUE

"Stand your ground. Don't fire unless fired upon. But if they mean to have a war let it begin here."
Captain John Parker of the Lexington Minutemen.

On April 19, 1775, some 700 British forces under General Gage advanced to Lexington and Concord to arrest Samuel Adams and John Hancock, and to seize stores of munitions held by the Americans. At Lexington Green they were met by about 50 hurriedly - armed minutemen. Someone fired a shot, and before the skirmish was over eight Americans had been killed. Soon afterwards a battle took place at Concord, where the Americans inflicted heavy losses on the British. The Revolution had begun.

M. 4/4/25

N. 4/4/25

O. 4/4/25

H. Huguenot monument in Mayport, Florida.
Same cities as **F** 5,659, 023
'25 .07 '45 1.40 '65 4.60
'35 .65 '55 3.00 75 11.50

I. Warren G. Harding. Regular issue. Also issued imperforate and in coils.
Washington, D.C.
'35 .05 '55 .15 '75 .75
'45 .07 '65 .28

J. Nathan Hale (1755 - 76), revolutionary hero who was hanged by the British as a

spy. Regular issue.
New Haven, Conn.
'35 .02 '55 .03 '75 .06
'45 .02 '65 .03

K. Woodrow Wilson (see p. 76). Regular issue.
New York, N.Y.;
Princeton, N.J.; Staunton, Va.
'35 .30 '55 .45 '75 3.25
'45 .36 '65 .70

L. Benjamin Harrison (1833 - 1901), 23rd president (1889 - 93). During his administration the Sherman Anti-Trust Act, which regulates monopolies,

was passed. Regular issue.
Indianapolis, Ind.;
North Bend, Ohio
'35 .25 '55 .55 '75 2.95
'45 .30 '65 .65

Lexington - Concord Issue.
Shown:

M. Washington at Cambridge, from an engraving in the Cambridge Public Library.
Boston, Cambridge, Concord, Concord Junction, and Lexington, Mass. 15,615,000
'35 .09 '55 .29 '75 1.50
'45 .15 '65 .52

N. Battle of Lexington, from an idealized painting by Henry Sandham (Town Hall, Lexington, Massachusetts).
Same cities as **M** 26,596,600
'35 .15 '55 .42 '75 3.25
'45 .28 '65 1.10

O. Minuteman, from a statue by Daniel Chester French at Concord, Massachusetts.
Same cities as **M** 5,348,800
'35 .55 '55 1.50 '75 8.00
'45 .90 '65 2.40

A. 5/18/25

B. 5/18/25

C. 8/3/27

D. 5/10/26

E. 5/29/26

F. *10/18/26*

G. 5/26/28

H. 10/20/28

A. Norse-American Issue, 100th anniversary of the arrival of the first Norwegian settlers in America on the sloop *Restaurationen* (shown).
Minneapolis, St. Paul, Benson, and Northfield, Minn.; Algona and Decorah, Iowa; Washington, D.C.   9,104,983

'35	.20	'55	.48
'45	.30	'65	.85
		'75	1.75

B. Norse-American Issue.
Shown: Viking ship.
Same cities as **A**   1,900,983

'35	.65	'55	2.65
'45	1.35	'65	4.00
		'75	7.50

C. Vermont, 150th anniversary of independence and the Battle of Bennington.
Bennington, Vt. and Washington, D.C.   39,974,900

'35	.09	'55	.17
'45	.08	'65	.25
		'75	.55

D. Sesquicentennial Exposition, 150th anniversary of American independence.
Philadelphia, Pa.; Boston, Mass.; Washington, D.C.   307,731,900

'35	.12	'55	.23
'45	.12	'65	.35
		'75	1.15

E. John Ericsson (1803-89), engineer who built the Union warship *Monitor*.
New York, N.Y.; Chicago, Ill.; Minneapolis, Minn.; Washington, D.C.   20,280,500

'35	.23	'55	.90
'45	.50	'65	1.50
		'75	3.50

F. Battle of White Plains, 150th anniversary of Washington's well-fought but losing effort. Also issued as a miniature sheet of 25, the first U.S. souvenir sheet.
Shown: Alexander Hamilton's battery.
White Plains and New York, N.Y.   40,639,485

'35	.08	'55	.23
'45	.14	'65	.45
		'75	1.10

G. Valley Forge, 150th anniversary of the terrible winter of 1777-78 which Washington's army spent at Valley Forge without adequate food and clothing.
West Chester, Valley Forge, Philadelphia, Lancaster, and Norristown, Pa.; Cleveland, Ohio; Washington, D.C.   101,330,328

'35	.07	'55	.13
'45	.06	'65	.19
		'75	.40

I. *8/3/27*

J. 12/12/28

L. 8/13/28

M. 6/17/29

K. 12/12/28

N. 2/25/29

H. Molly Pitcher Overprint on the 2c stamp of the 1922 - 23 regular issue. Perf. 11 by 10½. A tribute to the heroine of the Battle of Monmouth, New Jersey.
Freehold and Red Bank, N.J.; Washington, D.C. 9,779,896
'35 .10   '55 .15   '75 .45
'45 .08   '65 .25

I. Burgoyne Campaign, 150th anniversary of the Battles of Saratoga and Oriskany, the first major American victories of the Revolution. Shown:

The Surrender of Burgoyne, to General Gates after a painting by John Trumbull.
Albany, Rome, Syracuse, and Utica, N.Y.;
Washington, D.C. 25,268,450
'35 .20   '55 .38   '75 1.25
'45 .22   '65 .65

J. International Civil Aeronautics Conference of 1928.
Washington, D.C. 49,438,300
'35 .05   '55 .13   '75 .50
'45 .08   '65 .24

K. International Civil Aeronautics Conference.

Washington, D.C. 10,319,700
'35 .17   '55 .55   '75 2.10
'45 .30   '65 .80

L. Hawaii Overprint on the 2c and 5c stamps of the 1922 - 23 regular issue. Perf. 11 by 10½. In 1778 Captain Cook discovered the islands.
Honolulu, Hawaii and Washington, D.C. 1,459,897
'35 .50   '55 1.25   '75 4.75
'45 .50   '65 2.35

M. Sullivan Expedition, 150th anniversary of General John Sullivan's campaign against the

Iroquois in New York State. The stamp was first placed on sale at 15 cities in New York.
51,452,406
'35 .05   '55 .09   '75 .25
'45 .05   '65 .15

N. George Rogers Clark, 150th anniversary of his victory at Vincennes, which won the Old Northwest for the United States.
Vincennes, Ind. 16,684,674
'35 .06   '55 .16   '75 .35
'45 .06   '65 .24

A. Battle of Fallen Timbers, 135th anniversary.
Maumee, Perrysburg, Toledo, and Waterville, Ohio;
Erie, Pa. 29,338,274
'35 .06 '55 .20 '75 .50
'45 .08 '65 .28

B - C. In 1929 a set of definitives was prepared by overprinting "Kans." and "Nebr." on stamps of the regular issue of 1922 - 23 (see pp. 56 - 58). The stamps ranged from 1c to 10c in denomination and were perf. 11 by 10½. They were used experimentally in Kansas and Nebraska in an effort to reduce losses from post office burglaries.

B. Nebr. Overprint.
Washington, D.C.
'35 .23 '55 2.05 '75 6.50
'45 .90 '65 2.40

C. Kans. Overprint.
Washington, D.C.
'35 .25 '55 .70 '75 3.00
'45 .34 '65 .95

D. Edison, 50th anniversary of the invention of the incandescent light bulb (see p. 94). Perf. 11. Also issued perf. 11 by 10½ and in coils.
Menlo Park, N.J. 31,679,200
'35 .06 '55 .14 '75 .35
'45 .06 '65 .20

E. Ohio River Canalization, completion of the project between Cairo, Illinois and Pittsburgh, Pennsylvania.
Cairo, Ill.; Evansville, Ind.;
Louisville, Ky.; Cincinnati, Ohio;
Homestead and Pittsburgh, Pa.;
Wheeling, W.Va. 32,680,900
'35 .05 '55 .11 '75 .30
'45 .06 '65 .17

F. Massachusetts Bay Colony, 300th anniversary of its settlement by about 300 families of Puritans led by John Winthrop.
Boston and
Salem, Mass. 74,000,774
'35 .05 '55 .08 '75 .25
'45 .05 '65 .12

G. Charleston, South Carolina, 250th anniversary; Carolina Province, 260th anniversary (see p. 161).
Charleston, S.C. 25,215,574
'35 .09 '55 .17 '75 .50
'45 .12 '65 .27

A. 9/14/29

"Mad" Anthony Wayne (1745 - 96) was the daring general who defeated Chief Little Turtle at the Battle of Fallen Timbers in 1794 at Maumee, Ohio. During the Revolution he fought at Germantown and Stony Point, where he earned his nickname. In 1795 he negotiated a treaty with the Indians which led to the settlement of Ohio.

B. 5/1/29

C. 5/1/29

D. 6/5/29

E. 10/19/29

F. 4/8/30

G. 4/10/30

H. 7/9/30

I. *5/21/31*

L. 6/4/30

K. 9/17/30

J. 12/1/30

M. 1/16/31   N. 10/19/31

H. Battle of Braddock's Field, in which Americans under Braddock were defeated near Fort Duquesne, Pennsylvania in the French and Indian War.
Braddock, Pa.   25,609,470
'35 .08   '55 .12   '75 .40
'45 .07   '65 .23

I. American Red Cross, 50th anniversary (see pp. 98, 106).
Dansville, N.Y. and Washington, D.C.   99,074,600
'35 .04   '55 .06   '75 .10
'45 .03   '65 .08

J. Warren G. Harding. Regular issue. Also issued in coils.
Marion, Ohio
'35 .03   '55 .04   '75 .09
'45 .04   '65 .05

K. General Friedrich von Steuben (1730 - 94), German baron who fought for the Americans in the Revolution and helped train the Continental Army at Valley Forge.
New York, N.Y.   66,487,000
'35 .05   '55 .11   '75 .28
'45 .05   '65 .16

L. William Howard Taft (1857 - 1930), 27th president (1909 - 13), who also served as the chief justice of the Supreme Court. Regular issue. Also issued in coils.
Cincinnati, Ohio
'35 .06   '55 .10   '75 .15
'45 .06   '65 .10

M. General Casimir Pulaski (1748 - 79), who fought for Polish freedom in his native land and for American freedom at Germantown and Brandywine. The stamp was first placed on sale in 12 different cities.
'35 .05   '55 .07   '75 .13
'45 .05   '65 .09

N. Battle of Yorktown, 150th anniversary of the surrender of General Cornwallis to Washington. Yorktown, the last major battle of the Revolution, was marked by brilliant maneuvers on land and sea, in which Washington was aided by his French allies, De Grasse and Rochambeau.
Yorktown, Va. and Wethersfield, Conn.   25,006,400
'35 .05   '55 .08   '75 .15
'45 .05   '65 .10

WASHINGTON BICENTENNIAL ISSUE

Twelve stamps were released in 1932 in honor of the 200th anniversary of the birth of George Washington (1732 - 99). The designs were based on portraits of the general by some of the greatest artists of his age. Of these paintings those by Gilbert Stuart are the most familiar. They are classic and somewhat sublime portrayals of the nation's first great hero. But art historians and critics generally agree that the portraits by Charles Willson Peale are more realistic. Peale's paintings show us Washington as he really looked; Stuart's as we remember him.

A. *1/1/32*

B. 1/1/32

E. 1/1/32

C. 1/1/32

D. *1/1/32*

F. 1/1/32

A. After a miniature painted by Charles Willson Peale in 1777 (Metropolitan Museum of Art).
Washington, D.C.   87,969,700
| '35 | .01 | '55 | .03 | '75 | .05 |
| '45 | .02 | '65 | .03 | | |

B. After a profile bust made by Jean Antoine Houdon in 1785 (Mount Vernon).
Washington, D.C.   1,265,555,100
| '35 | .03 | '55 | .04 | '75 | .06 |
| '45 | .02 | '65 | .04 | | |

C. After the Virginia Colonel portrait, painted by Charles Willson Peale in 1772. It shows Washington in a regimental uniform he designed (Washington and Lee University).
Washington, D.C.   304,926,800
| '35 | .05 | '55 | .07 | '75 | .13 |
| '45 | .05 | '65 | .08 | | |

D. After the Athenaeum portrait, painted by Gilbert Stuart in 1796 (Boston Museum of Fine Arts).
Washington, D.C.   4,222,198,300
| '35 | .04 | '55 | .04 | '75 | .06 |
| '45 | .04 | '65 | .05 | | |

E. After portrait of Washington at Valley Forge, painted by Charles Willson Peale in 1777. It shows the general in uniform, wearing a cocked hat (State Normal School, West Chester, Pennsylvania).
Washington, D.C.   456,198,000
| '35 | .08 | '55 | .08 | '75 | .20 |
| '45 | .12 | '65 | .10 | | |

F. After a painting by Charles Willson Peale.
Washington, D.C.   151,201,300
| '35 | .08 | '55 | .08 | '75 | .15 |
| '45 | .06 | '65 | .10 | | |

G. Washington at the age of 63, after a portrait painted by Charles Willson Peale in 1795 (New York Historical Society).
Washington, D.C.   170,565,100
| '35 | .09 | '55 | .24 | '75 | .70 |
| '45 | .09 | '65 | .36 | | |

H. After a bust from the full - length portrait of Washington at Trenton, painted by John Trumbull in 1792 (Yale University Art Gallery).

G. 1/1/32

H. 1/1/32

I. 1/1/32

J. 1/1/32

K. 1/1/32

L. 1/1/32

OLYMPIC GAMES ISSUE

M. 1/25/32

O. *6/15/32*

N. 6/15/32

Washington, D.C. 111,739,400
'35 .12 '55 .37 '75 1.75
'45 .15 '65 .55

I. After a bust from a full-length portrait painted by John Trumbull in 1780 (Metropolitan Museum of Art).
Washington, D.C. 83,257,400
'35 .10 '55 .12 '75 .25
'45 .10 '65 .16

J. After a crayon drawing made by Charles B.J.F. Saint

Memin in 1798, the year before Washington died.
Washington, D.C. 96,506,100
'35 .14 '55 .27 '75 1.85
'45 .13 '65 .55

K. After a pastel portrait drawn from life by W. Williams in 1794 (Masonic Lodge, Alexandria, Virginia).
Washington, D.C. 75,709,200
'35 .16 '55 .36 '75 1.15
'45 .18 '65 .48

L. After the Gibbs-Channing-Avery portrait by Gilbert Stuart. This work is

a copy of the Vaughan portrait, which was painted in 1795 and was the first of the Stuart portraits.
Washington, D.C. 147,216,000
'35 .23 '55 .95 '75 4.75
'45 .20 '65 1.50

M-O. Three stamps were issued in 1932 to honor the 3rd Winter Olympics, held at Lake Placid, New York, February 4-13, and the 10th Summer Olympics, held at Los Angeles, July 30-August 14. Shown:

M. Ski Jumper.
Lake Placid, N.Y. 51,102,800
'35 .04 '55 .08 '75 .12
'45 .03 '65 .10

N. Runner.
Los Angeles, Calif. 168,885,300
'35 .07 '55 .13 '75 .20
'45 .08 '65 .16

O. *Discobolus* by Myron, a 5th century B.C. Greek sculptor. A globe appears in the background.
Los Angeles, Calif. 52,376,100
'35 .10 '55 .17 '75 .32
'45 .08 '65 .22

A. 4/22/32

B. 6/16/32

C. 10/24/32

D. 10/24/32

E. 5/25/33

F. 5/25/33

G. 10/9/33

H. 4/9/33

I. 2/12/33

A. Arbor Day, 60th anniversary of the setting aside of a day for planting trees in Nebraska.
Nebraska City, Ne.   100,869,300
'35   .04   '55   .07   '75   .10
'45   .03   '65   .08

B. George Washington, after a portrait by Gilbert Stuart. Regular issue for increase in first-class letter rate. Also issued in coils and booklets.
Washington, D.C.
'35   .04   '55   .06   '75   .10
'45   .06   '65   .08

C. Daniel Webster (1782-1852), secretary of state, senator, and champion of the Union, who won historic Supreme Court cases, including *Dartmouth College* v. *Woodward* (see p. 158). Shown: bust by Daniel Chester French.
Exeter, Franklin, and Hanover, N.H.   49,538,500
'35   .07   '55   .13   '75   .16
'45   .06   '65   .14

D. William Penn (1644-1718), English Quaker who founded the colony of Pennsylvania. He was the main author of "Concessions and Agreements" that established tolerance and democracy in the colonies.
New Castle, Del.; Chester and Philadelphia, Pa.   49,949,000
'35   .06   '55   .10   '75   .12
'45   .05   '65   .11

E-F. Chicago Century of Progress, issued for the Chicago World's Fair of 1933. Shown:

E. Fort Dearborn, the original site of Chicago.
Chicago, Ill.   348,266,800
'35   .02   '55   .05   '75   .06
'45   .02   '65   .05

F. Federal Building, which dominated the fairgrounds.
Chicago, Ill.   480,239,300
'35   .07   '55   .06   '75   .08
'45   .05   '65   .06

G. Byrd's Antarctic Expedition II, sold only through the Philatelic Sales Agency to enable stamp collectors to obtain a postmark from Little America, Richard E. Byrd's outpost in Antarctica.
Philatelic Agency   5,735,944
'35   .07   '55   .30   '75   .42
'45   .08   '65   .36

K. 7/7/34

J. *3/23/34*

L. 10/13/33

M. 8/15/33

N. *5/2/34*

H. Proclamation of Peace, issued by Washington in 1783 to bring the Revolution officially to an end. Shown: Washington's headquarters in Newburgh, New York, where the proclamation was issued.

Newburgh, N.Y. 73,382,400
'35 .06   '55 .06   '75 .09
'45 .05   '65 .08

I. Georgia Settlement, 200th anniversary. Shown: James Oglethorpe (1696-1785), who founded Georgia as a refuge for debtors in 1733.

Savannah, Ga. 61,719,200
'35 .06   '55 .09   '75 .12
'45 .05   '65 .12

J. Maryland, 300th anniversary. Founded by Lord Baltimore in 1632, Maryland was the first colony that tried to effect a separation of church and state. Shown: the *Ark* and *Dove,* which brought the first 200 settlers to Maryland.

St. Mary's City, Md. 46,258,300
'35 .07   '55 .09   '75 .13
'45 .05   '65 .10

K. Wisconsin, 300th anniversary of the landing of Jean Nicolet at Green Bay.

Green Bay, Wis. 64,525,400
'35 .06   '55 .08   '75 .12
'45 .05   '65 .10

L. Tadeusz Kosciuszko (1746-1817), Polish colonel who aided the Americans in the Revolution and planned the fortifications at West Point.

Kosciusko, Miss.; Boston, Mass.; Chicago, Ill.; St. Louis, Mo.; Detroit, Mich.; Pittsburgh, Pa.; Buffalo, N.Y.   45,137,700
'35 .10   '55 .27   '75 .35
'45 .11   '65 .30

M. National Recovery Act, part of President Roosevelt's program to relieve unemployment during the Great Depression.

Washington, D.C. 1,978,707,300
'35 .05   '55 .07   '75 .09
'45 .05   '65 .07

N. Mother's Day, perf. 11 by 10½. Also issued perf. 11. Shown: an adaptation of Whistler's *Arrangement in Grey and Black No. 1* (see p. 85).

Washington, D.C. 193,239,100
'35 .05   '55 .06   '75 .08
'45 .05   '65 .06

NATIONAL PARKS ISSUE

A. *7/16/34*

B. *7/24/34*

C. *9/25/34*

D. *9/5/34*

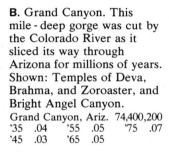

E. *10/2/34*

In honor of National Parks Year, 1934, ten stamps were issued by the postal service. The parks portrayed include:

A. Yosemite. Centuries of glacial movement carved the domes and valleys of this park in California's Sierra Nevada. The ancient sequoia redwoods in the park have been protected since 1864. Shown: El Capitan.

Yosemite, Calif.	84,896,350	
'35 .03	'55 .03	'75 .05
'45 .02	'65 .03	

B. Grand Canyon. This mile-deep gorge was cut by the Colorado River as it sliced its way through Arizona for millions of years. Shown: Temples of Deva, Brahma, and Zoroaster, and Bright Angel Canyon.

Grand Canyon, Ariz.	74,400,200	
'35 .04	'55 .05	'75 .07
'45 .03	'65 .05	

C. Mesa Verde. These multi-storied, hundred-room pueblos were inhabited by the Basket Makers and Cliff Dwellers from about 1 A.D. to 1300. Shown: Cliff Palace.

Mesa Verde, Colo.	19,178,650	
'35 .07	'55 .10	'75 .26
'45 .07	'65 .14	

D. Crater Lake. Indian legends tell of a war of the gods that caused the formation of this intensely blue caldera. Its rim once formed the sides of a 12,000-foot volcano whose last eruption created the lake. Shown: lake with Wizard Island.

Crater Lake, Ore.	16,923,350	
'35 .10	'55 .22	'75 .55
'45 .11	'65 .32	

E. Acadia. Located on the coast of Maine, Acadia is the only national park in New England. Shown: Great Head.

Bar Harbor, Maine	15,988,250	
'35 .10	'55 .18	'75 .30
'45 .11	'65 .20	

F. Mt. Rainier. Washington's 14,410-foot mountain is the largest single-peak glacier system in the contiguous

G. 7/30/34

F. *8/3/34*

H. 9/18/34

I. 8/27/34

J. 10/8/34

United States. Twenty-six glaciers originate on the summit. Shown: Mirror Lake. Longmire, Wash. 95,089,000
'35 .06 '55 .08 '75 .08
'45 .04 '65 .08

G. Yellowstone. Known for its spectacular geysers, this park is also one of the nation's foremost wildlife sanctuaries. It offers refuge to the bighorn sheep, white pelican, and the rare trumpeter swan, among

others. Shown: Old Faithful (see p. 170).
Yellowstone, Wyo. 30,980,100
'35 .08 '55 .15 '75 .30
'45 .09 '65 .15

H. Zion. This massive landmark in southern Utah is shaded from deep red at the bottom through pink to white at the top. Shown: Great White Throne.
Zion, Utah 15,288,700
'35 .12 '55 .26 '75 .75
'45 .14 '65 .50

I. Glacier. This park in northwestern Montana adjoins Waterton Lakes National Park in Canada to form the International Peace Park. Shown: Mt. Rockwell and Two Medicine Lake.
Glacier, Montana 17,472,600
'35 .14 '55 .27 '75 .60
'45 .14 '65 .40

J. Great Smoky Mountains. This park includes the last sizeable primeval hardwood forest in the South. Its

mountains are among the highest in the East. Shown: Mount Le Conte.
Gatlinburg, Tenn. 18,847,300
'35 .15 '55 .42 '75 1.50
'45 .18 '65 .70

Note: Twenty of the stamps and souvenir sheets issued in 1933 and 1934 under Postmaster General James A. Farley were released in complete, ungummed sheets through the Philatelic Sales Agency 1935. These so-called Farley special printings were imperforate, except for two (**G** and **H** on p. 66).

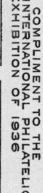

UNDER AUTHORITY OF
JAMES A. FARLEY, POSTMASTER GENERAL

PRINTED BY THE TREASURY DEPARTMENT, BUREAU OF ENGRAVING AND PRINTING

IN COMPLIMENT TO THE THIRD INTERNATIONAL PHILATELIC EXHIBITION OF 1936

CONNECTICUT TERCENTENARY 1635 1935
3¢ THE CHARTER OAK 3¢
UNITED STATES POSTAGE

CALIFORNIA PACIFIC INTERNATIONAL EXPOSITION 1535·SAN DIEGO·1935
3¢ U.S. POSTAGE 3¢

1835 MICHIGAN CENTENARY 1935
STATE SEAL OF MICHIGAN
3¢ U.S. POSTAGE 3¢

UNITED STATES POSTAGE TEXAS CENTENNIAL 1836-1936
SAM HOUSTON · STEPHEN F. AUSTIN
3¢ (THE ALAMO) 3¢

NEW YORK, N.Y., MAY 9-17, 1936
PLATE NUMBER 21558

A. 5/9/36

B. 6/15/36

C. 7/14/36

A. TIPEX, souvenir sheet, a compliment to the Third International Philatelic Exhibition, held in New York City, May 9-17, 1936. The sheet included four different stamps, all valid for postage, which were also issued individually. The stamps commemorate (clockwise from upper left):

Connecticut, 300th anniversary of the settlement of the colony by dissenters from Massachusetts led by Thomas Hooker. Shown: the Charter Oak, where colonists safely hid their charter in 1687 when it was recalled by the British.

California Pacific International Exposition, a world's fair held in San Diego.

Texas Independence, 100th anniversary. Once a part of Mexico, Texas was settled by Americans led by Stephen Austin in 1821. In 1836, Texas became a republic and Sam Houston was elected its first president.

Michigan Statehood, 100th anniversary. 26th state, admitted 1836. Capital, Lansing. The state leads the nation in motor vehicle production.
New York, N.Y.   111,236,156
'45 .28   '65 .55
'55 .55   '75 1.25

B. Arkansas Statehood, 100th anniversary. 25th state, admitted 1836. Capital, Little Rock. Leading industries include: forestry, cotton, and mineral production.

Little Rock, Ark.   72,992,650
'45 .05   '65 .06
'55 .06   '75 .07

C. Oregon Territory, 100th anniversary of the opening of this vast area, from which Idaho, Oregon, Washington, and parts of Wyoming and Montana were carved.
Lewiston, Idaho; Missoula, Mont.; Astoria, Ore.; Walla Walla, Wash.; Daniel, Wyo.   74,407,450
'45 .05   '65 .06
'55 .06   '75 .07

D. 8/26/36

E. *9/17/37*

F. 8/18/37

H. 9/30/35

I. 5/4/36

G. 7/13/37

D. Susan B. Anthony (1820-1906), crusader for women's rights, especially the right to vote.

Washington, D.C.   269,522,200
'45   .05   '65   .06
'55   .06   '75   .07

E. Constitution Sesquicentennial. In 1787, after four months of debate, the delegates to the Constitutional Convention signed the Constitution in Independence Hall. The document created three branches of government: legislative, executive, and judicial.

Philadelphia, Pa.   99,882,300
'45   .05   '65   .07
'55   .06   '75   .10

F. Virginia Dare, first English child born in America. Her birthplace was the site of Walter Raleigh's "lost colony" at Roanoke.

Manteo, N.C.   25,040,400
'45   .07   '65   .17
'55   .15   '75   .20

G. Ordinance of 1787, 150th anniversary. Sponsored by the Rev. Manasseh Cutler, this ordinance led to the creation of five new states from the Northwest Territory: Ohio, Indiana, Michigan, Illinois, and Wisconsin. The first settlement in the area was founded by Rufus Putnam.

Marietta, Ohio and
New York, N.Y.   84,825,250
'45   .05   '65   .08
'55   .05   '75   .09

H. Boulder Dam, a federal project on the Colorado River that was originally called Hoover Dam, a name that was restored in 1947.

Boulder City, Nev.   73,610,650
'45   .05   '65   .06
'55   .06   '75   .07

I. Rhode Island, 300th anniversary of the settlement of Providence by Roger Williams and his followers, who were fleeing from religious persecution in the Massachusetts Bay Colony.

Providence, R.I.   67,127,650
'45   .05   '65   .06
'55   .06   '75   .07

A. 12/15/36

B. *1/15/37*

In June of 1775, the Continental Congress resolved "That a general be appointed to command all the Continental forces, raised or to be raised for the defense of American liberty." After some debate, John Adams nominated George Washington for this post and by a unanimous vote he became the first commander-in-chief of an American army. A portrait of Washington, along with likenesses of other military heroes, appears on this tribute to the army.

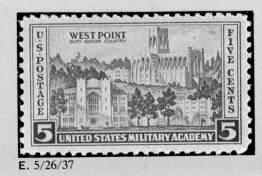

C. 2/18/37

D. 3/23/37

E. 5/26/37

A. The Continental Army. Shown: George Washington, who created a victorious army out of untrained soldiers and led the United States to independence; Nathanael Greene, who saved the South for the continental cause; and Mount Vernon.

Washington, D.C.   105,196,150
'45	.02	'65	.03
'55	.03	'75	.04

B. The Army in the War of 1812. Shown: Andrew Jackson, who fought against the Creek Indians and at New Orleans; Winfield Scott, who served at Lundy's Lane and Chippewa; and The Hermitage, Jackson's home in Tennessee.

Washington, D.C.   93,848,500
'45	.03	'65	.05
'55	.04	'75	.06

C. The Union Army in the Civil War. Shown: William T. Sherman, whose devastating, 32-day march through Georgia in 1864 helped to break the South; Ulysses S. Grant, who conducted the final campaign that led to Lee's surrender at Appomattox in 1865; and Philip H. Sheridan, who led a brilliant cavalry charge at Missionary Ridge, Tennessee, in 1863.

Washington, D.C.   87,741,150
'45	.05	'65	.06
'55	.06	'75	.08

D. The Confederate Army in the Civil War. Shown: Robert E. Lee, who reluctantly refused to take command of the Union army and then led the South against overwhelming odds; "Stonewall" Jackson, who used lightning movements and surprise strategies at Bull Run and Chancellorsville, where he was accidentally killed by his own men; and Stratford Hall, Lee's birthplace in Virginia.

Washington, D.C.   35,794,150
'45	.06	'65	.11
'55	.08	'75	.12

E. The U.S. Military Academy, established at West Point, New York, in 1802.

West Point, N.Y.   36,839,250
'45	.07	'65	.12
'55	.10	'75	.15

NAVY ISSUE

G. 1/15/37

F. *12/15/36*

H. 2/18/37

These five stamps honor the navy and its heroes. The navy was created in the Revolution, when the Continental Congress declared that "a swift - sailing vessel, to carry ten carriage guns, and a proportionate number of swivels, with eighty men," should be sent on a cruise to intercept British transports. In 1775, the congress voted to outfit thirteen ships to battle on the seas. Since then, the navy has carried American influence to all parts of the world.

I. 3/23/37

J. 5/26/37

F. The Navy in the Revolution. Shown: John Paul Jones, whose *Bonhomme Richard* was destroyed in 1779 when it seized the British *Serapis* in a great sea battle; John Barry, the first U.S. Navy officer to take a British ship, in 1776; and a warship of the day.
Washington, D.C. 104,773,450
'45 .02 '65 .03
'55 .03 '75 .04

G. The Navy in the Early 19th Century. Shown: Stephen Decatur, who took

the captured gunboat *Philadelphia* from the Barbary pirates in 1804 and was the commander of the frigate *United States* in the War of 1812; Thomas MacDonough, whose victory at Lake Champlain in 1814 kept the British from attacking both Vermont and New York; and a warship.
Washington, D.C. 92,054,550
'45 .03 '65 .05
'55 .04 '75 .06

H. The Navy in the Civil War. Shown: David Farragut

and his foster brother, David Dixon Porter, who helped seize the Mississippi from Confederate control with a victory at New Orleans. Farragut's famous order, "Damn the torpedoes!" came in his victory at Mobile Bay. A warship is also shown.
Washington, D.C. 93,291,650
'45 .05 '65 .06
'55 .06 '75 .08

I. The Navy in the Spanish - American War. Shown: William T. Sampson and Winfield S. Schley, who

demolished the Spanish fleet at Santiago, Cuba; and George Dewey, who crushed the Spanish at Manila Bay in the Philippines.
Washington, D.C. 34,552,950
'45 .06 '65 .11
'55 .08 '75 .12

J. The U.S. Naval Academy, established at Annapolis, Maryland, in 1845. Shown: seal of the academy and cadets in early and modern uniforms.
Annapolis, Md. 36,819,050
'45 .07 '65 .12
'55 .11 '75 .15

A. Benjamin Franklin.
Philadelphia, Pa.

| '45 | .01 | '65 | .02 |
| '55 | .01 | '75 | .03 |

B. George Washington. Also issued in coils and booklets.
Washington, D.C.

| '45 | .02 | '65 | .02 |
| '55 | .02 | '75 | .04 |

C. Martha Washington. Also issued in coils.
Washington, D.C.

| '45 | .03 | '65 | .04 |
| '55 | .03 | '75 | .04 |

D. John Adams. Also issued in coils and booklets.
Washington, D.C.

| '45 | .03 | '65 | .04 |
| '55 | .03 | '75 | .04 |

E. Thomas Jefferson. Also issued in coils and booklets.
Washington, D.C.

| '45 | .04 | '65 | .05 |
| '55 | .04 | '75 | .06 |

F. James Madison. Also issued in coils.
Washington, D.C.

| '45 | .05 | '65 | .07 |
| '55 | .06 | '75 | .11 |

G. The White House, oldest federal structure in Washington. Also issued in coils.
Washington, D.C.

| '45 | .06 | '65 | .08 |
| '55 | .07 | '75 | .11 |

H. James Monroe. Also issued in coils.
Washington, D.C.

| '45 | .06 | '65 | .08 |
| '55 | .07 | '75 | .13 |

I. John Quincy Adams (1767-1848), 6th president (1825-29). The diverse statesman also served nine terms with distinction in the House of Representatives. Also issued in coils.
Washington, D.C.

| '45 | .07 | '65 | .09 |
| '55 | .08 | '75 | .15 |

J. Andrew Jackson.
Washington, D.C.

| '45 | .09 | '65 | .11 |
| '55 | .09 | '75 | .16 |

K. Martin Van Buren (1782-1862), 8th president (1837-41), who was known as "the little magician".
Washington, D.C.

| '45 | .10 | '65 | .12 |
| '55 | .10 | '75 | .20 |

D. *6/3/38*

John Adams (1735-1826), 2nd president (1797-1801), was also the 1st vice president. It was he who attacked the Stamp Act of 1765 as taxation without representation. His support of the Declaration of Independence was vital.

A. 5/19/38

B. 4/25/38

C. 5/5/38

E. 6/16/38

F. 7/1/38

G. 7/11/38

H. 7/21/38

I. 7/28/38

J. 8/4/38

K. 8/11/38

L. 8/18/38

M. 9/2/38

N. 9/8/38

O. 9/14/38

P. 9/22/38

Q. 10/6/38

R. 10/13/38

S. 10/20/38

T. 10/27/38

U. 11/3/38

L. William Henry Harrison (1773 - 1841), 9th president (1841). His "log cabin and hard cider" campaign slogan reflected his long association with the Northwest Territory.
Washington, D.C.

'45	.11	'65	.13
'55	.11	'75	.24

M. John Tyler (1790 - 1862), 10th president (1841 - 45). Also issued in coils.
Washington, D.C.

'45	.12	'65	.14
'55	.12	'75	.22

N. James Polk (1795 - 1849), 11th president (1845 - 49).
Washington, D.C.

'45	.13	'65	.17
'55	.14	'75	.25

O. Zachary Taylor.
Washington, D.C.

'45	.14	'65	.22
'55	.15	'75	.30

P. Millard Fillmore (1800-74), 13th president (1850 - 53).
Washington, D.C.

'45	.16	'65	.20
'55	.17	'75	.35

Q. Franklin Pierce (1804 - 69), 14th president (1853 - 57).
Washington, D.C.

'45	.16	'65	.22
'55	.17	'75	.40

R. James Buchanan (1791 - 1868), 15th president (1857 - 61). During his administration seven states seceded.

'45	.18	'65	.23
'55	.18	'75	.30

S. Abraham Lincoln.
Washington, D.C.

'45	.19	'65	.25
'55	.20	'75	.40

T. Andrew Johnson (1808-75), 17th president (1865 - 69), who assumed office upon the death of Lincoln. His conflicts with radical Republican Congressmen led to his impeachment, which was not sustained by Senate vote.
Washington, D.C.

'45	.20	'65	.28
'55	.21	'75	.45

U. Ulysses S. Grant.
Washington, D.C.

'45	.21	'65	.29
'55	.23	'75	.45

A. 11/10/38

B. 11/10/38

C. 11/22/38

D. 11/22/38

E. 12/2/38

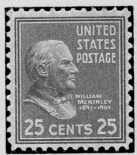

F. 12/2/38

G. 12/8/38

H. 12/8/38

I. *8/29/38*

J. 9/29/38

K. 11/17/38

A. Rutherford B. Hayes.
Washington, D.C.

'45	.23	'65	.32
'55	.24	'75	.50

B. James A. Garfield.
Washington, D.C.

'45	.23	'65	.30
'55	.24	'75	.45

C. Chester A. Arthur (1830-86), 21st president (1881-85), took office when Garfield was assassinated. He urged civil service reform.
Washington, D.C.

'45	.25	'65	.35
'55	.26	'75	.50

D. Grover Cleveland.
Washington, D.C.

'45	.26	'65	.39
'55	.28	'75	.60

E. Benjamin Harrison.
Washington, D.C.

'45	.29	'65	.40
'55	.30	'75	.65

F. William McKinley.
Washington, D.C.

'45	.30	'65	.38
'55	.30	'75	.55

G. Theodore Roosevelt.
Washington, D.C.

'45	.35	'65	.60
'55	.36	'75	1.35

H. William Howard Taft.
Washington, D.C.

'45	.58	'65	.95
'55	.60	'75	3.00

I. Woodrow Wilson (1856-1924), 28th president (1913-21), who led the nation through World War I. His hopes for strong American leadership in the League of Nations were dashed when the Senate failed to authorize U.S. membership.

Washington, D.C.

'45	1.15	'65	1.60
'55	1.25	'75	3.00

J. Warren G. Harding.
Washington, D.C.

'45	2.20	'65	3.25
'55	2.75	'75	7.75

K. Calvin Coolidge (1872-1933), 30th president (1923-29). He reduced the national debt and insisted on full payment of Europe's war debt.
Washington, D.C.

'45	5.50	'65	8.00
'55	5.50	'75	42.50

L. 11/12/37

M. 11/25/37

N. 12/15/37

O. 10/18/37

UNDER THE AUTHORITY OF
JAMES A. FARLEY, POSTMASTER GENERAL.

PRINTED BY THE
BUREAU OF ENGRAVING AND PRINTING.

GREAT SMOKY MOUNTAINS

10 CENTS
UNITED STATES POSTAGE

IN COMPLIMENT TO THE
43RD ANNUAL CONVENTION OF THE
SOCIETY OF PHILATELIC AMERICANS.

ASHEVILLE, N.C., AUGUST 26-28, 1937.
PLATE NUMBER 21695

P. 8/26/37

Territorial Issue, a tribute to United States possessions.

L. Alaska, now a state, was bought from Czarist Russia in 1867. Shown: Mount McKinley and contemporary views of the territory.
Juneau, Alaska 77,004,200
'45 .05 '65 .08
'55 .07 '75 .10

M. Puerto Rico, a Caribbean island obtained from Spain after the Spanish-American War of 1898. The island is now a commonwealth. Shown: La Fortaleza, the old Governor's Palace in San Juan.
San Juan, P.R. 81,292,450
'45 .05 '65 .08
'55 .07 '75 .10

N. Virgin Islands, a group of Caribbean islands bought from Denmark in 1917 for $25 million to protect the Panama Canal. The three major islands are St. Thomas, St. Croix, and St. John. Shown: view of city and harbor of Charlotte Amalie, the capital of the islands.
Charlotte Amalie, V.I. 76,474,550
'45 .05 '65 .07
'55 .06 '75 .10

O. Hawaii, a group of islands now a state, that were voluntarily annexed to the United States in 1898. Shown: statue of King Kamehameha I, who united the islands into the single kingdom, by sculptor T. R. Gould (Iolani Castle grounds, Honolulu, Hawaii).
Honolulu, Hawaii 78,454,450

'45 .05 '65 .08
'55 .06 '75 .10

P. Society of Philatelic Americans, souvenir sheet, honoring the 43rd annual S.P.A. convention at Asheville, North Carolina, August 26-28, 1937. Shown: imperforate reproduction in green of the Great Smoky Mountain design of the 10c 1934 National Park issue (see p. 69).
Asheville, N.C. 5,277,445
'45 .15 '65 .30
'55 .25 '75 .40

A. First Colony of the Swedes and Finns, 300th anniversary. Colonists led by Peter Minuit, a Dutchman, settled at the present site of Wilmington, Delaware, in 1630. Shown: *Landing of the Swedes,* painted by Stanley M. Arthurs.

Wilmington, Del.   58,564,368
'45	.05	'65	.13
'55	.12	'75	.15

B. Northwest Territory, 150th anniversary of settlement. Shown: memorial statue by Gutzon Borglum in Marietta, Ohio, site of the first settlement in the territory (see p. 71).

Marietta, Ohio   65,939,500
'45	.07	'65	.10
'55	.10	'75	.15

C. Golden Gate International Exposition, publicity for the 1939 fair on Treasure Island in San Francisco Bay. Shown: Tower of the Sun.

San Francisco, Calif. 114,439,600
'45	.05	'65	.07
'55	.07	'75	.15

D. Ratification of the Constitution, 150th anniversary. The oldest, written constitution of any major nation in the world became effective on June 21, 1788, when New Hampshire became the ninth state to ratify it. Shown: colonial courthouse in Williamsburg, Virginia.

Philadelphia, Pa.   73,043,650
'45	.05	'65	.13
'55	.12	'75	.15

E. Iowa Territory, 100th anniversary. The separate territory of Iowa was established on July 4, 1838. Shown: old capitol at Iowa City.

Des Moines, Iowa   47,064,300
'45	.05	'65	.13
'55	.12	'75	.15

F. Inauguration of Washington, 150th anniversary. Shown: Washington taking the oath of office as the first president on April 30, 1789, at Federal Hall, New York. After an engraving by Alonzo Chappel.

New York, N.Y.   72,765,550
'45	.05	'65	.13
'55	.12	'75	.15

A. *6/27/38*

B. 7/15/38

C. 2/18/39

D. 6/21/38

E. 8/24/38

F. 4/30/39

G. 4/1/39

H. 6/12/39

I. 11/2/39

J. 9/25/39

K. 8/15/39

G. New York World's Fair of 1939. Shown: the Trylon and the Perisphere.

New York, N.Y.   101,699,550
'45 .05   '65 .07
'55 .07   '75 .08

H. Baseball, 100th anniversary. Abner Doubleday diagrammed the game's base locations and player positions in 1839. Shown: sandlot baseball game.

Cooperstown, N.Y.   81,269,600
'45 .05   '65 .11
'55 .10   '75 .15

I. Montana, North Dakota, South Dakota, and Washington; 50th anniversary of their admission to the Union in 1889. These four states cover a large portion of the north central and northwestern United States. Their capitals are: Helena, Montana; Bismarck, North Dakota; Pierre, South Dakota; and Olympia, Washington. Separate first - day - of - issue ceremonies were held on the anniversary dates in each state.

Bismarck, N.D.   11/2/39
Pierre, S.D.   11/2/39
Helena, Mont.   11/8/39
Olympia, Wash.   11/11/39
66,835,000
'45 .05   '65 .08
'55 .07   '75 .09

J. Printing in Colonial America, 300th anniversary. Shown: the Stephen Daye press, which printed the *Freeman's Oath* in 1639 and the *Bay Psalm Book,* one of the most valuable books in the world, in 1640.

New York, N.Y.   71,394,750
'45 .05   '65 .08
'55 .07   '75 .09

K. Panama Canal, 25th anniversary of its opening in 1914. Shown: President Theodore Roosevelt, who authorized canal construction on a ten - mile wide strip of land leased from Panama; Colonel George W. Goethals, who directed the completion of the project, and the freighter *Andres F. Luchenbach* passing through the Gaillard Cut.

U.S.S. *Charleston,* C.Z.
67,813,350
'45 .05   '65 .11
'55 .11   '75 .13

A. Washington Irving (1783 - 1859), one of the nation's first great writers, drew upon the early history of New York to create "Rip Van Winkle" and "The Legend of Sleepy Hollow". These stories are included in his classic work, *The Sketch Book*. Irving also wrote the humorous *Diedrich Knickerbocker's History of New York*.

Tarrytown, N.Y.   56,348,320
'45 .02   '65 .04
'55 .03   '75 .04

B. James Fenimore Cooper (1789 - 1851), creator of adventure novels, wrote the *Leather - Stocking Tales*. The five books in this series immortalize the exploits of Natty Bumpo (or Hawk-eye), the first folk hero of the old frontier.

Cooperstown, N.Y.   53,177,110
'45 .03   '65 .04
'55 .04   '75 .06

C. Ralph Waldo Emerson (1803 - 82), poet, essayist, and lecturer, was a leader of the Transcendental movement in America. His writings include "Self - Reliance", "The American Scholar", and *Nature*.

Boston, Mass.   53,260,270
'45 .05   '65 .07
'55 .07   '75 .08

D. Louisa May Alcott (1832 - 88) began her literary career when she was a child. *Little Women,* her most famous book, was written to pay off family debts. Her other works include *Little Men* and *Jo's Boys*.

Concord, Mass.   22,104,950
'45 .09   '65 .10
'55 .09   '75 .15

E. Mark Twain (Samuel Langhorne Clemens, 1835 - 1910), humorist and satirist, was the creator of Tom Sawyer, Huckleberry Finn, and *Pudd'nhead Wilson*. He once wrote that *The Adventures of Tom Sawyer* "was made by Mr. Mark Twain, and he told the truth, mainly. There was things which he stretched, but mainly he told the truth."

Hannibal, Mo.   13,201,270
'45 .25   '65 .65
'55 .48   '75 1.00

A. 1/29/40

B. 1/29/40

C. 2/5/40

D. 2/5/40

E. *2/13/40*

Issue for Poets

F. *2/16/40*

G. 2/16/40

H. 2/20/40

I. 2/20/40

J. 2/24/40

F. Henry Wadsworth Longfellow (1807-82) wrote long narrative poems that are an inextricable part of the American tradition. These include *Evangeline, The Courtship of Miles Standish,* and *Hiawatha.* He is the only American honored in the Poet's Corner of Westminster Abbey, London.

Portland, Me.   51,603,580
'45	.03	'65	.07
'55	.07	'75	.08

G. John Greenleaf Whittier (1807-92), the son of frugal Quaker farmers, immortalized his family in his classic poem, *Snow-Bound.* An ardent abolitionist, he was also the author of religious hymns, ballads, and several volumes of prose and verse.

Haverhill, Mass.   52,100,510
'45	.04	'65	.05
'55	.05	'75	.06

H. James Russell Lowell (1819-91), poet, editor of the *Atlantic Monthly,* critic, and Harvard professor. His writings include *The Bigelow Papers, A Fable for Critics,* and *The Vision of Sir Launfal.*

Cambridge, Mass.   51,666,580
'45	.06	'65	.10
'55	.10	'75	.12

I. Walt Whitman (1819-92) is the celebrated author of *Leaves of Grass.* This book of poems, a milestone in the evolution of American literature, was revised by Whitman several times before his death. His other poems include "When Lilacs Last at the Dooryard Bloom'd", an elegy on the death of Lincoln.

Camden, N.J.   22,207,780
'45	.09	'65	.13
'55	.10	'75	.15

J. James Whitcomb Riley (1849-1916), the Hoosier poet, was a member of the American Academy of Arts and Letters. One of his best-remembered works is *The Old Swimmin' Hole and 'Leven More Poems,* purportedly written by an Indiana farmer.

Greenfield, Ind.   11,835,530
'45	.30	'65	1.00
'55	.95	'75	1.50

A. Horace Mann (1796 - 1859), regarded as the father of the American public school system, gave up a law career to fight for universal, free, nonsectarian education. He helped create the first normal school for teacher training and was instrumental in raising American educational standards.

Boston, Mass. 52,471,160

'45	.03	'65	.05
'55	.05	'75	.06

B. Mark Hopkins (1802 - 87), president of Williams College (1836 - 72), author, and moral philosopher. His principles of self - education and close student - faculty relations became the standard in U.S. liberal arts colleges.

Williamstown, Mass. 52,366,440

'45	.04	'65	.05
'55	.05	'75	.06

C. Charles W. Eliot (1834 - 1926) led Harvard University to a position of world prominence while serving as its president for 40 years. He also introduced mathematics and foreign languages into junior high curriculums, edited the *Harvard Classics,* and tried to broaden the education of high school students who were not preparing for college.

Cambridge, Mass. 51,636,270

'45	.07	'65	.17
'55	.17	'75	.20

D. Frances E. C. Willard (1839 - 98), teacher and organizer of the World's Woman's Christian Temperance Union. Her teaching career led her to the presidency of Evanston College for Ladies.

Evanston, Ill. 20,729,030

'45	.10	'65	.16
'55	.12	'75	.22

E. Booker T. Washington (1856 - 1915), self - taught educator and author who had 30 students when he founded Tuskegee Institute. Over 50,000 black Americans have since attended the school. His autobiographies are *Up from Slavery* and *My Larger Education* (see p. 112).

Tuskegee Institute, Ala. 14,125,580

'45	.25	'65	.58
'55	.45	'75	.75

Issue for Educators

A. 3/14/40

B. 3/14/40

C. 3/28/40

D. 3/28/40

E. *4/7/40*

Issue for Scientists

F. 4/8/40

G. 4/8/40

I. 4/17/40

H. 4/17/40

J. 4/26/40

F. John James Audubon (1785-1851), tireless and meticulous observer of nature. A migrant from Haiti, his principal work is the classic *Birds of America,* which remains unsurpassed in illustrating birds and their natural surroundings (see p. 136).
St. Francisville, La.   59,409,000
'45 .02   '65 .03
'55 .03   '75 .04

G. Crawford W. Long (1815-78), discoverer of the sulphuric ether process of anesthesia. His discovery did much to relieve pain and suffering during surgical procedures.
Jefferson, Ga.   57,888,600
'45 .03   '65 .05
'55 .05   '75 .05

H. Luther Burbank (1849-1926), biologist and plant breeder. A thorough student of Mendel's laws of heredity, he developed hundreds of plants, both food sources and flowers, for the economic benefit and pleasure of mankind.
Santa Rosa, Calif.   58,273,180
'45 .05   '65 .06
'55 .06   '75 .06

I. Walter Reed (1851-1902), bacteriologist and sanitarian responsible for the discovery of the mosquito as carrier of yellow fever. The U.S. Army surgeon, while serving in Cuba, proved that certain types of mosquito bites resulted in the contraction of yellow fever.
Washington, D.C.   23,779,000
'45 .09   '65 .13
'55 .09   '75 .14

J. Jane Addams (1860-1935) is best known for her work at Hull House, a settlement house she founded in the slums of Chicago. It gave the underprivileged civic, cultural, educational, and recreational opportunities. A co-winner of the Nobel Peace Prize in 1931, she also helped enact the first juvenile court law.
Chicago, Ill.   15,112,580
'45 .25   '65 .45
'55 .38   '75 .65

A. Stephen Collins Foster (1826 - 64) composed over 150 songs during a brief life of less than 40 years. These include "Old Black Joe", "Oh! Susanna", "Jeannie with the Light Brown Hair", and "My Old Kentucky Home". Despite their popularity, most of these songs earned Foster very little money, and he died in poverty.

Bardstown, Ky. 57,322,790
'45 .02   '65 .03
'55 .03   '75 .04

B. John Philip Sousa (1854 - 1932), "The March King", wrote "The Stars and Stripes Forever", "Semper Fidelis", "The Washington Post March", and other stirring melodies. He also led the U.S. Marine Corps band and his own band.

Washington, D.C. 58,281,580
'45 .03   '65 .05
'55 .05   '75 .05

C. Victor Herbert (1859 - 1924), Irish - born conductor and virtuoso musician, is best remembered for his many operettas, among them, *Babes in Toyland* and *Naughty Marietta.* He was also the founder of the American Society of Composers, Authors and Publishers (ASCAP).

New York, N.Y. 56,398,790
'45 .05   '65 .07
'55 .07   '75 .09

D. Edward A. MacDowell (1861 - 1908) was inspired by nature to compose such works as the classic *Woodland Sketches.* His farm near Peterborough, New Hampshire, is now the MacDowell Colony for artists, writers, composers, and sculptors.

Peterborough, N.H. 21,147,000
'45 .09   '65 .13
'55 .10   '75 .17

E. Ethelbert W. Nevin (1862 - 1901), concert pianist turned composer, was from the sentimentalist school. The brother of composer Arthur Finley Nevin, his works include "The Rosary", "Barchetta", and "A Day in Venice".

Pittsburgh, Pa. 13,328,000
'45 .30   '65 1.05
'55 .85   '75 1.65

A. 5/3/40

C. 5/13/40

B. *5/3/40*

D. 5/13/40

E. 6/10/40

Issue for Artists

F. *9/5/40*

G. *9/5/40*

H. *9/16/40*

I. *9/16/40*

J. *9/30/40*

F. Gilbert Stuart (1755 - 1828), Federalist portrait painter, was one of the most famous artists of his age. Born in Rhode Island, he spent 12 years in England and then returned to America, where he painted Washington three times from life and created likenesses of many heroes of the Revolutionary era. Several of his portraits have appeared on U.S. stamps.
Narragansett, R.I.   54,389,510
'45 .02   '65 .03
'55 .03   '75 .04

G. James Abbott McNeill Whistler (1834 - 1903), a witty and egotistical genius, spent most of his life in Europe. His most famous work is *Arrangement in Grey and Black No. 1,* better known as "Whistler's Mother" (see p. 67). He also created landscapes and prints.
Lowell, Mass.   53,636,580
'45 .03   '65 .04
'55 .04   '75 .05

H. Augustus Saint - Gaudens (1848 - 1907) revitalized American sculpture with the *Shaw Memorial, Abraham Lincoln* (see p. 52), the *Adams Memorial,* and other portraits. His studio in Cornish, New Hampshire, is a national historic site.
New York, N.Y.   55,313,230
'45 .05   '65 .05
'55 .05   '75 .06

I. Daniel Chester French (1850 - 1931) first won fame at the age of 25 for his statue of the *Minute Man* (see p. 59). His other works include two important statues of Lincoln (see pp. 100, 120).
Stockbridge, Mass.   21,720,580
'45 .09   '65 .14
'55 .10   '75 .20

J. Frederic Remington (1861 - 1909) began his art career as an illustrator for *Harper's Weekly.* He then turned to painting and sculpture, through which he captured the essence of the Old West (see p. 130).
Canton, N.Y.   13,600,580
'45 .25   '65 .60
'55 .48   '75 .95

A. Eli Whitney (1765 - 1825), inventor of the cotton gin. This device, which separates the cotton fiber from seeds and hulls, gave the American South a tremendous advantage in marketing its raw cotton to the world. Whitney, who applied the system of uniform parts in manufacturing muskets, is considered by many to be the father of the "mass production" concept.

Savannah, Ga.   47,599,580
'45	.02	'65	.06
'55	.06	'75	.08

B. Samuel F. B. Morse (1791 - 1872), inventor of the electric telegraph. Completion of the first transcontinental telegraph in 1861 virtually eliminated the Pony Express. Morse was also a painter of renown (see p. 89).

New York, N.Y.   53,766,510
'45	.03	'65	.05
'55	.05	'75	.05

C. Cyrus Hall McCormick (1809 - 84) revolutionized farming with the invention of the reaping machine in 1831. The principles of his reaper have been incorporated into all harvesting machines produced since then.

Lexington, Va.   54,193,580
'45	.05	'65	.09
'55	.09	'75	.11

D. Elias Howe (1819 - 67) patented the first practical sewing machine in 1846. The patent was the subject of lengthy litigation, during which time Isaac Singer developed a machine that became more popular than Howe's.

Spencer, Mass.   20,264,580
'45	.09	'65	.42
'55	.32	'75	.60

E. Alexander Graham Bell (1847 - 1922) transmitted the first sentence over a magnetoelectric telephone in 1876. His interest in transmitting speech electronically stemmed from his experiences as a teacher of speech to the deaf.

Boston, Mass.   13,726,580
'45	.30	'65	2.40
'55	1.90	'75	4.50

E. *10/28/40*

A. 10/7/40

B. 10/7/40

C. 10/14/40

D. 10/14/40

F. *4/3/40*

G. 10/16/40

H. 10/16/40

I. 10/16/40

J. *7/3/40*

K. *9/7/40*

F. Pony Express, 80th anniversary. Using slightly - built but expert riders, superb horses, and lightweight saddles, this famous service sped the mails from Missouri to California in about ten days. The record run of seven days, 17 hours bore the text of Lincoln's first inaugural address (see p. 123). St. Joseph, Mo. Sacramento, Calif.   46,497,400

'45	.06	'65	.29
'55	.26	'75	.32

National Defense Issue, three stamps which temporarily took the place of regular issues in order to focus on the impending crisis of World War II. The designs are based on original sketches by President Franklin D. Roosevelt. Shown:

G. Statue of Liberty. Washington, D.C.   6,081,409,300

'45	.03	'65	.03
'55	.03	'75	.03

H. 90mm. Anti - aircraft Gun. Washington, D.C.   5,211,708,300

'45	.03	'65	.03
'55	.03	'75	.04

I. Torch of Enlightenment. Washington, D.C.   8,384,867,600

'45	.05	'65	.07
'55	.06	'75	.08

J. Idaho Statehood, 50th anniversary. 43rd state, admitted 1890. Leading industries include mining, agriculture, and lumbering. Shown: capitol at Boise. Boise, Idaho   50,618,150

'45	.05	'65	.10
'55	.10	'75	.12

K. Coronado Expedition, 400th anniversary. In 1540, Francisco Vázquez de Coronado explored the American Southwest while searching for the gold of the Seven Cities of Cibola. He found no wealth, however, for the cities were the pueblo homes of Zuñi Indians. Shown: *Coronado and His Captains* by Gerald Cassidy. Albuquerque, N.M.   60,943,700

'45	.05	'65	.10
'55	.10	'75	.12

A. 4/14/40

B. 3/4/41

C. 6/1/42

D. 7/4/42

E. 1/14/43

F. 2/12/43

G. 7/10/40

A. Pan - American Union, founded in 1890 to promote trade and peace in the Americas. Shown: The Three Graces, from *Primavera* (Spring) by Italian Renaissance artist Sandro Botticelli.

Washington, D.C. 47,700,000
'45 .05   '65 .23
'55 .20   '75 .25

B. Vermont Statehood, 150th anniversary. Organized as an independent state in 1777, Vermont had a constitution which granted universal manhood suffrage. In 1791, it joined the Union as the 14th state. Shown: capitol at Montpelier, and shield with 14 stars.

Montpelier, Vt. 54,574,550
'45 .04   '65 .11
'55 .10   '75 .14

C. Kentucky Statehood, 150th anniversary. 15th state, admitted 1792. Leading industries include agriculture, tobacco, and mining. Shown: Daniel Boone and three frontiersmen looking at the site of the capital at Frankfort. The scene is from a mural by Gilbert White in the capitol.

Frankfort, Ky. 63,558,400
'45 .04   '65 .07
'55 .06   '75 .09

D-F. The following three stamps were issued to replace the National Defense Issue.

D. Win the War.
Washington, D.C.
20,642,793,310
'45 .04   '65 .05
'55 .05   '75 .07

E. United Nations.

Washington, D.C. 1,000,000,000
'45 .03   '65 .04
'55 .04   '75 .05

F. The Four Freedoms, enumerated by President Roosevelt in 1941.

Washington, D.C. 1,234,918,200
'45 .02   '65 .03
'55 .02   '75 .04

G. Wyoming Statehood, 50th anniversary. 44th state, admitted 1890. Capital, Cheyenne. Leading industries include mining, tourism, and wool production. Shown: state seal with "equal rights"

H. 7/7/42

J. *10/20/40*

I. 5/10/44

K. 5/22/44

L. 5/24/44

motto. Wyoming gave women the right to vote in 1869, while it was a territory.

Cheyenne, Wyo. 50,034,400

'45	.05	'65	.10
'55	.10	'75	.12

H. China, a tribute to five years of Chinese resistance to Japan.

Denver, Colo. 21,272,800

'45	.07	'65	.26
'55	.21	'75	.30

I. First Transcontinental Railroad, 75th anniversary of the joining of the Union Pacific Railroad and the Central Pacific Railroad at Promontory, Utah, in 1869. The new railroad promised to take travelers from Omaha to San Francisco "in less than four days". Shown: mural by John McQuarrie in the Union Pacific Station, Salt Lake City, Utah.

San Francisco, Calif.
Omaha, Nebr.
Ogden, Utah 61,303,000

'45	.04	'65	.07
'55	.06	'75	.08

J. Thirteenth Amendment, 75th anniversary of the abolition of slavery in the United States by constitutional amendment. Shown: Emancipation Monument in Lincoln Park, Washington, D.C., by Thomas Ball.

Flushing, N.Y. 44,389,550

'45	.05	'65	.13
'55	.11	'75	.15

K. S.S. *Savannah.* The first steamship to cross the Atlantic was a sailing ship equipped with steam power. It traveled from Georgia to England in 27 days.

Savannah, Ga.
Kings Point, N.Y. 61,001,450

'45	.04	'65	.06
'55	.05	'75	.08

L. Telegraph, 100th anniversary. In 1844, Samuel F. B. Morse sent the first words by telegraph, "What hath God wrought?" from Washington, D.C., to Baltimore, Maryland.

Baltimore, Md.
Washington, D.C. 60,605,000

'45	.04	'65	.06
'55	.05	'75	.08

Overrun Countries Issue,
a tribute to 13 countries occupied by Axis powers during World War II. Each stamp shows the flag of one of the overrun countries in natural colors. A phoenix appears on the left of each flag to symbolize the renewal of life. On the right, a kneeling female figure breaks the shackles of oppression. The multicolor stamps were printed by the American Bank Note Company. Flags shown are:

A. *6/22/43*

A. Poland.
Washington, D.C.
Chicago, Ill.   19,996,646
   '45 .08   '65 .14
   '55 .14   '75 .18

B. Czechoslovakia.
Washington, D.C.   19,996,646
   '45 .08   '65 .10
   '55 .09   '75 .10

C. Norway.
Washington, D.C.   19,996,646
   '45 .08   '65 .08
   '55 .08   '75 .10

B. 7/12/43

C. 7/27/43

D. Luxembourg.
Washington, D.C.   19,999,646
   '45 .08   '65 .08
   '55 .08   '75 .10

E. Netherlands.
Washington, D.C.   19,999,646
   '45 .08   '65 .08
   '55 .08   '75 .10

F. Belgium.
Washington, D.C.   19,999,646
   '45 .08   '65 .08
   '55 .08   '75 .10

G. France.
Washington, D.C.   19,999,646
   '45 .08   '65 .08
   '55 .08   '75 .10

F. 9/14/43

G. 9/28/43

H. Greece.
Washington, D.C.   14,999,646
   '45 .08   '65 .12
   '55 .12   '75 .16

I. Yugoslavia.
Washington, D.C.   14,999,646
   '45 .08   '65 .10
   '55 .10   '75 .15

J. 11/9/43

K. 11/23/43

J. Albania.
Washington, D.C.   14,999,646
   '45 .08   '65 .12
   '55 .12   '75 .12

K. Austria.
Washington, D.C.   14,999,646
   '45 .08   '65 .09
   '55 .09   '75 .13

L. Denmark.
Washington, D.C.   14,999,646
   '45 .08   '65 .12
   '55 .12   '75 .16

M. Korea.
Washington, D.C.   14,999,646
   '45 .07   '65 .14
   '55 .14   '75 .18

ROOSEVELT MEMORIAL ISSUE

Franklin Delano Roosevelt (1882 - 1945), bold and confident despite the effects of poliomyelitis, led the American people through the Great Depression and World War II. Unexcelled in winning popular support, he was the only president elected to that office for four terms (1933 - 45). He was also an enthusiastic stamp collector and designed several stamps issued during his presidency. The four memorial stamps shown at right were issued following his death in office in 1945.

N. 7/26/45

D. 8/10/43

E. 8/24/43

O. 8/24/45

H. 10/12/43

I. 10/26/43

P. 6/27/45

L. 12/7/43

M. 11/2/44

Q. 1/30/46

Roosevelt Memorial Issue.
N. Portrait of Roosevelt with his Hyde Park home.
Hyde Park, N.Y. 128,101,700
'55 .03 '65 .03 '75 .03

O. Roosevelt and "Little White House" at Warm Springs, Georgia.
Warm Springs, Ga. 67,255,000
'55 .04 '65 .05 '75 .05

P. Roosevelt and White House.
Washington, D.C. 133,856,950
'55 .05 '65 .06 '75 .07

Q. Roosevelt, Globe, and Freedoms Quote.
Washington, D.C. 76,455,400
'55 .07 '65 .09 '75 .09

A. *10/31/44*

B. 11/26/45

C. 9/27/44

D. 3/3/45

E. 4/25/45

F. 12/29/45

A. Motion Pictures, 50th anniversary of the first public showing of Edison's "Kinetoscope". The design of the stamp is a tribute to the contribution of the film industry to our armed forces. It depicts a motion picture being shown to U.S. troops in the South Pacific.
New York, N.Y.
Los Angeles, Calif.
Hollywood Station   53,479,400
　　'45 .04   '65 .06
　　'55 .05   '75 .08

B. Alfred E. Smith (1873 -

1944). Known as the "Happy Warrior", Smith served as governor of New York (1919 - 20, 1923 - 28) and ran for the presidency against Herbert Hoover in 1928.
New York, N.Y.   308,587,700
　　'55 .05   '65 .05   '75 .07

C. Corregidor, a rocky island in Manila Bay where forces under General Jonathan Wainwright repelled the Japanese for 27 days before surrendering on May 6, 1942.

Washington, D.C.   50,129,350
　　'45 .04   '65 .06
　　'55 .06   '75 .08

D. Florida Statehood, 100th anniversary. 27th state, admitted 1845. Capital, Tallahassee. Tourism is a major industry. The state also produces much of the nation's citrus fruit. Cape Canaveral has been the takeoff point for many historic space flights. Shown: gates of St. Augustine, oldest city in the state, and capitol

with state seal (see p. 143).
Tallahassee, Fla.   61,617,350
　'55 .05   '65 .05   '75 .07

E. United Nations Conference on International Organization. On April 25, 1945, delegates from 50 nations met in San Francisco to draw up the United Nations Charter. The conference was called by President Roosevelt, who died 13 days before it began.
San Francisco, Calif.   75,474,350
　'55 .07   '65 .08   '75 .09

ARMED FORCES ISSUE

G. 9/28/45

H. 10/27/45

J. 7/11/45

I. 11/10/45

K. 2/26/46

F. Texas Statehood, 100th anniversary. 28th state, admitted 1845 after nine years of independence. Capital, Austin. The state leads all others in cattle production. Other major industries are petroleum, manufacturing, and tourism. Shown: U.S. flag with beam from 28th state radiating to the Lone Star of the Texas flag.
Austin, Tex.   170,640,000
'55   .05   '65   .05   '75   .07

Armed Forces Issue, five stamps honoring those who served in World War II.

G. Army. A photograph of the liberation of Paris focuses on the infantry in Europe. U.S. troops are shown at the Arc de Triomphe with six bombers overhead.
Washington, D.C.   128,357,750
'55   .05   '65   .05   '75   .07

H. Navy. Faces of sailors at Corpus Christi Naval Air Station represent the thousands who fought gallantly and those who died.
Annapolis, Md.   138,863,000
'55   .05   '65   .05   '75   .07

I. Coast Guard. A landing craft with a supply ship in the background symbolizes the contribution of the military organization whose history can be traced from 1790.
New York, N.Y.   111,616,700
'55   .05   '65   .05   '75   .07

J. Marines. The stamp shows the famous photograph of the raising of the flag on Mount Suribachi, Iwo Jima, by Joe Rosenthal of the Associated Press. Marines captured the island from well-armed, determined Japanese forces.
Washington, D.C.   137,321,000
'55   .05   '65   .05   '75   .07

K. Merchant Marine. A Liberty ship unloading cargo symbolizes the contribution of this service in transporting men and materials.
Washington, D.C.   135,927,000
'55   .05   '65   .05   '75   .07

A. *8/10/46*

The Smithsonian Institution is named for James Smithson, an eccentric English chemist who left the United States $508,318.46 to build "an establishment for the increase & diffusion of knowledge among men." The gift baffled Congress, and for ten years it debated whether or not to accept the money, and how to spend it. During the proceedings, John Quincy Adams guarded the legacy. Largely through his efforts, one of the great museum complexes and research centers in the world was created in 1846.

B. 6/1/46

C. 8/3/46

D. 5/9/46

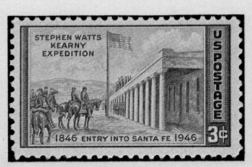

E. 10/16/46

F. 2/11/47

A. Smithsonian Institution, 100th anniversary. Shown: the original home of the Smithsonian, designed by James Renwick and completed in 1855.
Washington, D.C.   139,209,500
'55 .05   '65 .05   '75 .07

B. Tennessee Statehood, 150th anniversary. Once a part of North Carolina, Tennessee was briefly known as "Franklin" when it declared itself independent under John Sevier in 1785. In 1796 it became the 16th state, and Sevier was elected governor. Leading industries include: manufacturing, tobacco, forestry, and mineral production, chiefly zinc. Shown: Andrew Jackson, who led Tennessee volunteers in the War of 1812; John Sevier; and the capitol at Nashville.
Nashville, Tenn.   132,274,500
'55 .05   '65 .05   '75 .07

C. Iowa Statehood, 100th anniversary. 29th state, admitted 1846. Famous for its cattle, corn, and hogs, Iowa also manufactures home appliances, vending machines, office equipment, and other goods. In 1857, the capital was moved from Iowa City to Des Moines. Shown: outline map and state flag.
Iowa City, Iowa   132,430,000
'55 .05   '65 .05   '75 .07

D. Veterans of World War II, "Honoring Those Who Have Served". Shown: honorable discharge emblem.
Washington, D.C.   260,339,100
'55 .05   '65 .05   '75 .07

E. Kearny Expedition, 100th anniversary of this phase of the Mexican War. Shown: the *Capture of Santa Fe*, New Mexico, on August 18, 1846, by Stephen W. Kearny and his "Army of the West". After a painting by Kenneth Chapman.
Santa Fe, N.M.   114,684,450
'55 .05   '65 .05   '75 .07

F. Thomas A. Edison (1847-1931). The man who took out 1,093 patents for such things as the phonograph

G. 5/17/47

I. 4/10/47

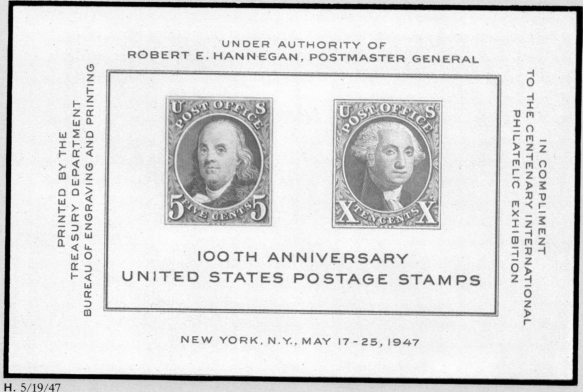

H. 5/19/47

and the incandescent light bulb was labeled as "addled" by his teachers. His major inventive achievements came between 1870 and 1880.
Milan, Ohio 156,540,510
'55 .05 '65 .05 '75 .07

G. United States Postage Stamps Centenary. Shown: portraits of Washington and Franklin that appeared on the first stamps, with various forms of transportation used to carry mail in the 19th and 20th centuries.

New York, N.Y. 127,104,300
'55 .05 '65 .05 '75 .07

H. CIPEX, souvenir sheet, a compliment to the Centenary International Philatelic Exhibition, held at Grand Central Palace, New York City, May 17-25, 1947. The central portion of the sheet contains reproductions of the first U.S. stamps, issued on July 1, 1847 (see p. 26). The 5c Franklin was reproduced in light blue rather than the original red

brown, and the 10c Washington was changed to red orange from black. The two stamps were valid for postage when cut out from the sheet.
New York, N.Y. 10,299,600
'55 .24 '65 .35 '75 .50

I. Joseph Pulitzer (1847-1911), Hungarian-born journalist who founded the Columbia University School of Journalism and endowed the Pulitzer Prizes, which are awarded annually for

excellence in journalism, drama, fiction, history, poetry, biography, and music. During his newspaper career, Pulitzer bought the *St. Louis Dispatch* and merged it with the *Post* to create the *Post-Dispatch.* In 1883, he bought the *New York World,* which became known for its forceful, independent editorials.
New York, N.Y. 120,452,600
'55 .05 '65 .05 '75 .07

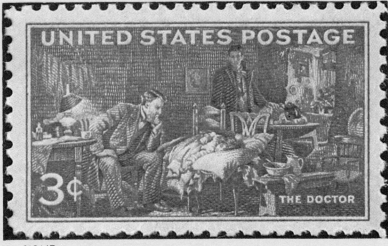

A. *6/9/47*

B. *12/5/47*

C. *1/5/48*

D. *7/24/47*

E. *1/24/48*

F. *4/7/48*

A. The Doctors, a tribute to physicians issued in conjunction with the 100th anniversary of the American Medical Association. Shown: *The Doctor* by Sir Luke Fildes.
Atlantic City, N.J.   132,902,000
'55   .05   '65   .05   '75   .07

B. Everglades National Park. Dedicated in 1947, this large area in southern Florida is a refuge for many forms of wildlife, including the Florida cougar, alligator, snowy egret, and great white heron (shown).
Florida City, Fla.   122,362,000
'55   .05   '65   .05   '75   .07

C. George Washington Carver (c. 1864-1943), slave-born agricultural-chemist whose research yielded many new uses for the farm crops of the South.
Tuskegee Institute, Ala. 121,548,000
'55   .05   '65   .05   '75   .07

D. Utah Settlement, 100th anniversary. Shown: Mormon settlers entering the valley of the Great Salt Lake in 1847 under the leadership of Brigham Young.
Salt Lake City, Utah 131,968,000
'55   .05   '65   .05   '75   .07

E. California Gold, 100th anniversary of the discovery of gold at Sutter's Mill by James W. Marshall. Soon afterwards, an estimated 80,000 gold-seekers poured into the area from all parts of the world. They included all the French inhabitants of the Marquesas Islands in Polynesia, with the lone exception of the governor.
Coloma, Calif.   130,709,500
'55   .05   '65   .05   '75   .07

F. Mississippi Territory, 150th anniversary. Shown: outline map of the territory, which included the present states of Mississippi and Alabama; the territorial seal, using the spelling Missisippi; and the first governor, Winthrop Sargent.
Natchez, Miss.   122,650,500
'55   .05   '65   .05   '75   .07

G. 5/29/48

H. 5/28/48

I. 6/4/48

J. 7/19/48

K. 7/31/48

L. *10/21/47*

G. Wisconsin Statehood, 100th anniversary. 30th state, admitted 1848. Capital, Madison. The state leads the nation in dairy production. Shown: outline map, state motto, and capitol.
Madison, Wis. 115,250,000
'55 .05   '65 .05   '75 .07

H. Four Chaplains, a tribute to George L. Fox, Clark V. Poling, John P. Washington, and Alexander D. Goode, who gave their life preservers to others and died in the sinking of the S.S. *Dorchester* on February 3, 1943.
Washington, D.C. 121,953,500
'55 .05   '65 .05   '75 .07

I. Swedish Pioneers, 100th anniversary of the immigration of 1½ million Swedish settlers to 12 midwestern states.
Chicago, Ill. 64,198,000
'55 .07   '65 .09   '75 .10

J. Progress of Women, 100th anniversary of the first women's rights convention, held at Seneca Falls, New York. Shown: Elizabeth Stanton, Carrie Chapman Catt, and Lucretia Mott, three leaders of the women's suffrage movement.
Seneca Falls, N.Y. 117,642,500
'55 .05   '65 .05   '75 .07

K. William Allen White (1868 - 1944), author and editor of the Kansas *Emporia Gazette* whose grass roots journalism made him famous. He also wrote novels, short stories, and biographies.
Emporia, Kans. 77,649,600
'55 .05   '65 .05   '75 .07

L. U.S. Frigate *Constitution,* 150th anniversary of the launching of the famous ship that captured the British *Guerrière* in one of the most memorable battles of the War of 1812. In 1830 she was almost scrapped, but Oliver Wendell Holmes aroused public sentiment to save her through his poem, "Old Ironsides".
Boston, Mass. 131,488,000
'55 .05   '65 .05   '75 .07

A. 8/2/48

B. 8/14/48

C. 9/7/48

D. 8/11/48

E. 9/21/48

F. 8/9/48

A. United States - Canada Friendship, 100th anniversary. Shown: the old Niagara Railway Suspension Bridge, completed in 1855.
Niagara Falls, N.Y.   113,474,500
'55 .05   '65 .05   '75 .07

B. Oregon Territory, 100th anniversary. In 1848, President Polk brought Oregon into the nation as a free territory after seven months of Congressional debate. Shown: Dr. John McLoughlin, who founded

Fort Vancouver in 1824; Jason Lee, the Methodist missionary who petitioned Congress for territorial organization in 1836; and a wagon on the Oregon Trail.
Oregon City, Ore.   52,214,000
'55 .06   '65 .07   '75 .08

C. Clara Barton (1821-1912), humanitarian and founder of the American Red Cross.
Oxford, Mass.   57,823,000
'55 .05   '65 .06   '75 .07

D. Salute to Youth, a tribute to Youth Month, 1948.

Washington, D.C.   77,800,500
'55 .05   '65 .05   '75 .07

E. Gold Star Mothers, a tribute to the mothers of the nation's war dead.
Washington, D.C.   77,149,000
'55 .05   '65 .05   '75 .07

F. Francis Scott Key (1779-1843), author of the national anthem. "The Star Spangled Banner" was written in 1814 after Key, a young lawyer, watched the bombing of Fort McHenry, Maryland, from a British ship (see p. 152). Shown: portrait of Key

draped by flags of 1814 and 1948. The Key home and Fort McHenry appear in the lower corners.
Frederick, Md.   120,868,500
'55 .05   '65 .05   '75 .07

G. Harlan Fiske Stone (1872-1946), chief justice of the the U.S. Supreme Court (1941-46).
Chesterfield, N.H.   53,958,100
'55 .06   '65 .07   '75 .09

H. Palomar Mountain Observatory, dedication. This California observatory houses the Hale telescope.

G. 8/25/48

H. 8/30/48

I. 9/9/48

J. 9/22/48

K. 10/4/48

L. 10/15/48

M. 10/27/48

Named for astronomer George Ellery Hale, it has a 200-inch mirror, which enables scientists to search and photograph one billion light years into space.
Palomar Mt., Calif. 61,120,010
'55 .06   '65 .07   '75 .18

I. Poultry Industry, 100th anniversary. Shown: light Brahma rooster.
New Haven, Conn. 52,975,000
'55 .05   '65 .07   '75 .08

J. Fort Kearney, Nebraska. Founded in 1848, this

outpost protected pioneers as they moved along the Platte Valley. Shown: bas-relief on the Nebraska capitol and view of the fort.
Minden, Nebr. 58,332,000
'55 .05   '65 .06   '75 .07

K. Volunteer Firemen. In 1647, the governor of New Amsterdam, Peter Stuyvesant, appointed the first fire wardens in the U.S. They patrolled the streets of Manhattan and carried noisemakers, which were used to sound alarms.

Dover, Del. 56,228,000
'55 .05   '65 .06   '75 .07

L. Indian Centennial, a memorial to the "Trail of Tears" removal of the Cherokee, Choctaw, Chickasaw, Muskogee, and Seminole Indians from their homes in the Southeast. Between 1830 and 1842, one-fourth of the population of the "five civilized tribes" died as they were driven to the territory which became Oklahoma.

Muskogee, Okla. 57,832,000
'55 .05   '65 .06   '75 .07

M. Rough Riders, 50th anniversary of Theodore Roosevelt's colorful regiment. During the Spanish-American War, they stormed Cuba's San Juan Hill on foot and helped the U.S. seize the Santiago Harbor. Shown: Solon Borglum's statue of Captain "Bucky" O'Neill, who was killed in the battle.
Prescott, Ariz. 53,875,000
'55 .05   '65 .08   '75 .08

A. Juliette Low (1860 - 1927), organizer of the Girl Scouts of America.
Savannah, Ga.   60,000,000
'55   .05   '65   .06   '75   .07

B. Fort Bliss, 100th anniversary. Located near El Paso, Texas, this fort has evolved from the largest U.S. cavalry post into the center for guided missile training.
El Paso, Tex.   63,490,000
'55   .07   '65   .07   '75   .25

C. Moina Michael (1870 - 1944), who developed the idea of selling poppies on Memorial Day to aid disabled veterans.
Athens, Ga.   64,079,500
'55   .05   '65   .06   '75   .07

D. Joel Chandler Harris (1848 - 1908), author of the "Uncle Remus" stories. His famous characters, Br'er Rabbit, Br'er Fox, and company, are styled after the oral literature of Africa.
Eatonton, Ga.   57,492,610
'55   .05   '65   .06   '75   .07

E. Gettysburg Address, 85th anniversary. These few sentences are among Lincoln's most memorable. They were delivered at the dedication of a military cemetery at the site of the Battle of Gettysburg.
Shown: statue of Lincoln by Daniel Chester French (Lincoln, Nebraska).
Gettysburg, Pa.   63,388,000
'55   .05   '65   .06   '75   .07

F. Minnesota Territory, created in 1849 and settled after treaties were negotiated with the Indians. The name Minnesota is from the Sioux for cloudy water.
St. Paul, Minn.   99,190,000
'55   .05   '65   .05   '75   .07

G. American Turners Society, 100th anniversary. The organization promotes health and physical fitness.
Cincinnati, Ohio   62,285,500
'55   .05   '65   .06   '75   .07

H. Will Rogers (1879 - 1935), rope - twirling humorist and philosopher who made America laugh at itself.
Claremore, Okla.   67,162,200
'55   .05   '65   .06   '75   .07

A. 10/29/48

B. 11/5/48

C. 11/9/48

D. 12/9/48

E. 11/19/48

F. 3/3/49

G. 11/20/48

H. 11/4/48

I. 4/12/49

J. 4/27/49

K. 10/7/49

L. 1/27/50

M. 5/23/49

N. 8/29/49

O. 1/3/50

I. Washington and Lee University, Lexington, Virginia. Founded in 1749, this university received an endowment from George Washington in 1798. Robert E. Lee served as its president after the Civil War.
Lexington, Va.   104,790,000
'55   .05   '65   .05   '75   .07

J. Puerto Rico Gubernatorial Election. In 1947 Congress passed a law which enabled this island Commonwealth to elect its chief executive.
San Juan, P.R.   108,805,000
'55   .05   '65   .05   '75   .07

K. Edgar Allan Poe (1809 - 49), poet and author who helped create the modern detective tale. His brooding imagination is reflected in "The Fall of the House of Usher", "The Pit and the Pendulum", and other stories.
Richmond, Va.   122,633,000
'55   .05   '65   .05   '75   .07

L. Samuel Gompers (1850 - 1924), self - educated, cigar - maker who founded the American Federation of Labor in 1886.
Washington, D.C.   128,478,000
'55   .05   '65   .05   '75   .07

M. Annapolis, 300th anniversary. Colonists of Lord Baltimore's Maryland Plantation settled this city in 1649 and named it for Queen Anne of England. It is now the capital of Maryland. Shown: 1718 map portraying ship entering the Severn River from the Chesapeake Bay and the crest of Lord Baltimore.
Annapolis, Md.   107,340,000
'55   .05   '65   .05   '75   .07

N. Grand Army of the Republic, noting the final encampment of the Civil War Union veterans association.
Indianapolis, Ind.   117,020,000
'55   .05   '65   .05   '75   .07

O. American Bankers Association, founded in 1875 at Saratoga Springs, New York.
Saratoga Springs, N.Y.
130,960,000
'55   .05   '65   .05   '75   .07

A. *11/22/50*

B. *4/20/50*

C. *6/12/50*

D. *8/2/50*

E. *4/29/50*

F. *6/3/50*

National Capital Sesquicentennial Issue.
Once described as a feverish swamp, the nation's capital was built on a site chosen by George Washington, who appointed French engineer Pierre Charles L'Enfant to design the city. In 1800, Henry Adams wrote that "...the half-finished White House stood in a naked field overlooking the Potomac... across a swamp, a mile and a half away, the shapeless, unfinished Capitol was seen..." From this humble start, Washington, D.C. evolved into a splendid showcase of monuments, spacious parks, and public buildings. Shown:

A. United States Capitol.
Washington, D.C.   129,980,000
'55 .05   '65 .05   '75 .07

B. Statue of Freedom by Thomas Crawford atop the Capitol dome.
Washington, D.C.   132,090,000
'55 .05   '65 .05   '75 .07

C. The White House.
Washington, D.C.   130,050,000
'55 .05   '65 .05   '75 .07

D. United States Supreme Court Building.
Washington, D.C.   131,350,000
'55 .05   '65 .05   '75 .07

E. Railroad Engineers of America. Shown: ancient and modern locomotives, and "Casey" Jones, who ran the "Cannonball Express". Balladeers still sing of his death in a crash on April 30, 1900.
Jackson, Tenn. 122,315,000
'55 .05   '65 .05   '75 .07

F. Kansas City, Missouri, 100th anniversary. "The Gateway to the West" was born in the age of the pioneers. Once called Westport Landing, it was a take-off point for settlers who traveled west on the Santa Fe and Oregon Trails. Shown: Westport Landing, 1850, and Kansas City, 1950.
Kansas City, Mo. 122,170,000
'55 .05   '65 .05   '75 .07

G. *6/30/50*

H. *7/4/50*

I. *9/9/50*

J. *5/30/51*

K. *7/14/51*

G. Boy Scouts of America, second National Jamboree. Scouting was started by Sir Robert Baden-Powell, who developed a training program for British recruits during the South African Boer War, and then adapted it for groups of boys. William Boyce brought scouting to America.
Valley Forge, Pa. 131,635,000
'55 .05 '65 .05 '75 .07

H. Indiana Territory, 150th anniversary. Shown: William Henry Harrison, the first territorial governor. His victory over the Shawnee at Tippecanoe in 1811 opened the area for settlement and gave him a winning campaign slogan in his race for the presidency. The first capitol at Vincennes is also shown.
Vincennes, Ind. 121,860,000
'55 .05 '65 .05 '75 .07

I. California Statehood, 100th anniversary. After gold was discovered at Sutter's Mill in 1848, the trickle of California-bound settlers swelled to a flood and in 1850 the territory entered the Union as the 31st state. Capital, Sacramento. Shown: gold panning and pioneers, flanked by the fruit and oil that are the modern "gold" of California. The S.S. *Oregon,* also shown, brought the news of statehood.
Sacramento, Calif. 121,120,000
'55 .05 '65 .05 '75 .07

J. United Confederate Veterans, issued for their final reunion.

Norfolk, Va. 119,120,000
'55 .05 '65 .05 '75 .07

K. Nevada Settlement, 100th anniversary. Founded as a summer trading post for miners moving west, the town of Mormon Station (now Genoa) was one of the first settlements in the state. Shown: log cabin and pioneer scene.
Genoa, Nev. 112,125,000
'55 .05 '65 .05 '75 .07

A. 7/24/51

B. 8/1/51

C. 9/4/51

D. 12/10/51

E. *2/28/52*

A. Landing of Cadillac, 250th anniversary. In 1701, Antoine de la Mothe Cadillac arrived at the site of Detroit, where he built Fort Pontchartrain du Detroit (of the strait). It was a French fur trading center until 1760, when it fell to the British as a result of the French and Indian War.
Detroit, Mich.   114,140,000
'55 .05   '65 .05   '75 .07

B. Colorado Statehood, 75th anniversary. 38th state;
nicknamed the "centennial state" because it entered the Union in 1876. Capital, Denver. Leading industries include: ranching, farming, tourism, and transportation.
Minturn, Colo.   114,490,000
'55 .05   '65 .05   '75 .07

C. American Chemical Society, 75th anniversary. Shown: emblem of the society and chemical instruments and structures.
New York, N.Y.   117,200,000
'55 .05   '65 .05   '75 .07

D. Battle of Brooklyn, 175th anniversary of what is also known as the Battle of Long Island, in which the British defeated the Americans and captured General John Sullivan. Two days later, on August 29, 1776, George Washington withdrew the remaining Americans across the East River in one of the brilliant maneuvers of the Revolutionary War.
Brooklyn, N.Y.   116,130,000
'55 .05   '65 .05   '75 .07

E. Baltimore and Ohio Railroad, 125th anniversary of the first common carrier in the United States. Service began in 1830 with live horsepower moving cars along the first 13 miles of track. Shown: "Pioneer Car", first type used for passenger service; "Tom Thumb", first steam locomotive; and modern diesel engine.
Baltimore, Md.   112,540,000
'55 .05   '65 .05   '75 .07

F. 1/2/52

G. 4/4/52

H. 1/15/52

I. 3/4/52

J. 6/13/52

K. 5/15/52

Mount Rushmore, South Dakota, is the site of Gustav Borglum's giant sculptures of the heads of Washington, Jefferson, Theodore Roosevelt, and Lincoln. The carvings, each about 60 feet tall, were created as a monument to American democracy. Borglum, who developed many new engineering methods for the project, died shortly before it was completed.

L. 8/11/52

F. Betsy Ross. An upholsterer by trade, she was probably commissioned to make the first U.S. flag (see p. 152), which was likely designed by Francis Hopkinson, a signer of the Declaration of Independence. Shown: painting by C. H. Weisgerber.
Philadelphia, Pa. 116,175,000
'55 .05 '65 .05 '75 .07

G. North Atlantic Treaty Organization, third anniversary of the signing of a mutual defense pact by the United States, Canada, and ten West European nations.
Washington, D.C. 2,899,580,000
'55 .05 '65 .05 '75 .07

H. 4-H Clubs, rural youth organization. The 4-H clover symbol stands for "head, heart, hands, and health".
Springfield, Ohio 115,945,000
'55 .05 '65 .05 '75 .07

I. American Automobile Association, 50th anniversary. The organization promotes safety and provides many services for its members.
Chicago, Ill. 117,415,000
'55 .05 '65 .05 '75 .07

J. Marquis de La Fayette, 175th anniversary of his arrival in America. The Marquis came here at his own expense and soon became a close friend of George Washington. A good soldier, he also helped secure French support for the Americans.
Georgetown, S.C. 113,135,000
'55 .07 '65 .05 '75 .07

K. Grand Coulee Dam, the world's largest concrete dam. It is built across the Columbia River in Washington. The stamp also marks 50 years of river development in the West.
Grand Coulee, Wash. 114,540,000
'55 .05 '65 .05 '75 .07

L. Mount Rushmore, 25th anniversary.
Keystone, S.D. 116,255,000
'55 .05 '65 .05 '75 .07

A. *10/4/52*

B. *9/6/52*

C. *9/11/52*

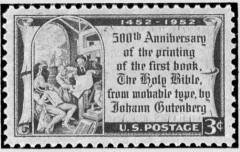

D. *9/30/52*

E. *11/21/52*

F. *2/23/53*

A. Newspaperboys of America. Countless men have received training in the free enterprise system while serving as newsboys.
Philadelphia, Pa.   115,430,000
'55   .05   '65   .05   '75   .07

B. American Society of Civil Engineers, 100th anniversary. Shown: crest of the society, a covered bridge of 1852, and the George Washington Bridge between New York and New Jersey.

Chicago, Ill.   113,860,000
'55   .05   '65   .05   '75   .07

C. Women in Our Armed Services, a tribute to these women, especially the 40,000 who served in World War II.
Washington, D.C.   124,260,000
'55   .05   '65   .05   '75   .07

D. Gutenberg Bible, 500th anniversary. This superb edition of the Holy Bible, the first book printed from movable type, is named for Johann Gutenberg (c. 1400 - 68). A native of Mainz,

Germany, Gutenberg is generally accepted as the inventor of western printing. Shown: a reproduction of Edward Laning's painting, *Gutenberg Showing a Proof to the Elector of Mainz.*
Washington, D.C.   115,735,000
'55   .05   '65   .05   '75   .07

E. International Red Cross. This humanitarian society was created largely through the efforts of Jean Henri Dunant, who won the first Nobel Peace Prize in 1901.

New York, N.Y.   136,220,000
'55   .05   '65   .05   '75   .07

F. National Guard, the oldest military organization in the United States. It originated as a volunteer colonial militia.
Washington, D.C.   114,894,600
'55   .05   '65   .05   '75   .07

G. Washington Territory, 100th anniversary. This majestic land offered settlers fertile soil, timber, and untapped mineral resources. Railroad-building spurred its

G. 3/2/53

H. 3/2/53

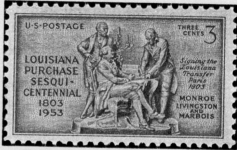

I. 4/30/53

J. 7/14/53

K. 8/24/53

L. 9/14/53

M. 10/13/53

population growth, and in 1889 it became a state.
Olympia, Wash.   114,190,000
'55 .05   '65 .05   '75 .07

H. Ohio Statehood, 150th anniversary. 17th state and the first to be created from the Northwest Territory. Ohio is a leading producer of tires, metal products, glassware, and other items. In 1817 the capital was moved from Chillicothe to Columbus.
Chillicothe, Ohio   118,706,000
'55 .05   '65 .05   '75 .07

I. Louisiana Purchase, 150th anniversary. Bought from France in 1803 for about 4c an acre, this huge area doubled the size of the United States. Thirteen states were created from it. Shown: Karl Bitter's sculptured plaque illustrating the transfer of the land.
St. Louis, Mo.   113,990,000
'55 .05   '65 .05   '75 .07

J. Opening of Japan, 100th anniversary. The Treaty of Kanagawa, negotiated by Commodore Matthew Perry

in 1853, opened Japan to trade after 200 years of virtual isolation.
Washington, D.C.   89,289,600
'55 .07   '65 .09   '75 .10

K. American Bar Association, 75th anniversary. Shown: the figures of Wisdom, Justice, Divine Inspiration, and Truth, from a frieze in the Supreme Court Room.
Boston, Mass.   114,865,000
'55 .05   '65 .05   '75 .07

L. Sagamore Hill, national shrine. This 22 - room

Victorian mansion in Oyster Bay, New York, was the home of Theodore Roosevelt. It served as the summer White House from 1901 to 1909 and houses his hunting trophies.
Oyster Bay, N.Y.   115,780,000
'55 .05   '65 .05   '75 .07

M. Future Farmers of America, 25th anniversary. Shown: student future farmer viewing agricultural scene.
Kansas City, Mo.   115,244,600
'55 .05   '65 .05   '75 .07

A. *11/20/53*

B. 10/27/53

C. 11/11/53

D. 12/30/53

E. 4/9/54

F. 1/4/54

G. 6/24/54

A. New York City, 300th anniversary. Incorporated as New Amsterdam by the Dutch in 1653, this city became an English colony under the Duke of York in 1664. Shown: Dutch ship in New Amsterdam Harbor and the modern city.
New York, N.Y. 115,759,600
'55 .05   '65 .05   '75 .07

B. American Trucking Association, 50th anniversary.
Los Angeles, Calif. 123,709,600
'55 .05   '65 .05   '75 .07

C. General George S. Patton, Jr. (1885 - 1945), commander of the Third Army in World War II. The stamp was also a tribute to the Armored Forces of the U.S. Army.
Ft. Knox, Ky. 114,789,600
'55 .05   '65 .05   '75 .07

D. Gadsden Purchase, 100th anniversary. This triangle of land south of the Gila River in New Mexico and Arizona was bought from Mexico to provide a convenient railway route to California. It was the last addition to the contiguous continental United States.
Tucson, Ariz. 116,134,600
'55 .05   '65 .05   '75 .07

E. Statue of Liberty, a gift from France which stands in the harbor of New York. It was created by Frédéric A. Bartholdi. Regular issue.
Washington, D.C.
'55 .11   '65 .14   '75 .16

F. Columbia University, 200th anniversary. Founded by a group of New Yorkers in 1754, Columbia was once known as Kings College.

Shown: Low Memorial Library.
New York, N.Y. 118,540,000
'55 .05   '65 .05   '75 .07

G. Statue of Liberty. Regular issue. Also issued in coils and booklets.
Albany, N.Y.
'55 .04   '65 .05   '75 .06

H. Nebraska Territory, 100th anniversary. Shown: statue of *The Sower* on the capitol dome at Lincoln.
Nebraska City, Nebr.
115,810,000
'55 .05   '65 .05   '75 .07

H. 5/7/54

I. 5/31/54

J. 7/12/54

K. 8/26/54

L. 9/15/54

M. 6/21/55

N. 7/28/54

I. Kansas Territory, 100th anniversary. Kansas, like Nebraska, was created by the Kansas-Nebraska Act, which allowed the territories to choose between "slave" and "free" status. The fighting that followed helped to spark the Civil War.
Fort Leavenworth, Kans. 113,603,700
'55 .05   '65 .05   '75 .07

J. George Eastman (1854-1932), whose Kodak camera made home photography possible. One of the

originators of profit sharing, he gave $75 million to education.
Rochester, N.Y.   121,100,000
'55 .05   '65 .05   '75 .07

K. George Washington, after a portrait by Gilbert Stuart (National Gallery of Art, Washington, D.C.). Regular issue. Also issued in coils.
Chicago, Ill.
'55 .02   '65 .02   '75 .03

L. Thomas Jefferson, after a portrait by Gilbert Stuart

(Bowdoin College Museum, Brunswick, Maine). Regular issue. Also issued in coils.
San Francisco, Calif.
'55 .03   '65 .03   '75 .04

M. New Hampshire, 150th anniversary of the discovery of The Old Man of the Mountains, a natural landmark near Franconia Notch. Hawthorne immortalized it in "The Great Stone Face".
Franconia, N.H.   125,944,400
'65 .05   '75 .07

M. Lewis and Clark Expedition, 150th anniversary. Shown: Meriwether Lewis and William Clark, the first U.S. explorers to reach the Pacific Ocean over land; Sacajawea, the Shoshone guide who led them across the Great Divide; and Charbonneau, her French-Canadian husband. A keelboat is also shown.
Sioux City, Ia.   116,078,150
'55 .05   '65 .05   '75 .07

A. Pennsylvania Academy of Fine Arts, 150th anniversary. Shown: *Peale in His Museum,* a self-portrait by one of the founders of the academy, Charles Willson Peale (1741-1827). One of the most important artists of his day, Peale had 17 children, including painters Rembrandt Peale, Raphaelle Peale, Rubens Peale, and Titian Ramsey Peale.
Philadelphia, Pa.   116,139,800
'65   .05   '75   .07

B. Abraham Lincoln, after a portrait by Douglas Volk (National Gallery of Art, Washington, D.C.). Regular issue. Also issued in coils and booklets.
New York, N.Y.
'55   .06   '65   .06   '75   .07

C. James Monroe, after a portrait by Rembrandt Peale (Monroe Law Office and Museum, Fredericksburg, Virginia). Regular issue.
Fredericksburg, Va.
'55   .06   '65   .07   '75   .10

D. First Land-Grant Colleges, built by Michigan and Pennsylvania on public lands donated by the federal government.
East Lansing, Mich.   120,484,800
'65   .05   '75   .07

E. Rotary International, 50th anniversary of this organization of business and professional men.
Chicago, Ill.   53,854,750
'65   .11   '75   .15

F. Armed Forces Reserve, a tribute to the men of the Marines, Coast Guard, Army, Navy, and Air Force Reserves.
Washington, D.C.   176,075,000
'65   .05   '75   .07

G. Soo Locks, 100th anniversary of this vital link between Lakes Superior and Huron. The stamp was issued in conjunction with the Soo Locks Exposition.
Sault Sainte Marie, Mich.
122,284,600
'65   .05   '75   .07

H. Atoms for Peace. The quote on the stamp is from President Eisenhower's United Nations speech on the subject.
Washington, D.C.   133,638,850
'65   .05   '75   .10

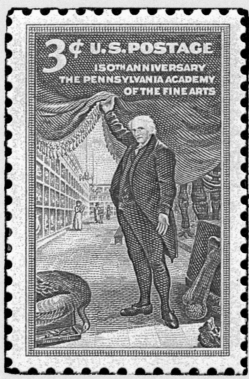

A. *1/15/55*

B. 11/19/54

C. 12/2/54

D. 2/12/55

E. 2/23/55

F. 5/21/55

G. 6/28/55

H. 7/28/55

I. 8/25/55

J. 9/21/55

K. 9/18/55

L. 9/24/55

M. 10/7/55

N. 10/20/55

O. 11/18/55

P. 12/20/55

Q. 1/10/56

I. Susan B. Anthony, after a photograph in the Library of Congress. Regular issue.
Louisville, Ky.
'65 .70 '75 1.00

J. Robert E. Lee (1807-70), commanding general of the Confederate armies in the Civil War. Regular issue. Shown: photograph of Lee by Mathew Brady.
Norfolk, Va.
'65 .40 '75 .60

K. Fort Ticonderoga, 200th anniversary. Built by the French, it was taken by the British in the French and Indian War. At the start of the Revolution, it was seized by Ethan Allen, who is shown on the stylized stamp, along with a plan of the fort and artillery.
Fort Ticonderoga, N.Y.
118,664,600
'65 .05 '75 .07

L. John Marshall, after a painting by Rembrandt Peale. Regular issue.
Richmond, Va.
'65 .54 '75 .80

M. Patrick Henry (1736 - 99), statesman, revolutionary orator, and supporter of the Bill of Rights; after a portrait by Alonzo Chappel. Regular issue.
Joplin, Mo.
'65 1.25 '75 3.35

N. Benjamin Franklin, after a portrait by J. S. Duplessis. Regular issue.
Washington, D.C.
'65 .02 '75 .03

O. Theodore Roosevelt, after a portrait by Philip A. de Laszlo. Regular issue.
New York, N.Y.
'65 .09 '75 .11

P. Andrew W. Mellon (1855-1937), secretary of the treasury and financier, who donated his art collection to the nation as the basis for the National Gallery of Art.
Washington, D.C. 112,434,000
'65 .05 '75 .07

Q. Woodrow Wilson, after a drawing by F. Graham Cootes. Regular issue.
Staunton, Va.
'65 .10 '75 .13

A. *1/17/56*

B. 2/22/56

C. 3/19/56

D. 4/13/56

E. 6/14/56

F. 4/5/56

G. 4/30/56

A. Benjamin Franklin, 250th anniversary of the birth of this phenomenal inventor, statesman, folk philosopher, and bon vivant. Shown: *Franklin Taking Electricity from the Sky* by Benjamin West.
Philadelphia, Pa.   129,384,550
   '65   .05   '75   .07

B. Mount Vernon, plantation home of George Washington near Alexandria, Virginia. Regular issue.
Mt. Vernon, Va.
   '65   .03   '75   .04

C. Alexander Hamilton, after a painting by John Trumbull (National Gallery of Art, Washington, D.C.). Regular issue.
Paterson, N.J.
   '65   5.95   '75 15.00

D. Monticello, classical-revival style home of Thomas Jefferson near Charlottesville, Virginia. Jefferson designed the building, which contains a bed on pulleys, the first dumbwaiter, and other devices, some of which he invented. Regular issue.
Charlottesville, Va.
   '65   .28   '75   .35

E. The Alamo, a Spanish mission where Colonel William Travis and 186 patriots were annihilated by General Santa Anna and a Mexican Army of 4,000 in 1836. Regular issue.
San Antonio, Tex.
   '65   .13   '75   .17

F. Booker T. Washington (1856-1915), slave-born educator who founded the Tuskegee Institute in Alabama to train black students for industry.
Booker T. Washington Birthplace, Va.   121,184,600
   '65   .05   '75   .07

G. FIPEX, issued for the Fifth International Philatelic Exhibition. Shown: the New York Coliseum, where the exhibition was held, and the Columbus Monument.
New York, N.Y.   119,784,200
   '65   .05   '75   .07

H. 4/28/56

I. 7/4/56

J. 8/5/56

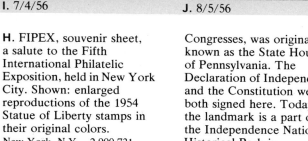

K. 9/22/56

H. FIPEX, souvenir sheet, a salute to the Fifth International Philatelic Exposition, held in New York City. Shown: enlarged reproductions of the 1954 Statue of Liberty stamps in their original colors.
New York, N.Y.   2,900,731
       '65   .60   '75 3.50

I. Independence Hall. This historic shrine, the home of the Liberty Bell and the site of both the First and Second Continental Congresses, was originally known as the State House of Pennsylvania. The Declaration of Independence and the Constitution were both signed here. Today, the landmark is a part of the Independence National Historical Park in Philadelphia. Regular issue.
Philadelphia, Pa.
       '65   .14   '75 .18

J. Wheatland, the home of President James Buchanan. Located near Lancaster, Pennsylvania, the mansion is an architectural period piece as well as a historical shrine.
Lancaster, Pa.   125,475,000
       '65   .05   '75 .07

K. Nassau Hall, 200th anniversary of the oldest building of the College of New Jersey, now Princeton University. Named for William of Nassau (William III of England), it was the largest academic structure in the American colonies. It was here, while Princeton was the nation's capital in 1783, that official news of the Peace of Paris was received. This treaty marked the formal end of the Revolution. Shown: Nassau Hall after a 1764 engraving by Dawkins.
Princeton, N.J.   122,100,000
       '65   .05   '75 .07

WILDLIFE CONSERVATION · WILD TURKEY · 3¢ UNITED STATES POSTAGE 3¢

A. 5/5/56

WILDLIFE CONSERVATION · PRONGHORN ANTELOPE · 3¢ UNITED STATES POSTAGE 3¢

B. 6/22/56

WILDLIFE CONSERVATION · KING SALMON · 3¢ UNITED STATES POSTAGE 3¢

C. 11/9/56

LABOR DAY · LABOR IS LIFE —CARLYLE · U.S. POSTAGE · 3¢

D. *9/3/56*

U.S. POSTAGE · 3¢ · 50th ANNIVERSARY DEVILS TOWER NATIONAL MONUMENT

E. 9/24/56

UNITED STATES POSTAGE · 3¢ · HARVEY W. WILEY · 50TH ANNIVERSARY PURE FOOD AND DRUG LAWS

F. 6/27/56

A. Wild Turkey, the largest and fastest of the flying upland game birds. Once threatened with extinction, they now inhabit wooded areas in the eastern, southwestern, and midwestern states. First stamp in the *Wildlife Conservation Series.*
Fond du Lac, Wis. 123,159,400
    '65 .05 '75 .08

B. Pronghorn Antelope. Though their once vast population was reduced to a low of 17,000 by the march of civilization, these graceful animals now exist in large herds in several western states. *Wildlife Conservation Series.*
Gunnison, Colo. 123,138,800
    '65 .05 '75 .08

C. King Salmon, large fish who migrate upstream to their spawning grounds. Man has helped this difficult process by introducing fish ladders and elevators as routes around dams and waterfalls. *Wildlife Conservation Series.*
Seattle, Wash. 109,275,000
    '65 .05 '75 .08

D. Labor Day. The Knights of Labor held their first annual parade in honor of workers on the first Monday in September in 1882. Shown: the central subject of a mural by Lumen M. Winter in the AFL - CIO building in Washington, D.C.
Camden, N.J. 117,855,000
    '65 .05 '75 .07

E. Devils Tower, 50th anniversary of the oldest national monument in the U.S. Shown: the prismatic formation of volcanic rock which rises 1200 feet above the Belle Fourche River near Moorcroft, Wyoming.
Devils Tower, Wyo. 118,180,000
    '65 .05 '75 .07

F. Pure Food and Drug Laws, 50th anniversary of Harvey W. Wiley's successful fight to require government

G. 1/11/57

H. 12/15/56

I. 1/15/57

J. 5/22/57

K. 11/22/57

L. 2/11/57

M. 2/23/57

inspection and accurate labeling of food and drugs.
Washington, D.C.   112,932,200
   '65   .05   '75   .07

G. Alexander Hamilton (1757 - 1804), first secretary of the treasury. Hamilton fought in the Revolution, established the Bank of the United States, and gave the nation a solid financial basis. In helping to structure the Constitution, he emphasized a strong central government.
New York, N.Y.   115,299,450
   '65   .05   '75   .07

H. Children's Stamp. High school student Ronald Dias chose "Friendship—the Key to World Peace" as the theme for his winning entry in a nationwide contest.
Washington, D.C.   100,975,000
   '65   .05   '75   .07

I. Polio, a tribute to those who fought against this dread disease. In 1955, Dr. Jonas Salk developed the first effective anti-polio vaccine.
Washington, D.C.   186,949,250
   '65   .05   '75   .07

J. Steel Industry, 100th anniversary. The United States is the world's largest producer of steel.
New York, N.Y.   112,010,000
   '65   .05   '75   .07

K. Whooping Cranes, rare birds who migrate from Canada to Texas in the winter. *Wildlife Conservation Series.*
New York, N.Y.
Corpus Christi, Tex.
New Orleans, La.   174,372,800
   '65   .05   '75   .07

L. Coast and Geodetic Survey, 150th anniversary. This service charts coastal navigation routes and records tides.
Seattle, Wash.   115,235,000
   '65   .05   '75   .07

M. Architects of America, 100th anniversary of the American Institute of Architects.
New York, N.Y.   106,647,500
   '65   .05   '75   .07

A. 6/10/57

B. 6/14/57

C. 8/31/57

D. 8/15/57

E. 12/27/57

F. 7/1/57

G. 7/4/57

A. International Naval Review - Jamestown Festival, honoring both the naval review whose theme was "Freedom of the Seas" and the 350th anniversary of the founding of Jamestown (see p. 50).
Norfolk, Va.   118,399,600
    '65   .05   '75   .07

B. Oklahoma Statehood, 50th anniversary. 46th state, admitted 1907. Capital, Oklahoma City. Leading industries include: petroleum, natural gas, agriculture, and food processing.
Oklahoma City, Okla.
102,219,500
    '65   .05   '75   .08

C. Ramon Magsaysay (1907 - 1957), president of the Philippines (1953 - 57). First stamp in the *Champions of Liberty Series.*
Washington, D.C.   41,601,600
    '65   .12   '75   .17

D. Shipbuilding, 350th anniversary of the *Virginia of Sagadahock,* the first American - built ship to engage in international shipping.
Bath, Me.   126,321,580
    '65   .06   '75   .07

E. Religous Freedom, 300th anniversary of the signing of the Flushing Remonstrance, an early acknowledgment of the right to freedom of worship.
Flushing, N.Y.   114,365,000
    '65   .05   '75   .07

F. Teachers of America, 100th anniversary of the National Education Association. The stamp honored the work of teachers and educators.
Philadelphia, Pa.   103,045,000
    '65   .05   '75   .07

G. American Flag, a salute to "Old Glory". First stamp printed on the multicolor Giori press.
Washington, D.C.   84,054,400
    '65   .06   '75   .08

H. 3/15/58

I. 3/22/58

K. 9/6/57

J. 4/18/58

L. 10/27/58

M. 4/17/58

N. 4/28/58

H. Gardening - Horticulture, honoring botanist Liberty Hyde Bailey (1858 - 1954).
Ithaca, N.Y.   122,765,200
　　'65   .05   '75   .07

I. Statue of Liberty. Regular issue, redesigned for use on the Giori Press (see p. 108).
Cleveland, Ohio
　　'65   .11   '75   .15

J. Paul Revere (1735 - 1818), patriot and craftsman who warned Massachusetts colonists of the advancing

British on April 18, 1775. A leading silversmith, he later cast hundreds of church bells and worked closely with Robert Fulton to perfect copper boilers for steamboats. Regular issue. Also issued in coils. Shown: portrait painted in 1813 by Gilbert Stuart.
Boston, Mass.
　　'65   .34   '75   .42

K. Marquis de La Fayette (1757 - 1834), French general and statesman who joined Washington's revolutionary

army in 1777. Wounded at Brandywine, he also served at Valley Forge and Yorktown.
Easton, Pa.
Louisville, Ky.
Fayetteville, N.C.   122,990,000
　　'65   .05   '75   .07

L. Forest Conservation. The stamp also marked the 100th anniversary of the birth of President Theodore Roosevelt, a leading conservationist.
Tucson, Ariz.   156,600,200
　　'65   .07   '75   .08

M. Brussels Exhibition, honoring the 1958 World's Fair held in Belgium.
Detroit, Mich.   113,660,200
　　'65   .05   '75   .07

N. James Monroe (1758 - 1831), fifth president (1817 - 25). His famous Monroe Doctrine declared the Americas closed to further European colonization. Shown: portrait by Gilbert Stuart.
Montross, Va.   120,196,580
　　'65   .05   '75   .07

A. Minnesota Statehood, 100th anniversary. 32nd state, admitted 1858. Capital, St. Paul. Leading industries include: agriculture, food processing, iron mining, machinery, chemicals, lumber, and tourism. Shown: sketch emphasizing the state's lakes and natural beauty.
St. Paul, Minn. 120,805,200
'65 .05 '75 .07

B. International Geophysical Year, an 18-month period of scientific study. Shown: an area of solar activity and a part of Michelangelo's fresco *The Creation of Adam.*
Chicago, Ill. 125,815,200
'65 .05 '75 .20

C. Simon Bolivar (1783-1830), South American revolutionary whose leadership led to the independence of Venezuela, Colombia, and Ecuador. *Champions of Liberty Series.*
Washington, D.C. 115,745,280
'65 .07 '75 .08

D. Simon Bolivar.
Washington, D.C. 39,743,640
'65 .12 '75 .17

E. Lajos Kossuth (1802-94), Hungarian patriot and a leading figure in the 1848 revolution. *Champions of Liberty Series.*
Washington, D.C. 120,561,260
'65 .07 '75 .08

F. Lajos Kossuth.
Washington, D.C. 44,064,576
'65 .12 '75 .17

G. John Jay (1745-1829), first chief justice of the Supreme Court (1789-95), and author of five of the *Federalist* papers, which urged acceptance of the Constitution. Regular issue. Shown: portrait by Gilbert Stuart (National Gallery of Art, Washington, D.C.).
Washington, D.C.
'65 .19 '75 .25

H. Gunston Hall, home of George Mason, whose *Virginia Resolves* influenced the Declaration of Independence.
Lorton, Va. 108,415,200
'65 .05 '75 .07

A. 5/11/58

B. 5/31/58

E. 9/19/58

F. 9/19/58

C. 7/24/58

D. 7/24/58

G. 12/12/58

H. 6/12/58

I. Journalism - Freedom of the Press, 50th anniversary of the University of Missouri School of Journalism, oldest in the United States.

Columbia, Mo. 118,390,200
'65 .07 '75 .08

J. Overland Mail, 100th anniversary of the arrival of the first Butterfield land

coach in San Francisco. It carried mail and passengers from Tipton, Missouri.
San Francisco, Calif.
125,770,200
'65 .07 '75 .08

I. 9/22/58

J. *10/10/58*

K. 10/16/58

L. 6/25/58

M. *11/25/58*

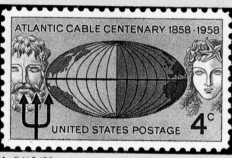

N. 8/15/58

K. Noah Webster (1758 - 1843). His dictionary made his name a household word. West Hartford, Conn. 114,114,280
'65 .07 '75 .08

L. Mackinac Bridge, dedication. The bridge spans the Mackinac Straits.
Mackinaw City and St. Ignace, Mich. 107,195,200
'65 .05 '75 .07

M. Fort Duquesne, an outpost in Pennsylvania taken by the English from the French in 1758 and renamed Fort Pitt. Pittsburgh, Pa. 124,200,200
'65 .07 '75 .08

N. Atlantic Cable, 100th anniversary of the first telegraphic link between North America and Europe. New York, N.Y. 114,570,200
'65 .07 '75 .08

LINCOLN SESQUICENTENNIAL ISSUE

A. *8/27/58*

B. *2/12/59*

Abraham Lincoln (1809 - 65), the self - educated son of a poor Kentucky farmer, was the 16th president of the United States (1861 - 65). He led the Union through the "fiery trial" of the Civil War, a test he faced with courage and decisiveness. "I do the very best I can," he once remarked. "If the end brings me out all right, what is said against me won't amount to anything. If the end brings me out wrong, ten angels swearing I was right would make no difference."

C. *2/27/59*

D. *5/30/59*

A. Lincoln addressing potential voters with Stephen A. Douglas awaiting his turn to speak at one of the 1858 Lincoln - Douglas debates. The debates thrust Lincoln into national prominence, and while Douglas defeated him for the U.S. Senate, Lincoln was elected president two years later. The stamp design is a reproduction of an old print.
Freeport, Ill. 114,860,200
    '65 .07   '75 .08

B. George P. A. Healy's "Beardless Lincoln". This oil portrait of the new president was painted from life in 1860 at Springfield, Illinois. It was first placed on sale at the post office nearest Lincoln's birthplace.
Hodgenville, Ky. 120,400,200
    '65 .02   '75 .03

C. Gutzon Borglum's 1906 marble sculpture of Lincoln, now on view in the Capitol rotunda. First placed on sale at the site of the historical Cooper Union speech of 1860, in which Lincoln said: "Let us have faith that right makes might, and in that faith let us to the end dare to do our duty as we understand it."
New York, N.Y. 91,160,200
    '65 .05   '75 .07

D. Daniel Chester French's statue in the Lincoln Memorial, Washington, D.C. The rendering of the stamp is by Fritz Busse.
Washington, D.C. 126,500,000
    '65 .06   '75 .08

E. Oregon Statehood, 100th anniversary. 33rd state, admitted 1859. Capital, Salem. Known as the beaver state, Oregon cuts more lumber than any other state. Other leading industries are fishing and dairying. Shown: Mount Hood, highest point in the state (11,235 ft.), and a covered wagon used to carry pioneers over the Oregon Trail.
Astoria, Ore. 120,740,200
    '65 .07   '75 .08

E. 2/14/59

F. 2/25/59

G. 2/25/59

H. 4/1/59

I. 4/6/59

J. 6/6/59

K. 4/20/59

L. 6/8/59

F. José de San Martin (1778 - 1850), Argentinian general who was instrumental in the liberation of Chile from Spanish rule. *Champions of Liberty Series.*
Washington, D.C.   133,623,280
'65   .07   '75   .08

G. José de San Martin.
Washington, D.C.   45,569,088
'65   .12   '75   .17

H. NATO, 10th anniversary. Shown: emblem and motto of the North Atlantic Treaty Organization.
Washington, D.C.   122,493,280
'65   .07   '75   .08

I. Arctic Explorations, 50th anniversary of Admiral Robert Peary's dogsled trek to the North Pole. The stamp was also a tribute to the voyage of the first atomic submarine, the U.S.S. *Nautilus,* and her sister ship, the U.S.S. *Skate,* to the Pole in 1959.
Cresson, Pa.   131,260,200
'65   .07   '75   .08

J. Benjamin Harrison, after a photograph by Charles Parker. Regular issue.
Oxford, Ohio
'65   .17   '75   .21

K. World Peace Through World Trade. Issued for the 17th Congress of the International Chamber of Commerce, held in Washington, D.C. in 1959.
Washington, D.C.   47,125,200
'65   .12   '75   .14

L. Silver Centennial, 100th anniversary of the Comstock Lode discovery at Mount Davidson, Nevada. During its first 20 years of mining, it yielded about $300 million worth of silver. Shown: design based on an old print of Henry Comstock at the discovery site.
Virginia City, Nev.   123,105,000
'65   .07   '75   .08

A. 3/16/59

B. 7/4/59

C. 6/17/59

D. 9/29/59

E. 9/29/59

F. 8/26/59

G. *6/26/59*

H. 8/27/59

A. The Hermitage, home of Andrew Jackson near Nashville, Tennessee. It is furnished with original Jackson family pieces. Regular issue. Also issued in coils.
Hermitage, Tenn.
  '65 .06   '75 .10

B. Forty - nine star Flag, noting the admission of Alaska to the Union.
Auburn, N.Y.   209,170,000
  '65 .07   '75 .08

C. Bunker Hill Monument, Boston, Massachusetts. The first major battle of the Revolutionary War, the Battle of Breed's Hill, was fought here on June 17, 1775. Regular issue. Also issued in coils.
Boston, Mass.
  '65 .05   '75 .05

D. Ernst Reuter (1889 - 1953), mayor of West Berlin (1948 - 53). *Champions of Liberty Series.*
Washington, D.C.   111,685,000
  '65 .07   '75 .08

E. Ernst Reuter.
Washington, D.C.   43,099,200
  '65 .12   '75 .14

F. Soil Conservation, a reminder of the importance of soil and water conservation to life in America.
Rapid City, S. Dak.   120,835,000
  '65 .07   '75 .08

G. St. Lawrence Seaway Opening. President Eisenhower and Queen Elizabeth II dedicated this

joint U.S. - Canadian project on June 26, 1959. Canada issued a stamp of the same design on the same day.
Massena, N.Y.   126,105,050
  '65 .07   '75 .08

H. Petroleum Industry, 100th anniversary. Edwin L. Drake succeeded in putting his Titusville, Pennsylvania, oil well into operation in 1859.
Titusville, Pa.   115,715,000
  '65 .07   '75 .08

I. 12/3/59

J. 9/14/59

K. 10/10/60

L. 3/7/60

M. 3/7/60

N. 7/19/60

O. 2/18/60

P. 7/4/60

Q. 8/29/60

I. Ephraim McDowell (1771 - 1830), who performed the first successful ovariotomy in America in 1809.
Danville, Ky.   115,444,000
       '65   .07   '75   .08

J. Dental Health, 100th anniversary of the American Dental Association.
New York, N.Y.   118,445,000
       '65   .07   '75   .08

K. Robert A. Taft (1889 - 1953), senator from Ohio who promoted social welfare measures and co - sponsored the Taft - Hartley Labor - Management Relations Act of 1947.
Cincinnati, Ohio   115,171,000
       '65   .07   '75   .08

L. Thomas G. Masaryk (1850 - 1937), first president of Czechoslovakia (1918 - 35). *Champions of Liberty Series.*
Washington, D.C.   113,792,000
       '65   .07   '75   .08

M. Thomas G. Masaryk.
Washington, D.C.   44,215,200
       '65   .12   '75   .17

N. Pony Express, 100th anniversary. This renowned relay service carried mail from St. Joseph, Missouri, to Sacramento, California, in about ten days. In 1861 the transcontinental telegraph eliminated the need for such a service.
Sacramento, Calif.   119,665,000
       '65   .07   '75   .08

O. Eighth Olympic Winter Games, held at Squaw Valley, California, in 1960.
Tahoe City, Calif.   124,445,000
       '65   .07   '75   .08

P. Fifty - star Flag, noting the admission of Hawaii to the Union.
Honolulu, Hawaii   153,025,000
       '65   .07   '75   .10

Q. Fifth World Forestry Congress, held in Seattle, Washington. Its theme was the "Multiple Use of Forest Lands."
Seattle, Wash.   118,185,000
       '65   .07   '75   .08

AMERICAN CREDO ISSUE

A. 1/20/60

B. 3/31/60

C. 5/18/60

D. 9/14/60

E. 11/19/60

F. 1/11/61

American Credo Issue. Each design presents a statement by a great American in the style and manner of colonial currency. The designs also include facsimiles of the authors' signatures and appropriate symbolic devices.

A. George Washington Credo, from his Farewell Address of 1796, in which he outlined the course he hoped the new nation would follow. The scales of justice symbolize his intent.

Mount Vernon, Va. 126,470,000
'65   .07   '75   .10

B. Benjamin Franklin Credo, from the 1740 edition of *Poor Richard's Almanack,* a work he called "the gleanings…of the sense of all ages and nations." The device portrays a dove encircled by olive branches.
Philadelphia, Pa. 124,560,000
'65   .07   '75   .10

C. Thomas Jefferson Credo, from his *Collected Writings,* Volume 10. A flaming sword represents Jefferson's ideals.
Charlottesville, Va. 115,455,000
'65   .07   '75   .10

D. Francis Scott Key Credo, from the "Star Spangled Banner". The device showing "bombs bursting in air" calls to mind the writing of the national anthem.
Baltimore, Md.   122,060,000
'65   .07   '75   .10

E. Abraham Lincoln Credo, from a letter he wrote to H.L. Pierce of Boston in 1859. The symbol shows the figure of freedom holding an olive branch.
New York, N.Y.   120,540,000
'65   .07   '75   .10

F. Patrick Henry Credo, from his speech delivered on March 23, 1775, at Saint John's Episcopal Church in Richmond, Virginia. A flaming torch is shown.
Richmond, Va.   113,075,000
'65   .07   '75   .10

G. 2/8/60

H. 4/7/60

I. 10/8/60

J. 10/8/60

K. 4/18/60

L. 6/2/60

M. 10/26/60

N. 10/26/60

G. Boy Scouts of America, Golden Jubilee. Shown: a Norman Rockwell design of a Boy Scout with his arm raised in the traditional sign.
Washington, D.C.   139,325,000
'65 .07   '75 .08

H. World Refugee Year, July 1, 1959 - June 30, 1960. The United States participated in a multi-nation effort to awaken concern for the homeless of the world.
Washington, D.C.   113,195,000
'65 .07   '75 .08

Washington, D.C.   113,195,000
'65 .07   '75 .08

I. Ignacy Jan Paderewsky (1860 - 1941), world famous concert pianist who carried on a lifelong fight for a free Poland. *Champions of Liberty Series.*
Washington, D.C.   119,798,000
'65 .07   '75 .08

J. Ignacy Jan Paderewsky.
Washington, D.C.   42,696,000
'65 .12   '75 .17

K. Water Conservation, issued in conjunction with the Seventh National Watershed Congress. The design depicts the dependence of life on the watershed area.
Washington, D.C.   120,570,000
'65 .07   '75 .08

L. American Woman. Shown: mother, daughter, and open book honoring women in the home. Designs in corner niches recognize the contributions of women to civic affairs, education,

the arts, and industry.
Washington, D.C.   111,080,000
'65 .07   '75 .08

M. Baron Karl Gustaf Emil Mannerheim (1867 - 1951), Finnish statesman who fought for his country's freedom and served as its president. *Champions of Liberty Series.*
Washington, D.C.   124,796,000
'65 .07   '75 .08

N. Baron Karl Gustaf Emil Mannerheim.
Washington, D.C.   42,076,800
'75 .12   '75 .17

A. United States - Japan Centennial, 100th anniversary of the first goodwill treaty between the two nations, ratified in 1860. Shown: a branch of Japanese cherry blossoms against the Washington Monument.
Washington, D.C.　125,010,000
　　'65　.07　'75　.08

B. Palace of Governors, a historic shrine built in 1610 in Santa Fe, New Mexico. The stamp was available in post offices only in precancelled form. Unused, it was sold on June 17, 1960, at the Santa Fe post office and for a limited time through the Philatelic Sales Agency. Regular issue. Also issued in coils.
Santa Fe, N. Mex.
　　'65　.04　'75　.04

C. SEATO, issued for the sixth meeting of the South - East Asia Treaty Organization.
Washington, D.C.　115,353,000
　　'65　.07　'75　.08

D. Walter F. George (1878 - 1957), senator from Georgia who served as ambassador to NATO in 1957. Shown: portrait based on photograph by Hank Walker of *Life*.
Vienna, Ga.　124,117,000
　　'65　.07　'75　.08

E. Andrew Carnegie (1835 - 1919), a Scottish immigrant who became a leader of the world steel industry by the age of 30. His philanthropies total over $300 million, including a $10 million Endowment for International Peace, established in 1910 without restrictions, because "Lines of future action cannot wisely be laid down."
New York, N.Y.　119,840,000
　　'65　.07　'75　.08

F. First Automated Post Office. Issued for dedication of new facility in Providence, Rhode Island, where newly designed machinery began a new era in postal service.
Providence, R.I.　127,970,000
　　'65　.07　'75　.08

A. 9/28/60

The Washington Monument, one of the most beautiful sites in the nation's capital, is a towering 555 - foot obelisk built in the 19th century. The monument has an observatory at the 500 - foot level which affords visitors a panoramic view of the capital.

B. 6/17/60

C. 5/31/60

D. 11/5/60

E. 11/25/60

F. 10/20/60

G. 10/18/60

H. 12/15/60

I. 10/15/60

J. 9/16/60

K. 11/2/60

L. 11/2/60

M. 8/28/60

G. Boys Clubs of America, 100th anniversary of the establishment of recreational organizations for underprivileged boys.
New York, N.Y.   123,690,000
   '65   .07   '75   .08

H. Echo I - Communications for Peace. The first passive communications satellite, Echo I, was balloon - like and weighed 300 pounds. It was placed in orbit around the earth on August 12, 1960.
Washington, D.C.   125,290,000
   '75   .07   '75   .40

I. Wheels of Freedom, issued in conjunction with the opening of the 1960 National Automobile Show in Detroit, Michigan.
Detroit, Mich.   109,695,000
   '65   .07   '75   .08

J. Mexican Independence, 150th anniversary. The stamp was part of a joint issue with Mexico. Shown: the independence bell at the entrance to the Palacio Nacional in Mexico City, which is rung every year by the president of Mexico. It was brought there from Dolores by Miguel Hidalgo, the priest who led the first thrust against Spanish rule in 1810.
Los Angeles, Calif.   112,260,000
   '65   .07   '75   .08

K. Giuseppe Garibaldi (1807 - 82), freedom fighter who was instrumental in unifying his native Italy. *Champions of Liberty Series.*
Washington, D.C.   126,252,000
   '65   .07   '75   .08

L. Giuseppe Garibaldi.
Washington, D.C.   42,746,400
   '65   .12   '75   .17

M. Employ the Handicapped. Stamp stresses the theme of the Eighth World Congress of the International Society for the Welfare of Cripples, sponsored by the President's Committee on Employment of the Physically Handicapped.
New York, N.Y.   117,855,000
   '65   .07   '75   .08

CIVIL WAR CENTENNIAL ISSUE

E. 4/9/65

B. 4/7/62

C. 7/1/63

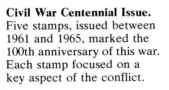

A. 4/12/61

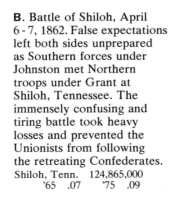

D. 5/5/64

Civil War Centennial Issue.
Five stamps, issued between 1961 and 1965, marked the 100th anniversary of this war. Each stamp focused on a key aspect of the conflict.

A. Fort Sumter, April 12, 1861. The war began when Confederate forces bombarded this federal fort in South Carolina for over 30 hours and took it from the Union.
Charleston, S.C.   101,125,000
      '65   .07   '75   .13

B. Battle of Shiloh, April 6 - 7, 1862. False expectations left both sides unprepared as Southern forces under Johnston met Northern troops under Grant at Shiloh, Tennessee. The immensely confusing and tiring battle took heavy losses and prevented the Unionists from following the retreating Confederates.
Shiloh, Tenn.   124,865,000
      '65   .07   '75   .09

C. Battle of Gettysburg, July 1 - 4, 1863. As Lee turned north into Pennsylvania, he was met and defeated by Meade in the battle which turned the tide for the Union.
Gettysburg, Pa.   139,860,000
      '65   .08   '75   .10

D. Battle of the Wilderness, May 5 - 6, 1864. With this hard - fought, two - day battle in a densely wooded area near Fredericksburg, Virginia, Grant began his final push toward Richmond.
Fredericksburg, Va.   125,410,000
      '65   .08   '75   .10

E. Appomattox. "Here on Sunday April 9, 1865 after four years of heroic struggle in defense of principles believed fundamental to the existence of our government Lee surrendered 9000 men… to 118,000 men under Grant." (Inscription on plaque at Appomattox, Virginia.) The quote on the stamp is from President Lincoln's second inaugural address.
Appomattox, Va.   112,845,000
      '75   .13

G. 2/2/61

F. 12/6/60

I. 1/26/61

H. 2/3/61

K. 11/1/60

J. 1/26/61

L. 11/6/61

F. John Foster Dulles (1888 - 1959), international jurist and secretary of state (1953 - 59), during the Eisenhower administration. One of his successful diplomatic efforts was the negotiation of the 1950 peace treaty with Japan, signed by 49 nations.
Washington, D.C.   117,187,000
    '65   .07   '75   .08

G. Range Conservation, a reminder of the value of grassland and livestock to the nation's agriculture.

Shown: *The Trail Boss* by Charles M. Russell and a modern range scene.
Salt Lake City, Utah
110,850,000
    '65   .07   '75   .08

H. Horace Greeley (1811 - 72), editor and founder of *The New York Tribune* (1841). Under his leadership the newspaper became a literate and influential voice of social and educational reform. Its editorials took stands against such things as slavery

and gambling.
Chappaqua, N.Y.   98,616,000
    '65   .07   '75   .08

I. Mahatma Gandhi (1869 - 1948), nonviolent leader of India and a major force in his nation's struggle for independence. *Champions of Liberty Series.*
Washington, D.C.   112,966,000
    '65   .07   '75   .08

J. Mahatma Gandhi.
Washington, D.C.   41,644,200
    '65   .12   '75   .17

K. Camp Fire Girls, 50th anniversary of the founding, in 1910, of the first interracial, nonsectarian organization for girls.
New York, N.Y.   116,215,000
    '65   .07   '75   .08

L. Naismith - Basketball. In 1891 Dr. James A. Naismith invented basketball. Early players used soccer balls and peach baskets.
Springfield, Mass.   109,110,000
    '65   .07   '75   .08

A. Frederick Remington (1861 - 1909), painter, sculptor, and author noted for his Western subjects, especially Indians and U.S. soldiers. Shown: a detail from *The Smoke Signal* (Amon Carter Museum of Art, Fort Worth, Texas). First stamp in the *American Painting Series.*
Washington, D.C.   111,600,000
　　'65   .07　　'75   .12

B. Statue of Liberty. Regular issue, denomination added for international surface rate.
Washington, D.C.
　　'65   .15　　'75   .20

C. John J. Pershing (1860 - 1948), commander of the American Expeditionary Force in Europe during World War I and the first active General of the Army. Regular issue.
New York, N.Y.
　　'65   .11　　'75   .15

D. Workmen's Compensation Law, 50th anniversary. In 1911, Wisconsin passed the first successful legislation in this field in the U.S. The law provided compensation for employees injured or disabled in the course of their employment.
Milwaukee, Wis.   121,015,000
　　'65   .07　　'75   .08

E. Sun Yat-sen (1866 - 1925), first president of the Republic of China, founded in 1911.
Washington, D.C.   110,620,000
　　'65   .07　　'75   .08

F. Kansas Statehood, 100th anniversary. 34th state, admitted 1861. Capital, Topeka. Leading industries include: agriculture, aircraft, and railroad equipment. Shown: sunflower (state flower) and pioneer family.
Council Grove, Kans.
106,210,000
　　'65   .07　　'75   .08

G. George W. Norris (1861 - 1944), senator from Nebraska who jointly introduced the bill that created the Tennessee Valley Authority in 1933. The TVA provides electric power, flood control, and navigation routes

A. *10/4/61*

B. 6/15/61

C. 11/17/61

D. 9/4/61

E. 10/10/61

through a system of rivers, reservoirs and dams. One of these, shown on the stamp, is named for him.
Washington, D.C.   110,810,000
　　'65   .07　　'75   .08

H. Naval Aviation, 50th anniversary. The first naval airplane was a 1911 Curtiss Biplane.
San Diego, Calif.   116,995,000
　　'65   .07　　'75   .08

I. Nursing, a profession whose original training programs were formulated during the Civil War.
Washington, D.C.   145,350,000
　　'65   .07　　'75   .08

F. 5/10/61

G. 7/11/61

H. 8/20/61

I. 12/28/61

J. 4/11/62

K. *2/14/62*

J. Charles Evans Hughes (1862 - 1948), Chief Justice of the Supreme Court (1930-41), secretary of state (1921-25), and two-term governor of New York. Hughes helped shape American policy regarding the formation of the United Nations.
Washington, D.C.   124,595,000
'65   .07   '75   .08

K. Arizona Statehood, 50th anniversary. 48th state, admitted 1912. Capital, Phoenix. Leading industries include: tourism, electrical machinery, and transportation equipment. Shown: night scene on the desert, with giant saguaro cactus (state flower).
Phoenix, Ariz.   121,820,000
'65   .07   '75   .08

A. New Mexico Statehood, 50th anniversary. 47th state, admitted 1912. Capital, Santa Fe. Leading industries: uranium, petroleum, and potash. Shown: Shiprock, sacred mountain of the Navajo Indians.
Santa Fe, N. Mex.   112,870,000
  '65   .07   '75   .08

B. Project Mercury, a tribute to the first orbital space flight by a U.S. astronaut. Distributed in secret and released at the exact hour Colonel John Glenn completed his flight, this was the first U.S. commemorative issued simultaneously with the event it commemorated.
Cape Canaveral, Fla. and
at all post offices.   289,240,000
  '65   .07   '75   .30

C. Malaria Eradication, acknowledgment of American support for the World Health Organization's fight against malaria. The disease had been fatal to millions every year. Shown: Great Seal of the United States with World Health Organization emblem.
Washington, D.C.   120,155,000
  '65   .07   '75   .08

D. George Washington, after a bust by Jean Antoine Houdon (Mount Vernon, Virginia). Regular issue. Also issued in coils and booklets.
New York, N.Y.
  '65   .08   '75   .09

E. Louisiana Statehood, 150th anniversary. 18th state, admitted 1812. Capital, Baton Rouge. Leading industries: chemicals and petroleum. Shown: steamboat on the Mississippi River.
New Orleans, La.   118,690,000
  '65   .07   '75   .08

F. Seattle World's Fair, America's first space-age fair. Shown: 550-foot Space Needle and a high-speed monorail, two spectacular features of the exposition.
Seattle, Wash.   147,310,000
  '65   .07   '75   .08

A. *1/6/62*

B. 2/20/62

C. 3/30/62

D. 11/23/62

E. 4/30/62

F. 4/25/62

G. 5/20/62

H. 7/24/62

I. 9/16/62

J. 7/28/62

K. 8/31/62

G. Homestead Act, 100th anniversary. This 1862 legislation enabled settlers to acquire 160 acres of land for $10 by living on it for five years or by cultivating it for the same amount of time. Shown: sod hut dwelling and homesteaders.
Beatrice, Nebr.   122,730,000
'65   .07   '75   .08

H. Girl Scouts, 50th anniversary. This movement for girls began in 1912 with 12 members. Over three million people now belong. Shown: intermediate scout and a portion of the U.S. flag.
Burlington, Vt.   126,515,000
'65   .07   '75   .08

I. Sam Rayburn (1882 - 1961), congressman from Texas (1913 - 61). He served as Speaker of the House of Representatives for a longer term than any other congressman in history — 17 years. Shown: Capitol and portrait of "Mr. Sam", based upon a photograph in House Document 247 of the 87th Congress.
Bonham, Tex.   120,715,000
'65   .07   '75   .08

J. Brien McMahon (1903 - 52), senator from Connecticut. He promoted the constructive use of atomic energy through the creation of the U.S. Atomic Energy Commission. Shown: atomic symbol and portrait based on photograph by Glogau of Washington, D.C.
Norwalk, Conn.   130,960,000
'65   .07   '75   .08

K. Apprenticeship, 25th anniversary of National Apprenticeship Act. Under legislation enacted in 1937, the U.S. Department of Labor, organized labor, and business management jointly sponsor apprenticeship training in 375 crafts. Shown: symbolic transfer of skills from the artisan to the apprentice.
Washington, D.C.   120,055,000
'65   .07   '75   .08

A. *12/15/62*

D. 11/1/62

B. 10/23/62

E. 1/9/63

C. 11/16/62

F. 11/14/62

A. Winslow Homer (1836 - 1910), realistic painter who captured the dramatic essence of the sea in his works. Shown: *Breezing Up* (National Gallery of Art, Washington, D.C.). The painting depicts a group of fishermen returning home to Gloucester, Massachusetts. *American Painting Series.*
Gloucester, Mass.   117,870,000
   '65   .07   '75   .12

B. Dag Hammarskjöld (1905 - 61), United Nations Secretary General (1953 - 61). The Swedish statesman's independent approach to his international responsibilities won him worldwide respect.
New York, N.Y.   121,440,000
   '65   .07   '75   .08

C. Dag Hammarskjöld, yellow background inverted. The discovery of this mistake led the Post Office to reprint it, so that anyone who desired an example of the error could obtain one.
Washington, D.C.   40,270,000
   '65   .10   '75   .11

D. Christmas. The first special U.S. stamp for holiday mail.
Pittsburgh, Pa.   861,970,000
   '65   .07   '75   .08

E. Flag and White House, a design inspired by Mrs. John F. Kennedy, who wanted to use a stamp showing the White House on White House mail. Regular issue.
Washington, D.C.   3,066,890,000
   '65   .08   '75   .09

F. Higher Education, issued in connection with the centennial of the Morrill Act, which created land grant colleges and universities.
Washington, D.C.   120,035,000
   '65   .07   '75   .08

G. Food for Peace - Freedom from Hunger, a tribute to the World Food Congress held in Washington, D.C. Shown: stalk of wheat, symbolic of the world campaign against hunger.
Washington, D.C.   135,620,000
   '65   .08   '75   .09

G. 6/4/63

H. 3/22/63

I. 4/6/63

J. 6/20/63

K. 8/16/63

L. *10/26/63*

H. Andrew Jackson, after a presidential medal designed by Moritz Furst and struck by the United States Mint in 1829. Regular issue. Also issued in coils.
New York, N.Y.
'65 .02   '75 .03

I. Carolina Charter, 300th anniversary. In 1663, Charles II granted the Carolina Territory to eight Englishmen. Its boundaries lay roughly between what is now Virginia and Florida. The original charter is on view at the Hall of History, Raleigh, North Carolina.
Edenton, N.C. 129,445,000
'65 .08   '75 .09

J. West Virginia Statehood, 100th anniversary. 35th state, admitted 1863. Capital, Charleston. Leading industries include: coal mining, natural gas, chemicals, and glass. Shown: outline map and state capitol.
Wheeling, W. Va. 137,540,000
'65 .08   '75 .09

K. Emancipation Proclamation, 100th anniversary of the freeing of all slaves in the Confederacy by President Lincoln. The stamp was issued on the first day of the Centenary of Negro Progress Exposition in Chicago. Shown: a severed chain, symbol of the end of slavery.
Chicago, Ill. 132,435,000
'65 .08   '75 .09

L. City Mail Delivery, 100th anniversary. In 1863 Congress authorized the free delivery of letters in cities with a population of more than 20,000. Shown: city letter carrier of 1863 by Norman Rockwell.
Washington, D.C. 128,450,000
'65 .08   '75 .09

A. *12/7/63*

B. 10/11/63

C. 8/17/63

D. 10/29/63

E. 10/14/63

F. 11/1/63

A. John James Audubon (1785 - 1851), ornithologist and artist. His great work, *The Birds of America,* included 435 hand - colored folio plates. Shown: *Columbia Jays* (National Gallery of Art, Washington, D.C.). The birds portrayed are actually magpie jays. *American Painting Series.*
Henderson, Ky. 175,175,000
  '65 .08 '75 .10

B. Eleanor Roosevelt (1884 - 1962), author, lecturer, diplomat, and wife of Franklin D. Roosevelt. She devoted her energies to educational, sociological, and political affairs, and headed the commission that drafted the Universal Declaration of Human Rights at the United Nations.
Washington, D.C. 133,170,000
  '65 .08 '75 .09

C. Alliance for Progress, a program of inter - American cooperation for economic and social development started in 1961. Shown: official emblem of the Alliance for Progress.
Washington, D.C. 135,520,000
  '65 .08 '75 .09

D. International Red Cross, 100th anniversary. Founded at Geneva, Switzerland, this organization assists people throughout the world. The stamp was also a tribute to the role played by the Red Cross in the Cuban prisoner exchange of 1963. Shown: Red Cross flag over the *S.S. Morning Light* and Cuban refugees.
Washington, D.C. 118,665,000
  '65 .08 '75 .09

E. The Sciences, 100th anniversary of the National Academy of Sciences, an organization of scientists and and engineers. Their work extends to such diverse fields as highway safety, the effects of atomic radiation, and environmental pollution.
Washington, D.C. 130,195,000
  '65 .08 '75 .10

H. 4/22/64

G. 10/5/63

I. 5/29/64

J. 1/10/64

K. *7/22/64*

F. Christmas. Shown: National Christmas Tree on the Ellipse opposite the White House.
Santa Claus, Ind.   1,291,250,000
'65   .08   '75   .09

G. Cordell Hull (1871 - 1955), secretary of state (1933 - 44). He was awarded a Nobel Peace Prize in 1945 for his contribution to the founding of the United Nations.
Carthage, Tenn.   131,420,000
'65   .08   '75   .09

H. New York World's Fair, held at Flushing, New York, 1964 - 65. Shown: view of the Unisphere and Donald De Lue's *Rocket Thrower.*
Flushing, N.Y.   145,700,000
'75   .11

I. John F. Kennedy (1917 - 63), 35th president (1961 - 63). The youngest man ever elected chief executive, Kennedy was also the fourth U.S. president killed by an assassin. His energetic administration saw the creation of the Peace Corps and the signing of a nuclear test ban treaty by the U.S. and the U.S.S.R. Shown: Kennedy, quotation from 1961 inaugural address, and eternal flame at Arlington National Cemetery gravesite.
Boston, Mass. and any post office.
511,750,000   '75   .09

J. Sam Houston (1793 - 1863), hero of Texas independence who served as president of the Republic of Texas before it became a state. He was also a U.S. senator and a champion of the rights of Indians. Shown: drawing by Tom Lea based on 1848 lithograph.
Houston, Tex.   125,995,000
'65   .08   '75   .10

K. Nevada Statehood, 100th anniversary. 36th state, admitted 1864. Capital, Carson City. Leading industry is tourism. Shown: Virginia City and outline map.
Carson City, Nev.   122,825,000
'75   .09

A. *3/19/64*

B. *6/15/64*

C. 8/1/64

D. 8/14/64

E. *4/29/64*

A. Charles M. Russell (1864 - 1926), frontier artist. Shown: *Jerked Down* (Thomas Gilcrease Institute of American History and Art, Tulsa, Oklahoma). *American Painting Series.*
Great Falls, Mont. 128,025,000
'65 .08 '75 .11

B. New Jersey, 300th anniversary of English settlement. One of the founding Thirteen Colonies and the third state to ratify the Constitution, New Jersey was originally part of the Dutch colony of New Netherland. In 1664 it was granted to the English Duke of York, but was soon regranted to Lord Berkeley and Sir William Carteret. It was named New Jersey in honor of Carteret, who governed the Isle of Jersey during the English Civil War.
Elizabeth, N.J. 123,845,000
'65 .08 '75 .09

C. Register - Vote, publicity to attract more voters to the polls. Shown: American flag.
Washington, D.C. 453,090,000
'65 .08 '75 .09

D. William Shakespeare (1564 - 1616), 400th anniversary of the birth of the English poet. The stamp was first placed on sale at Stratford, Connecticut, home of the American Shakespeare Festival Theatre and Academy. Shown: artist's conception of Shakespeare standing before the proscenium of an Elizabethan theater, among symbols of the stage and his plays.
Stratford, Conn. 123,245,000
'65 .08 '75 .09

E. John Muir (1838 - 1914), writer, naturalist, and conservationist. A Scottish immigrant, Muir lived most of his adult life in California and was noted for his efforts to preserve the giant redwoods. Shown: Muir and redwood trees.
Martinez, Calif. 120,310,000
'65 .08 '75 .09

F. 10/26/64

G. 10/15/64

H. 11/9/64

I. 9/11/64

J. 12/15/64

K. 11/21/64

F. Homemakers, 50th anniversary of the Smith-Lever Act, which created an extension service through which home economists offer advice to women on feeding and clothing their families.
Honolulu, Hawaii 121,250,000
   '65 .08 '75 .09

G. American Music, 50th anniversary of the American Society of Composers, Authors, and Publishers (ASCAP).
New York, N.Y. 126,970,000
   '65 .08 '75 .09

H. Christmas. These four stamps, printed on the same sheet, were the first U.S. adhesives issued in this form. They are usually collected as a block. Shown (clockwise from upper left): holly, mistletoe, conifer, and poinsettia.
Bethlehem, Pa. 1,407,760,000
   '65 .40 (block) .09 (ea.)
   '75 .85 (block) .20 (ea.)

I. Doctors Mayo, two brothers who established the Mayo Foundation for Medical Education and

Research in 1915. The foundation is affiliated with the Mayo Clinic and is part of the University of Minnesota at Rochester, Minnesota. Shown: William J. Mayo and Charles H. Mayo by sculptor James Earle Fraser.
Rochester, Minn. 123,355,000
   '65 .08 '75 .09

J. Amateur Radio, 50th anniversary. The American Radio Relay League was founded in 1914. Amateur

radio "hams" often provide communications as a public service in emergencies.
Anchorage, Alaska 122,230,000
   '65 .08 '75 .09

K. Verrazano-Narrows Bridge, dedication. The world's longest suspension bridge connects Staten Island and Brooklyn, New York. It is named for the explorer who discovered New York Bay in 1524.
Staten Island, N.Y. 120,005,000
   '65 .08 '75 .09

A. Fine Arts. Shown: a lithograph by modernist Stuart Davis. The design was the winning entry in an invitational competition sponsored by the Society of American Graphic Artists, Inc.
Washington, D.C. 125,800,000
'75 .09

B. Physical Fitness - Sokol, 100th anniversary of the founding of the Sokol program in the United States. The program, promoted mostly among Americans of Czechoslovak, Polish, and Yugoslav descent, combines gymnastic, cultural, and educational activities. Shown: statue of a discus thrower inspired by Myron's *Discobolus*. The statue stands near the Department of State in Washington, D.C.
Washington, D.C. 115,095,000
'75 .09

C. Crusade against Cancer, a campaign to conquer this disease. It is a major cause of death among Americans. Shown: a microscope and stethoscope symbolizing the importance of early diagnosis.
Washington, D.C. 119,560,000
'75 .09

D. Battle of New Orleans, 150th anniversary. On January 8, 1815, Americans under Andrew Jackson defeated British troops led by Sir Edward Pakenham at New Orleans. Due to lapses in communication, however, the battle was fought a full two weeks after the Treaty of Ghent brought the War of 1812 to an end. The treaty also marked the start of 150 years of unbroken peace between the United States and England. Shown: Jackson leading troops into battle and the sesquicentennial medal designed by Angela Gregory.
New Orleans, La. 115,695,000
'75 .09

A. *12/2/64*

B. 2/15/65

C. 4/1/65

D. *1/8/65*

E. 5/13/65

H. 7/2/65

I. 8/10/65

F. 6/15/65

G. 6/26/65

J. 7/17/65

E. Winston Churchill (1874 - 1965), British statesman, prime minister (1940 - 45, 1951 - 55), and World War II leader who was granted honorary American citizenship in 1963. Shown: portrait based upon the *Angry Lion* photograph by Canadian Yousuf Karsh.
Fulton, Mo.   125,180,000
                '75   .09

F. Magna Carta, 750th anniversary. This charter, signed by King John in 1215, is the basis of English and American common law. The design of the stamp is symbolic of the great event, which marked the first successful challenge to the principle of the divine right of kings. Shown: procession of barons above a crown.
Jamestown, Va.   120,135,000
                '75   .09

G. International Cooperation Year - United Nations, 20th anniversary. In 1965, the United States joined many U.N. members in recognizing International Cooperation Year.
San Francisco, Calif.
115,405,000   '75   .09

H. Salvation Army, 100th anniversary. This religious and charitable movement was founded in London, England, by William Booth in 1865. It now carries on its work in countries around the world.
New York, N.Y.   115,855,000
                '75   .09

I. Herbert Hoover (1874 - 1964), 31st president (1929 - 33). Hoover was also a mining engineer and an international relief administrator. Shown: portrait based on photograph by Louis Fabian Bachrach, Sr.
West Branch, Iowa   114,840,000
                '75   .09

J. Dante Alighieri (1265 - 1321), 700th anniversary of the birth of the Italian poet, who is best known for *The Divine Comedy.* Shown: simulated 16th century Italian painting.
San Francisco, Calif.   115,340,000
                '75   .09

A. 9/17/65

B. 8/19/65

C. 9/3/65

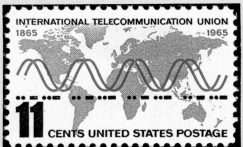

D. 10/6/65

E. 11/2/65

F. 11/19/65

A. John Singleton Copley (1738 - 1815), one of the finest colonial artists America produced. Shown: Elizabeth Clarke Copley, the artist's daughter; a detail from *The Copley Family*, painted c. 1785 (National Gallery of Art, Washington, D.C.). *American Painting Series.*
Washington, D.C.   114,880,000
'75   .10

B. Robert Fulton (1765 - 1815), engineer and artist who developed the first successful steamboat, the *Clermont*, in 1807. He also developed a type of submarine, the *Nautilus*, but was unable to interest any government in producing it. His last venture was a floating fort. Shown: bust of Fulton by Jean Antoine Houdon and the *Clermont*.
Clermont, N.Y.   116,140,000
'75   .09

C. Traffic Safety, stressing goals that can be met through enforcement, education, and engineering.
Baltimore, Md.   114,085,000
'75   .10

D. International Telecommunication Union, 100th anniversary. The ITU, a specialized agency of the United Nations, has 124 members. Shown: map of the world, symbolic radio sine wave, and ITU spelled out in Morse Code four times.
Washington, D.C.   26,995,000
'75   .30

E. Christmas. Shown: a watercolor rendering of an early American weather vane by Lucille Gloria Chabot (Index of American Design, National Gallery of Art, Washington, D.C.).
Silver Bell, Ariz.   1,139,930,000
'75   .09

F. Abraham Lincoln. Regular issue. Also issued in coils. Shown: portrait based on photograph by Mathew Brady, with log cabin in background.
New York, N.Y.   '75   .06

G. 8/28/65

H. 3/16/66

I. 10/23/65

J. 5/2/66

K. 4/16/66

L. 7/1/66

G. Settlement of Florida, 400th anniversary of the founding of St. Augustine, oldest city in the United States. It was built by Spain on the site of a French colony and remained a part of Spain's colonial empire until 1821, when Florida was formally ceded to the United States. Shown: Spanish explorer with royal banner. A stamp of the same design was simultaneously released by Spain.

St. Augustine, Fla.   116,900,000
'75   .10

H. Migratory Bird Treaty, 50th anniversary of joint U.S. - Canadian treaty to protect migratory birds.
Pittsburgh, Pa.   116,835,000
'75   .09

I. Adlai E. Stevenson (1900 - 65), ambassador to the United Nations (1961 - 65), lawyer, and presidential candidate in 1952 and 1956.
Bloomington, Ill.   128,495,000
'75   .10

J. American Circus, a salute to the spectacle which entertains countless people every year.
Delavan, Wis.   131,270,000
'75   .09

K. Indiana Statehood, 150th anniversary. 19th state, admitted 1816. Capital, Indianapolis. Leading industries include: mining, farming, steel manufacturing, and food processing.
Corydon, Ind.   123,770,000
'75   .09

L. Bill of Rights, 175th anniversary of the passage of the first ten amendments to the Constitution. They provided guarantees of such civil liberties as freedom of religion, freedom of speech, and freedom of the press.
Miami Beach, Fla.   114,160,000
'75   .09

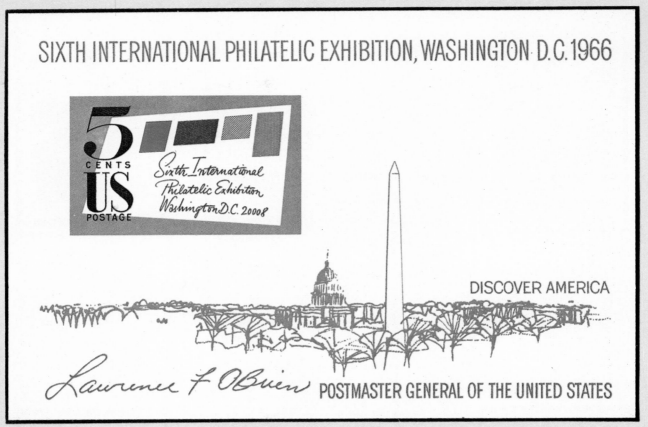

SIXTH INTERNATIONAL PHILATELIC EXHIBITION, WASHINGTON D.C.1966

5 CENTS US POSTAGE

Sixth International Philatelic Exhibition Washington D.C. 20008

DISCOVER AMERICA

Laurence F. O'Brien POSTMASTER GENERAL OF THE UNITED STATES

B. 5/23/66

C. 1/29/66

A. 5/21/66

D. 2/22/66

A. Sixth International Philatelic Exhibition (SIPEX), the first international stamp show held in Washington, D.C. Shown: a representation of an entire envelope complete with simulated stamps and address as would be retained by a "cover" collector. In addition to this stamp, the postal service released a souvenir sheet (**B**) and an international air mail post card for the occasion.
Washington, D.C. 122,285,000
'75 .09

B. SIPEX, souvenir sheet, a compliment to the Sixth International Philatelic Exhibition. Shown: a reproduction of the commemorative stamp issued for the occasion (**A**) and a panoramic view of the nation's capital. The phrase "Discover America" promoted President Johnson's campaign to encourage people to visit all parts of the United States.
Washington, D.C. 14,680,000
'75 .12

C. Franklin D. Roosevelt. Regular issue. Also issued in coils and booklets. Shown: portrait based on 1941 photograph taken at the signing of the Atlantic Charter.
Hyde Park, N.Y. '75 .09

D. George Washington. Regular issue. Also issued in coils. Shown: idealized portrait painted by Rembrandt Peale in 1823 and subsequently copied by him 79 times. The first day of issue ceremony was held in the office of the vice president, where the original painting hangs.
Washington, D.C. '75 .08

A. 3/14/66

B. 4/9/66

C. 6/8/66

D. 7/30/66

E. 8/29/66

F. 9/24/66

G. 8/25/66

H. 9/12/66

A. Albert Einstein (1879 - 1955), noted physicist who developed the theory of relativity. Regular issue.
Princeton, N.J.   '75 .11

B. American Society for the Prevention of Cruelty to Animals, 100th anniversary. Shown: Babe, a mongrel dog owned by stamp designer Norman Todhunter, who makes a plea for the humane treatment of animals.
New York, N.Y. 117,470,000   '75 .09

C. Frank Lloyd Wright (1869 - 1959), architect. Regular issue. Shown: Wright and one of his most famous designs, the Guggenheim Museum of New York.
Spring Green, Wis.   '75 .04

D. Poland's Millennium, 1000th anniversary of the adoption of Christianity.
Washington, D.C. 128,475,000   '75 .09

E. Marine Corps Reserve, 50th anniversary. Shown:

Marines of World Wars I and II, a frogman, and modern combat Marine. A fifth Marine in colonial uniform recalls the founding of the Corps in 1775.
Washington, D.C. 125,110,000   '75 .09

F. Johnny Appleseed (John Chapman, 1774 - 1847), American folk hero who spent his life planting apple trees in Ohio, Pennsylvania, and Indiana. First stamp in the *American Folklore Series*.

Leominster, Mass. 124,290,000   '75 .09

G. National Park Service, 50th anniversary. Shown: Park Service emblem, which symbolizes the three categories of parks — natural, historical, and recreational.
Yellowstone Natl. Park, Wyo.
119,535,000   '75 .09

H. General Federation of Women's Clubs, founded 1891.
New York, N.Y. 114,853,200   '75 .09

A. Beautification of America. Shown: Jefferson Memorial wreathed in cherry blossoms.
Washington, D.C.   128,460,000
'73   .10

B. Great River Road, 5,600 - mile Mississippi River parkway from the Canadian border to the Gulf of Mexico.
Baton Rouge, La.   127,585,000
'75   .09

C. Servicemen - Savings Bonds, tribute to servicemen on the 25th anniversary of the U.S. savings bond program.
Sioux City, Iowa   115,875,000
'75   .09

D. John Bassett Moore (1860 - 1947), professor of international law, government adviser, and judge on The Hague Tribunal and the Permanent Court of International Justice. Regular issue.
Smyrna, Del.   '75   6.25

E. Christmas. Shown: detail from *Madonna and Child with Angels* by Hans Memling, a 15th century Flemish master (National Gallery of Art, Washington, D.C.).
Christmas, Mich.   1,173,547,420
'75   .09

F. Mary Cassatt (1845 - 1926), impressionist painter who spent much of her life in France. She was greatly influenced by impressionist artists Edouard Manet and Edgar Degas and associated herself with their style. Shown: *The Boating Party,* painted in 1893 (National Gallery of Art, Washington, D.C.). *American Painting Series.*
Washington, D.C.   114,015,000
'75   .12

G. Canada, 100th anniversary. On July 1, 1867, the provinces of Canada united under a central government. This was the first U.S. stamp that carried an official first day cancellation from another nation.
Montreal, Canada   132,045,000
'75   .09

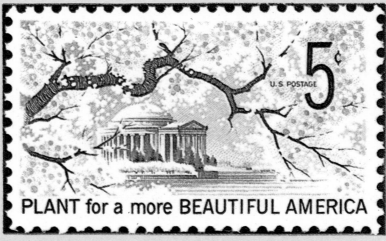

A. *10/5/66*

B. 10/21/66

C. 10/26/66

D. 12/3/66

E. *11/1/66*

H. National Grange, 100th anniversary. Agrarian movement organized primarily for social and educational purposes. The movement also promoted cooperative enterprises as a means of redress against economic abuse of farmers.
Washington, D.C.   121,105,000
'75   .09

I. Erie Canal, 150th anniversary. This 363 - mile - long canal linked Lake Erie with the Hudson River.
Rome, N.Y.   118,780,000
'75   .09

F. *11/17/66*

J. 1/30/67

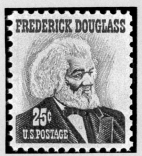

K. 2/14/67

G. 5/25/67

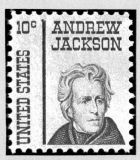

L. 3/15/67

H. 4/17/67

I. 7/4/67

M. 5/29/67

J. Albert Gallatin (1761 - 1849), secretary of the treasury 1802 - 14. Regular issue.
Washington, D.C.   52,030,000
           '75   .06

K. Frederick Douglass (1817- 95), editor, abolitionist, public servant, and minister to Haiti, who was born a slave. Regular issue.
Washington, D.C.   '75   .34

L. Andrew Jackson, after a portrait by Thomas Sully (National Gallery of Art, Washington, D.C.). Regular issue.
Hermitage, Tenn.   '75   .14

M. John F. Kennedy, after a photograph by Jacques Lowe in *The Kennedy Years.* Regular issue.
Brookline, Mass.   '75   .18

A. 7/5/67

B. 7/29/67

C. 9/16/67

Historian Francis Parkman is famous for works about the old Northwest and Canada. His most famous book is *The Oregon Trail.*

D. 10/16/67

E. 9/29/67

A. Search for Peace, the theme of an essay contest for young people sponsored by Lions International in connection with its 50th anniversary. Shown: dove and laurel branch, the ancient Greek symbol for peace, as adapted by Bradbury Thompson from Jacob Bryant's *Analysis of Ancient Mythology.*
Chicago, Ill. 121,985,000
          '75 .09

B. Nebraska Statehood, 100th anniversary. 37th state,

admitted 1867. Capital, Lincoln. Major industries are insurance, railroads, meat-packing, farming and food processing. Corn, livestock, and wheat are important related products. Shown: Hereford steer and ear of corn.
Lincoln, Nebr. 117,225,000
          '75 .09

C. Francis Parkman (1823-93). Regular issue.
Boston, Mass.   '75 .05

D. Eugene O'Neill (1888-1953), possibly the greatest dramatist America has produced. His plays include *The Iceman Cometh, Mourning Becomes Electra,* and *Emperor Jones.* Regular issue. Also issued in coils.
New London, Conn. '75 1.25

E. United States Space Accomplishments, the first twin stamps in U.S. postal history. Usually collected as a pair. Shown (left to right): astronaut during space-walk and Gemini 4 capsule

with the earth in the background. The designs, created by artist Paul Calle, were inspired by the 1965 flight of Gemini 4, which marked the first time that a U.S. astronaut walked in outer space.
Kennedy Space Center, Fla.
120,865,000
     '75 2.50 (pair) .75 (ea.)

F. Henry David Thoreau (1817-62), poet and essayist whose beliefs have influenced millions. His best-known work is *Walden,*

F. 7/12/67

G. 8/17/67

H. 8/1/67

I. 10/2/67

J. 10/6/67

K. 11/6/67

which has appeared in some 150 editions in 50 languages. The book is based on his experiences at Walden Pond where he lived in seclusion for two years. Shown: portrait by Leonard Baskin based on an 1856 daguerrotype.
Concord, Mass.   111,850,000
'75   .09

G. Davy Crockett (1786 - 1836), frontiersman, trapper, and Congressman who died at the Alamo. A native of Tennessee, Crockett is the subject of many colorful legends. *American Folklore Series.*
San Antonio, Tex.   114,270,000
'75   .09

H. Voice of America, 25th anniversary. This stamp, which also marked the 14th anniversary of the U.S. Information Agency, paid tribute to the organization that broadcasts programs to people all over the world, including those behind the Iron Curtain.
Washington, D.C.   111,515,000
'75   .09

I. Plan for Better Cities, issued in connection with a meeting of experts interested in the future of city life. Shown: a bird's - eye view of a planned city.
Washington, D.C.   110,675,000
'75   .10

J. Finnish Independence, 50th anniversary. This northern European nation was conquered by Sweden in the 12th century and ceded to Russia in 1809. It became a fully independent nation in 1917. Shown: Finnish coat of arms.
Finland, Minn.   110,670,000
'75   .10

K. Christmas. This stamp includes more of the painting than shown in the 1966 version (*Madonna and Child with Angels* by Hans Memling), and is nearly twice as large (see p. 146).
Bethlehem, Ga.   1,208,700,000
'75   .09

A. Thomas Eakins (1844 - 1916), painter and teacher. Eakins, who was thoroughly schooled in anatomy, is best - known for outdoor scenes, sports subjects, and realistic portraits. He served as an instructor at the Pennsylvania Academy of Fine Arts and was a founder of the Art Students League of Philadelphia. Shown: *The Biglin Brothers Racing* (National Gallery of Art, Washington, D.C.). First U.S. stamp printed by gravure, at the Photogravure and Color Company, Moonachie, New Jersey. *American Painting Series.*
Washington, D.C.   113,825,000
   '75   .12

B. George C. Marshall (1880 - 1959), General of the Army and secretary of state who initiated the European Recovery Plan, commonly known as the Marshall Plan, during the Truman administration. The plan extended U.S. aid to war - ravaged nations after World War II. Regular issue.
Lexington, Va.   '75   .28

C. George Washington, new version of 1966 design (see p. 144), reengraved to remove harsh highlights and to subdue shadow areas. Regular issue.
New York, N.Y.   '75   .10

D. Illinois Statehood, 150th anniversary. 21st state, admitted 1818. Capital, Springfield. Major industries include: farming, mining, steel manufacturing, publishing, and printing. Shown: rural scene by George Barford, winner in contest held by Illinois Sesquicentennial Commission.
Shawneetown, Ill.   141,350,000
   '75   .11

E. HemisFair '68, an exposition held in San Antonio, Texas. Its theme was "The Confluence of Civilizations in the Americas".
San Antonio, Tex.   144,345,000
   '75   .11

A. *11/2/67*

B. 10/24/67

C. 11/17/67

D. 2/12/68

E. 3/30/68

F. 12/11/67

G. 1/12/68

H. 1/29/68

I. 2/28/68

J. 3/8/68

K. *1/24/68*

F. Mississippi Statehood, 150th anniversary. 20th state, admitted 1817. Capital, Jackson. Principal industry is agriculture; leading crop is cotton. Shown: magnolia blossom, the state flower.
Natchez, Miss.   113,330,000
                        '75   .10

G. Thomas Jefferson, after a painting by Rembrandt Peale (The White House, Washington, D.C.). Regular issue. Also issued in coils and booklets.
Jeffersonville, Ind.   '75   .03

H. Thomas Paine (1737 - 1809), eloquent and controversial author of *Common Sense* and *The Crisis,* which helped to inflame the American Revolutionary spirit. Regular issue. Shown: portrait by John Wesley Jarvis (National Gallery of Art, Washington, D.C.).
Philadelphia, Pa.   '75   .54

I. Franklin D. Roosevelt, vertical version of coil stamp issued in 1967 (see p. 144) and found unsatisfactory for most dispensing machines. Regular issue.
Washington, D.C.   '75   .16

J. Oliver Wendell Holmes (1841 - 1935), associate justice of the U.S. Supreme Court. His liberal interpretation of the Constitution stemmed from long experience as a Massachusetts jurist and professor of common law. He was the son of the poet and essayist of the same name. Regular issue.
Washington, D.C.   '75   .20

K. Flag over White House, a new version of the flag design of 1963 (see p. 134). First stamp to carry both "Mail Early in the Day" and "Use Zip Code" slogans in the margin. Regular issue. Also issued in coils.
Washington, D.C.   '75   .11

Historic Flag Issue.

Usually collected in strips of ten, the stamps portray nine flags of the era of the Revolutionary War and the Fort McHenry flag of the War of 1812. Pittsburgh, Pa. 228,040,000

A. First Stars and Stripes, the flag authorized on June 14, 1777, by the Continental Congress. Varieties exist, the most familiar being with a circle of stars in the field.
'75 .30

B. Fort Moultrie Flag, reportedly recovered and raised again after having been shot away during a British bombardment of Fort Sullivan in Charleston Harbor. The fort was renamed to honor its defender, then Col. William Moultrie.
'75 .35

C. Fort McHenry Flag, the flag that inspired Francis Scott Key to write the "Star Spangled Banner" in 1814. The flag flew above the fort during a British attack which threatened Baltimore. It now hangs in the Smithsonian Institution.
'75 .35

D. Washington's Cruisers Flag, carried by Washington's six cruisers prior to the designation of the first naval ensign.
'75 .30

E. Bennington Flag, carried by militiamen, possibly at the Battle of Bennington. The flag is kept by the Bennington Battle Monument and Historical Association, Bennington, Vermont.
'75 .30

F. Rhode Island Flag, carried by the 400 troops of the First Rhode Island Regiment in the battles of Brandywine, Trenton, and Yorktown. The flag is in the State House at Providence.
'75 .30

A. 7/4/68

B, C, D. 7/4/68

E, F, G. 7/4/68

K. 4/4/68

L. 5/17/68

H, I, J. 7/4/68

M. 8/13/68

N. 6/27/68

G. Bunker Hill Flag, the colonial flag on Breed's Hill. The blue version of the flag, preferred by historians, contrasts with artist John Trumbull's red flag.
'75 .30

H. Grand Union Flag, the flag raised in January 1776 by Gen. George Washington near Cambridge, Massachusetts, as the Continental Army came into being. The first national flag of the United States, it was also the first naval ensign.
'75 .30

I. Philadelphia Light Horse Flag, the banner of the elite troop that often served as escort to General Washington. The flag is retained by the First City Troop in its Philadelphia armory.
'75 .30

J. First Navy Jack, believed to have been flown by Commodore Esek Hopkins when he captured New Providence in the Bahamas in 1775.
'75 .30

K. Airlift, special rate for parcels mailed to servicemen overseas. Shown: eagle design inspired by 19th century wood carving (Index of American Design, National Gallery of Art, Washington, D.C.).
Seattle, Wash. '75 1.40

L. Law and Order, a salute to law enforcement officers, the friends and protectors of the citizen.
Washington, D.C. 130,125,000
'75 .11

M. Lucy Stone (1818-93), a crusader for women's rights who was also active in the antislavery and temperance movements. Regular issue.
Dorchester, Mass. '75 .70

N. Register and Vote, a reminder of a civic responsibility. Shown: eagle weathervane.
Washington, D.C. 158,070,000
'75 .11

A. *9/11/68*

B. 5/1/68

C. 9/20/68

D. 9/26/68

E. 10/21/68

F. 7/30/68

A. Walt Disney (1901 - 66), animated film maker whose genius created Mickey Mouse, Donald Duck, and other cherished characters. His films include *Fantasia* and *Pinocchio.* Shown: Disney and parade of children; designed by two staff members of Disney Productions.
Marceline, Mo.   153,015,000
'75   .15

B. Support our Youth, a tribute to the Benevolent and Protective Order of Elks, which sponsored a National Youth Week during its centennial year.
Chicago, Ill.   147,120,000
'75   .11

C. Jacques Marquette (1637 - 75), French Jesuit missionary who explored the Mississippi River with Louis Jolliet. In 1668 he founded Sault Ste. Marie, the first permanent settlement in Michigan.
Sault Ste. Marie, Mich.
132,560,000   '75   .11

D. Daniel Boone (1734 - 1820), frontier hero. Immortalized as a hunter, trapper, soldier, and public servant, Boone blazed the Wilderness Road into Kentucky and founded Boonesboro on the Kentucky River. *American Folklore Series.*
Frankfort, Ky.   130,385,000
'75   .11

E. John Dewey (1859 - 1952), philosopher, psychologist, and educator. He believed in learning through experience, a philosophy that was basic to progressive education. Regular issue.
Burlington, Vt.   '75   .40

F. Henry Ford (1863 - 1947), pioneer automobile maker. His mass - produced, inexpensive, standardized car helped make the Ford Motor Company one of the largest automobile manufacturers in the world.

Chief Joseph · National Portrait Gallery

United States Postage 6¢

G. *11/4/68*

WATERFOWL CONSERVATION

6¢

UNITED STATES

H. 10/24/68

UNITED STATES POSTAGE

6¢

ARKANSAS RIVER NAVIGATION

I. 10/1/68

UNITED STATES 6¢

"BATTLE OF BUNKER'S HILL"

John Trumbull
AMERICAN ARTIST

J. *10/18/68*

Regular issue. Shown: portrait of Ford superimposed over 1909 Model T touring car.
Dearborn, Mich.   '75   .17

G. Chief Joseph (c. 1840 - 1904), Nez Percé (Pierced Nose) warrior noted for his war strategy and consideration for his enemies. Shown: portrait after painting by Cyrenius

Hall (National Portrait Gallery, Washington, D.C.). The stamp also commemorated the dedication of the National Portrait Gallery.
Washington, D.C.   125,100,000
                        '75   .11

H. Waterfowl Conservation, a salute to the work of Ducks Unlimited, a conservation group. Shown: two wood ducks in flight, by California artist Stanley

W. Galli. This was voted a popular stamp design of 1968.
Cleveland, Ohio   142,245,000
                        '75   .11

I. Arkansas River Navigation. Issued for the opening of the $1.2 billion waterway, which is expected to provide Kansas, Oklahoma, and Arkansas with a barge route and hydroelectric power.
Little Rock, Ark.   132,265,000
                        '75   .11

J. John Trumbull (1756 - 1843), American painter noted for his works depicting Revolutionary War scenes. Shown: Second Lieutenant Thomas Grosvenor and Peter Salem, a group study from *The Battle of Bunker's Hill,* finished in 1786 (Yale University Art Gallery, New Haven, Connecticut. See p. 12).
New Haven, Conn.   128,295,000
                        '75   .11

A. *11/1/68*

B. 5/17/69

C. 10/15/68

D. *5/1/69*

A. Christmas. Shown: the Angel Gabriel, a detail from *The Annunciation* by 15th century Flemish artist Jan van Eyck (National Gallery of Art, Washington, D.C.). First stamp printed on the nine - color Huck press.
Washington, D.C. 1,410,585,000
'75 .11

B. W. C. Handy (1873 - 1958), jazz musician and composer of "The Saint Louis Blues", "The Memphis Blues", and "The Beale Street Blues". Shown: Handy and his trumpet, based upon one of Bernice Kochan's winning entries in a nationwide design contest sponsored by the Memphis Sesquicentennial Committee.
Memphis, Tenn. 125,555,000
'75 .11

C. Cherokee Strip, 75th anniversary. On September 16, 1893, 100,000 aspirants raced into this former Indian hunting ground to claim 40,000 homesteads. The land had been closed to settlers until Congress paid the Indians $1.40 per acre for it.
Ponca City, Okla. 124,775,000
'75 .11

D. Grandma Moses, familiar name for primitive artist Anna Mary Robertson Moses (1860 - 1961), who took up painting at the age of 76. Her works portray everyday American life. Shown: a detail from *July Fourth,* painted in 1951 when she was 91 (The White House, Washington, D.C.). *American Folklore Series.*
Washington, D.C. 139,475,000
'75 .11

E. 1/16/69

F. 10/9/68

G. 3/15/69

H. 5/5/69

E. Beautification of America. Usually collected in blocks of four, the stamps publicize President and Mrs. Johnson's "Beautify America" campaign. Shown (clockwise from upper left): Capitol Building in Washington, D.C., with azaleas and tulips, the Washington Monument and the Potomac River with daffodils, a highway with poppies and lupine, and a street lined with flowering crab apple. The designs represent actual parks in the nation's capital and road scenes typical of many parts of the country.
Washington, D.C. 192,570,000
'75 3.50 (block) .85 (ea.)

F. Lief Erikson, 11th century Norse explorer credited with being the first European to set foot on North American soil, probably in Labrador. Shown: statue of Erikson in Reykjavik, Iceland, by American sculptor Stirling Calder.

Seattle, Wash. 128,710,000
'75 .11

G. American Legion, 50th anniversary. A salute to the organization founded in Paris in 1919 by representatives of the American Expeditionary Force of World War I. Its subsequent growth absorbed veterans of all wars. Shown: eagle adapted from the Great Seal of the United States.
Washington, D.C. 148,770,000
'75 .11

H. Apollo 8, a tribute to the space mission that placed men in orbit around the moon for the first time. Shown: the earth photographed from outer space and the first words of the Book of Genesis, from which the astronauts read in a Christmas Eve message radioed to earth from their space capsule.
Houston, Tex. 187,165,000
'75 .25

A. California Settlement, 200th anniversary. On July 16, 1769, Father Junipero Serra and Captain Gaspar de Portala founded the San Diego Mission, first permanent settlement in California. Shown: bells of the Carmel Mission, where Father Serra is buried.
San Diego, Calif. 144,425,000
'75 .11

B. John Wesley Powell (1834 - 1902), geologist, ethnologist, and founder of the U.S. Bureau of American Ethnology at the Smithsonian Institution, for which he classified American Indian languages. In 1869 he led an expedition through the Grand Canyon and traced the Green and Colorado Rivers for 1,000 miles.
Page, Ariz. 133,100,000
'75 .11

C. Alabama Statehood, 150th anniversary. 22nd state, admitted 1819. Capital, Montgomery. Major industries include: agriculture (chiefly cotton), iron, and steel. Shown: camellia, the state flower, and the yellowhammer or flicker, the state bird.
Huntsville, Ala. 151,110,000
'75 .11

D. Dartmouth College Case, 150th anniversary. In 1819 Daniel Webster successfully argued this celebrated case before the U.S. Supreme Court. The opinion, rendered by John Marshall, preserved for college charters the sanctity due all contracts. Shown: portrait of Webster by John Pope and sketch of Dartmouth Hall.
Hanover, N.H. 124,075,000
'75 .11

E. Christmas. Shown: *Winter Sunday in Norway, Maine,* a primitive painting by an unknown artist (New York State Historical Association, Cooperstown, New York). This stamp was precancelled as follows for trial use in four cities: Atlanta, Ga.; Baltimore, Md.; Memphis, Tn.; and New Haven, Ct.
Christmas, Fla. 1,710,795,000
'75 .11

A. 7/16/69

B. 8/1/69

C. 8/2/69

D. 9/22/69

E. *11/3/69*

F. Botanical Congress Issue. Usually collected in blocks of four. Shown (clockwise from upper left): Douglas fir, lady's slipper, Franklinia tree, and ocotillo.

Seattle, Wash. 158,695,000
'75 3.95 (block) .95 (ea.)

G. Dwight D. Eisenhower (1890 - 1969), 34th president (1953 - 61) and General of

the Army who led the Allied forces in Europe during World War II. He also served as the first supreme commander of the Allied

F. 8/23/69

H. 9/24/69

G. 10/14/69

I. 9/26/69

forces under the North Atlantic Treaty Organization (NATO) from 1950 to 1952. Shown: portrait based on photograph by Bernie Noble of the *Cleveland Press.*

Abilene, Kans.   138,976,000
            '75   .11

H. Professional Baseball, 100th anniversary. Salaried baseball players were first

used by the Red Stockings of Cincinnati in 1869.
Cincinnati, Ohio   129,925,000
            '75   .11

I. College Football, 100th anniversary. Rutgers

defeated Princeton, its New Jersey rival, in the first intercollegiate game of football on November 6, 1869.
New Brunswick, N.J.
129,860,000   '75   .11

A. William M. Harnett (1848 - 92), Irish - born American artist noted for his realistic works. Shown: *Old Models,* one of his last and finest works. The painting is signed and dated 1892 (Boston Museum of Fine Arts). *American Painting Series.*
Boston, Mass.   124,729,600
     '75   .11

B. National Society for Crippled Children and Adults (the sponsor of Easter Seals), 50th anniversary. Shown: hope for the crippled, symbolized by a child rising from a wheelchair.
Columbus, Ohio   124,565,000
     '75   .11

C. Edgar Lee Masters (1869 - 1950), poet best remembered for *Spoon River Anthology,* an exposé of small - town mores. First stamp in the *American Poet Series.*
Petersburg, Ill.   137,660,000
     '75   .10

A. *12/3/69*

B. 11/20/69

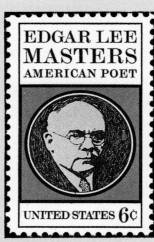

C. 8/22/70

D. 7/20/70

E. 8/6/70

F. 8/26/70

G. 9/12/70

H. *7/9/70*

D. American Bison (buffalo), giant animal whose numbers have decreased from an estimated 200 million to about 30,000. The largest remaining herd is at Custer Battlefield National Monument in Montana. *Wildlife Conservation Series.*
Custer, S. Dak.   142,185,000
'75   .09

E. Dwight D. Eisenhower. Regular issue. Also issued in coils and booklets.
Washington, D.C. 1,722,890,000
'75   .09

F. Woman Suffrage, 50th anniversary. The stamp was issued at the birthplace of Susan B. Anthony, one of the crusaders for women's rights whose efforts culminated in the passage of the 19th amendment, giving women the right to vote. Shown: suffragettes of 1920 and woman voter of 1970.
Adams, Mass.   135,125,000
'75   .10

G. South Carolina, 300th anniversary of the founding of Charles Towne, the first permanent English settlement in the state. In 1680 the settlement was moved to the site of Charleston, which later became one of the leading cities in the Thirteen Colonies. South Carolina was admitted to the Union in 1788 as the eighth state. Shown: drawings representative of the state's development, including St. Philip's Church in Charleston and a cannon from Fort Sumter, where the Civil War began in 1861.
Charleston, S.C.   135,395,000
'75   .10

H. Maine Statehood, 150th anniversary. 23rd state, admitted 1820. Capital, Augusta. Major industries include: wood products, textiles, shoes, farming, lumbering, fishing, mining, and tourism. Shown: *The Lighthouse at Two Lights* by Edward Hopper (Metropolitan Museum of Art, New York, N.Y.).
Portland, Me.   171,850,000
'75   .09

A. 9/19/70

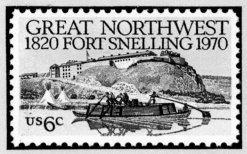

B. 10/17/70

C. 5/6/70

A. Stone Mountain Memorial to Thomas J. "Stonewall" Jackson, Jefferson Davis, and Robert E. Lee. The mammoth carving of the mounted Confederate heroes fills a niche 305 feet across and 195 feet tall in the 825-foot-high face of the largest isolated block of granite in Stone Mountain Park near Atlanta, Georgia.
Stone Mountain, Ga.
132,675,000   '75   .10

B. Fort Snelling, 150th anniversary of the founding of the first outpost west of the Mississippi River. The fort, named for Col. Joshiah Snelling, was built near present-day St. Paul, Minnesota. It played a key role in the opening of the Northwest to settlement. Shown: old fort, Indian tepees, and keelboat at juncture of Minnesota and Mississippi Rivers.
St. Paul, Minn.   134,785,000
                    '75   .10

C. American Museum of Natural History, New York City, 100th anniversary. The four stamps, usually collected as a block, also focus attention on environmental problems, including extinction in the past as well as survival in the future. Shown: the bald eagle, African elephant herd, and Haida Indian canoe (based on actual exhibits at the museum), and the central portion of *The Age of Reptiles*, a 110-foot mural

by Rudolph Zallinger (Peabody Museum, Yale University).
New York, N.Y.   201,794,600
     '75   .55 (block)   .13 (ea.)

D. Landing of the Pilgrims, 350th anniversary. Shown: the *Mayflower* and a group of Pilgrims. The *Mayflower* was also shown on one of three stamps issued in 1920 to honor the Pilgrims (see p. 55).
Plymouth, Mass.   129,785,000
          '75   .10

D. 11/21/70

E. 10/28/70

F. 11/24/70

G. 11/20/70

E. Anti - Pollution, issued to call attention to a worldwide problem that threatens our environment. Usually collected in blocks of four. Shown: stylized globe coupled with wheat blowing in the wind (save our soil), a view of a city playground (save our cities), a seagull (save our air), and a fish (save our water). The stamps were printed by rotogravure process at Guilford Gravure, Inc., Guilford, Connecticut, on presses manned by Bureau of Engraving and Printing crews.
San Clemente, Calif.
161,590,000
    '75 .90 (block)   .22 (ea.)

F. Disabled American Veterans, 50th anniversary, and a tribute to Americans being held as prisoners of war or missing in action in Southeast Asia. The two stamps, printed side by side in sheets, are usually collected in pairs.
Cincinnati, Ohio;

Montgomery, Ala.   134,388,000
    '75   .25 (pair)   .13 (ea.)

G. United Nations, 25th anniversary. Founded in 1945, the U.N. promotes international peace and security through its six principal organs: the General Assembly, the Security Council, the Economic and Social Council, the Trusteeship Council, the International Court of Justice, and the Secretariat. Postal administrations frequently recognize the United Nations and its specialized agencies or their activities through stamps. Notable examples are issues publicizing UNICEF (United Nations Children's Fund), the Food and Agricultural Organization's campaign against hunger, and the World Health Organization's efforts to eliminate malaria.
New York, N.Y.   127,110,000
    '75 .10

A. 11/5/70

B. 1/19/71

C. 3/12/71

D. 1/26/71

A. Christmas, Antique Toys. Usually collected in blocks of four. Shown (clockwise from upper left): locomotive (after a drawing), horse on wheels, doll carriage, and mechanical tricycle (after the *Golden Age of Toys* by Fondin and Remise).
Washington, D.C.   928,905,000
'75   2.50 (block)   .50 (ea.)

B. American Wool Industry, 450th anniversary of the arrival of the first sheep in America. The animals were imported for food and wool. Shown: ewe and lamb.
Las Vegas, Nev.   132,785,000
'75   .10

C. Blood Doners, issued to help increase participation in the blood bank program. Shown: giving blood saves lives, a poster design.
New York, N.Y.   128,910,000
'75   .10

D. Gen. Douglas MacArthur (1880 - 1964), Chief of Staff (1930 - 35), Five Star General, and Supreme Commander of the Allied Powers in the Pacific during World War II. He also was in charge of the Allied occupation of Japan after the war. The stamp was issued in Norfolk, Virginia, the site of the MacArthur Memorial Foundation. Shown: portrait based upon a photograph taken in 1944 aboard a flying fortress aircraft.
Norfolk, Va.   131,840,000
'75   .10

E. Ernie Pyle (1900 - 45), Pulitzer Prize winning World War II correspondent killed by enemy fire in the Pacific on April 18, 1945.
Regular issue.
Washington, D.C.   87,230,000
'75   .22

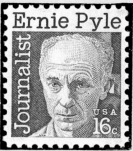
E. 5/7/71

F. 5/10/71

G. 5/10/71

H. 5/10/71

I. *11/5/70*

J. 5/8/71

K. 6/23/71

F. Flag over White House. Regular issue. Also issued in coils.
Washington, D.C. 3,019,435,000
'75 .13

G. Dwight D. Eisenhower. Regular issue.
Washington, D.C.   '75 .11

H. Dwight D. Eisenhower. Regular coil issue. Also issued in booklets.
Washington, D.C.   '75 .12
1,295,220,000 **(G & H)**

I. Christmas. Shown: *The Nativity* by Italian artist Lorenzo Lotto (National Gallery of Art, Washington, D.C.). Lotto (c. 1480 - 1556) was born in Venice but spent his early life in Treviso and always remained apart from the main Venetian art tradition.
Washington, D.C. 996,975,000
'75 .15

J. Missouri Statehood, 150th anniversary. 24th state, admitted 1821. Capital, Jefferson City. Major industries include food, transportation equipment, chemicals. Shown: a detail from *Independence and the Opening of the West,* a mural by Thomas Hart Benton (Harry S. Truman Library, Independence, Missouri).
Independence, Mo. 150,650,000
'75 .13

K. Antarctic Treaty, 10th anniversary of pact among Argentina, Australia, Belgium, Chile, France, Japan, New Zealand, South Africa, the Soviet Union, the United Kingdom, and the United States, pledging to cooperate in the peaceful exploration and development of Antarctica. Shown: official emblem showing map of Antarctica.
Washington, D.C. 133,470,000
'75 .13

A. 6/12/71

B. 7/4/71

C. 8/28/71

D. 9/12/71

A. *Wildlife Conservation Series,* 1971. Usually collected in blocks of four. Shown: trout, alligator, polar bear with cubs, and California condor. Trout are found in many parts of the world. One species, the lake trout, was once one of the most valuable commercial fish in North America. The alligator lives in the southeastern United States. Its numbers have been reduced by those who use its hide for luggage, shoes, and handbags. The polar bear, a native of the Arctic, is frequently hunted by trophy seekers. Cubs, like the ones shown here weigh about two pounds at birth and stay with their mothers for about 17 months. The California condor, one of the rarest birds in North America, is also one of the largest. About 40 of them survive.
Avery Island, La.   136,646,400
        '75   .70 (block)   .17 (ea.)

B. American Revolution Bicentennial. First stamp in a series planned for issuance through 1976. Shown: official emblem of the Bicentennial Commission.
Washington, D.C.   136,435,000
        '75   .13

C. Emily Dickinson (1830 - 86), poet and author of over 1700 lyrics, many of which rank among the finest in American literature. A spinster, she lived in seclusion in her home in Amherst, Massachusetts. The bulk of her poetry was discovered after her death. *American Poet Series.*
Amherst, Mass.   134,245,000
        '75   .13

D. San Juan, 450th anniversary. The city is the capital of Puerto Rico. Shown: the sentry box of El Morro, a fortress built by Spain in the 16th century.
San Juan, P.R.   139,730,000
        '75   .13

E. 7/1/71

F. 8/2/71

G. 10/29/71

E. United States Postal Service. The stamp was issued on July 1, which marked the official inception of the U.S.P.S. Shown: Postal Service emblem.
All post offices 342,610,000
'75 .11

F. United States Space Achievements, a tribute to a decade of historic exploration in which the United States landed men upon the moon. The two stamps are usually collected as a pair. Shown (left to right): landing craft on the moon and the lunar rover, a jeeplike buggy first used by the Apollo 15 astronauts to explore the moon. David Scott, a member of the crew of Apollo 15, announced the release of these stamps on the moon on August 2, 1971. At the same time he cancelled an envelope bearing the two stamps.
Kennedy Space Center, Fla.; Houston, Tex.; Huntsville, Ala. 175,295,000
'75 .40 (pair) .20 (ea.)

G. Historic Preservation. Usually collected as a block of four, these stamps call attention to the work of the National Trust for Historic Preservation. Shown: Decatur House, a mansion built in 1819 by Commodore Stephen Decatur (see p. 73) on Lafayette Square in Washington, D.C.; the Charles W. Morgan, last of the 19th century whaling ships, now moored in Mystic, Connecticut; San Xavier del Bac Mission, near Tucson, Arizona, consecrated in 1797 and considered the finest surviving colonial mission in the United States; and a San Francisco cable car, a form of transportation first used in 1873 and still operational on a curtailed 10-mile route.
San Diego, Calif. 164,272,000
'75 .70 (block) .18 (ea.)

A. John Sloan (1871 - 1951), American artist noted for city subjects, landscapes, and figures. He was also a teacher and was associated with the Art Students League from 1916 to 1938. His students included Alexander Calder and David Smith. *American Painting Series.*
Lock Haven, Pa.   141,355,000
'75   .13

B. CARE (Cooperative of American Relief Everywhere), a humanitarian project that provides assistance to people all over the globe. The project was started by the United States and Canada in 1946.
New York, N.Y.   127,340,000
'75   .13

C. Drug Abuse Prevention Week. Shown: a solitary figure against a blue - green background.
Dallas, Tex.   132,205,000
'75   .13

D. Christmas. Shown: *The Adoration of the Shepherds* by Giorgione (National Gallery of Art, Washington, D.C.). The painting was done on wood about 1510 by the Venetian artist (c. 1478 - 1510) who studied under Giovanni Bellini with Titian.
Washington, D.C.   1,074,280,000
'75   .13

E. Christmas. Shown: *Partridge in a Pear Tree* by Jamie Wyeth, son of artist Andrew Wyeth and grandson of illustrator N. C. Wyeth. The painting is based upon the first line of the folk carol "Twelve Days of Christmas."
Washington, D.C.   979,520,000
'75   .13

F. Mail Order Business, 100th anniversary. The stamp was issued in Chicago, where the industry began in 1872 when Aaron Montgomery Ward distributed a one - page catalogue offering 163 items for sale.
Chicago, Ill.   184,355,000
'75   .12

A. *8/2/71*

B. 10/27/71

John Sloan's dramatic rendering of a ferry ride between Manhattan Island and Jersey City is the subject of *Wake of the Ferry,* which is reproduced on this stamp. The painting was completed in 1907 (Phillips Collection, Washington, D.C.).

C. 10/4/71

D. *11/10/71*

G. Sidney Lanier (1842 - 81), poet, Confederate soldier, and flutist (Peabody Orchestra of Baltimore). His works include "The Symphony" and "A Ballad of Trees and the Master". *American Poet Series.*
Macon, Ga.   137,355,000
'75   .13

H. Benjamin Franklin. Regular issue.
Philadelphia, Pa.   '75   .10

— 168 —

E. 11/10/71

F. *9/27/72*

G. 2/3/72

This stamp portrays a 19th century country store - post office. The design was based on the Headsville, West Virginia post office now in the National Museum of History and Technology, Smithsonian Institution, Washington, D.C. The post office is operational and has its own cancellation.

H. 10/20/72

J. 2/11/72

I. 4/24/72

K. 3/18/72

I. Fiorello La Guardia (1882 - 1947), Congressman and Mayor of New York City (1934 - 45). As mayor he balanced the city budget, reorganized the machinery of city government, and was involved with slum clearance and construction projects. Regular issue.
New York, N.Y.   '75   .20

J. Peace Corps, volunteer aid program for developing nations. Shown: poster design by David Battle.
Washington, D.C.   148,650,000
                          '75   .13

K. Family Planning focuses attention on an area of major concern in much of the world.
New York, N.Y.   153,025,000
                          '75   .12

NATIONAL PARKS CENTENNIAL ISSUE

A. 4/5/72

B. 3/1/72

C. 6/26/72

D. 7/28/72

National Parks Centennial Issue, 100th anniversary of Yellowstone National Park, Wyoming. The park, oldest and largest of its kind in the world, was created in 1872 as a result of the Yellowstone Act, which forbade the destruction of its wilderness and set it aside for public use.
The issue consists of eight stamps, one for air mail use (see p. 196). The designs portray the great diversity of the country's 35 national parks, ten of which were shown on a set of stamps issued in 1934 (see pp. 68-69). Parks honored here include:

A. Cape Hatteras National Seashore, 45 square miles of beachland stretching across North Carolina's barrier islands in the Atlantic Ocean. Four stamps, usually collected as a block, make up the total design. Shown (clockwise from upper left): ship's hull in the Atlantic, Cape Hatteras lighthouse, two gulls on driftwood, and three gulls on driftwood.
Hatteras, N.C.   172,730,000
'75 .20 (block) .05 (ea.)

B. Yellowstone, a 2,221,773-acre tract which contains more geysers than the rest of the world combined. Shown: Old Faithful, the park's most reliable geyser, from a combination of photographs and sketches made in 1971 by Robert Handville while he was chairman of Artists in the Park.
Yellowstone Natl. Park, Wyo.; Washington, D.C.   164,096,000
'75 .13

C. Wolf Trap Farm, a 118-acre cultural park with music theater in Virginia.
Vienna, Va.   104,000,000
'75 .11

D. Mt. McKinley, 3,030 square miles in Alaska. The park's namesake is the highest peak (20,320 ft.) in North America.
Mt. McKinley National Park, Alaska 53,920,000
'75 .25

E. 8/17/72

F. 8/17/72

G. 8/17/72

H. *10/13/72*

I. 9/15/72

Olympic Games Issue, a salute to the 11th Winter Olympics, held at Sapporo, Japan, February 3 - 13, and the 20th Summer Olympics, held at Munich, Germany, August 26 - September 11, 1972. Athletes from 35 countries took part in the winter events, in which 16 - year-old Anne Henning of the United States was the youngest person to receive a gold medal (500-meter speed skating). At the summer games, in which 124 countries participated,

American Mark Spitz won seven gold medals in swimming.

The issue consists of four stamps, one for use on air mail (see p. 196). The stamp designs are based on the official Olympic emblems for the sports portrayed. Shown:

E. Cycling
Washington, D.C. 67,000,000
'75 .11

F. Bobsled Racing
Washington, D.C. 179,675,000
'75 .12

G. Footracing
Washington, D.C. 46,260,000
'75 .22

H. Tom Sawyer, fictional folk hero created by Mark Twain in the classic book of the same name. The book, written in 1876, describes the adventures of a boy who lived along the Mississippi River about 1845. Shown: the famous fence whitewashing scene from a painting by Norman Rockwell created for a 1936 edition of *The Adventures of*

Tom Sawyer (Heritage Press). *American Folklore Series.*
Hannibal, Mo. 162,789,000
'75 .12

I. Parent Teacher Association, 75th anniversary. The PTA strives to improve the quality of education and to promote the welfare of young people.
San Francisco, Calif.
178,890,000 '75 .12

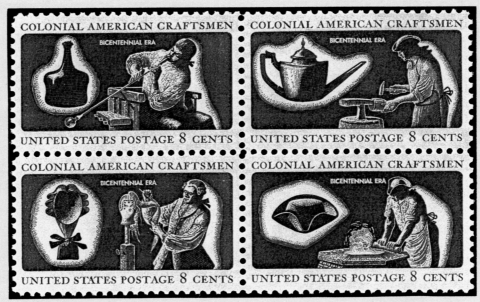

A. 7/4/72

B. 10/9/72

C. 11/9/72

D. 11/9/72

A. *American Revolution Bicentennial Series,* Colonial American Craftsmen. Usually collected in blocks of four. These four stamps — a tribute to the role of the craftsman in the growth of the Thirteen Colonies — were issued in Williamsburg, the restored colonial city which was once the capital of Virginia. Shown (clockwise from upper left): a glassmaker, a silversmith, a hatter, and a wigmaker. American silversmithing had its birth in Boston, where patriot Paul Revere was one of its most famous exponents. The other colonial crafts were first developed in Virginia.
Williamsburg, Va. 201,890,000
    '75 .50 (block) .13 (ea.)

B. American Osteopathic Association, 75th anniversary. Osteopathic medicine is a healing art that was pioneered by Dr. Andrew Still, a Civil War physician who derived the principles of osteopathic medicine from his studies of anatomy.

Miami, Fla. 161,325,000
    '75 .12

C. Christmas. Shown: two angels, a detail from *Mary, Queen of Heaven* by an unknown artist of the 15th century who is identified as the Master of the St. Lucy Legend (National Gallery of Art, Washington, D.C.).
Washington, D.C.   '75 .12

D. Christmas. Shown: Santa Claus, whose origin can be traced to St. Nicholas, a 4th century Bishop of Myra in Asia Minor. St. Nicholas, known as the Wonder Worker, was the patron saint of schoolchildren. The custom of exchanging gifts on his feast day was brought to America by the Dutch, who called him Sinter Claes. When the Dutch colony of New Amsterdam was taken by the English and renamed New York he became Santa Claus.
Washington, D.C.   '75 .12
2,000,000,000 **(C & D)**

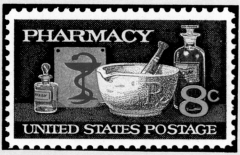

E. 11/10/72

F. 11/17/72

G. 9/20/72

E. American Pharmaceutical Association, 120th anniversary. Shown: mortar and pestle with familiar Rx, two medicine bottles, and the symbol of Hygeia, who was the Greek goddess of health, represented by a snake.
Cincinnati, Ohio   165,895,000
'75   .12

F. Stamp Collecting. Issued during the 125th year of U.S. postage stamps. Shown: one of the most common tools of the stamp collector, a magnifying glass, and a reproduction of the first U.S. stamp, issued in 1847 (see p. 26).
New York, N.Y.   165,476,000
'75   .12

G. *Wildlife Conservation Series,* 1972. Usually collected in blocks of four. Shown: four types of wildlife indigenous to different parts of the nation — the fur seal, the cardinal, the bighorn sheep, and the brown pelican. The Alaskan fur seal migrates in the winter as far south as the northern coast of California. In the spring it returns to its breeding grounds on the Pribilof Islands. The cardinal or redbird is a member of the finch family and is most numerous in the East. The bighorn or Rocky Mountain sheep is found in Canada, Alaska, and the western part of the United States. The pelican is a native of the Atlantic seaboard. It has a large pouch under its beak in which it holds its fish.
Warm Springs, Ore. 198,364,800
'75   .50 (block)   .13 (ea.)

A. Nicolaus Copernicus (1473 - 1543), Polish astronomer whose revolutionary work *Concerning the Revolutions of the Heavenly Spheres* set forth the theory that the earth revolves around the sun. Until this book was published in 1543, most people accepted the Ptolemaic concept of astronomy, which stated that the earth was the center of the universe. Shown: Copernicus, after an 18th century engraving.
Washington, D.C.   160,000,000
'75   .11

B. Lyndon B. Johnson (1908 - 73), 36th president (1963 - 69). Johnson, who became president following the assassination of John F. Kennedy, won legislative approval for more social innovations in a single term than did any other 20th century president. Shown: portrait after a painting by Elizabeth Shoumatoff, said to be Mr. Johnson's favorite likeness of himself (The White House, Washington, D.C.).
Austin, Tex.   150,000,000
'75   .11

C. Harry S. Truman (1884 - 1972), 33rd president (1945 - 53). Truman was thrust into office upon the sudden death of Franklin D. Roosevelt. His immediate and momentous decisions in the closing days of World War II won him respect throughout the world. Shown: a favorite portrait of Mr. Truman by Kansas City photographer Leo Stern.
Independence, Mo.   163,000,000
'75   .11

D. Amadeo P. Giannini (1870 - 1949), who developed the Bank of America into the world's largest private bank and opened the bank door to the common man. Regular issue.
San Mateo, Calif.   '75   .28

E. Special Stamp for Someone Special, designed for use on mail that expresses special sentiments. Shown: *Love* by pop sculptor

A. *4/23/73*

B. *8/27/73*

C. 5/8/73

D. 6/27/73

E. 1/26/73

Robert Indiana.
Philadelphia, Pa.   328,580,000
'75   .11

F. Printer and Patriots Examining a Pamphlet.

Portland, Ore.   165,000,000
'75   .11

G. Posting a Broadside.
Atlantic City, N.J.   140,000,000
'75   .11

H. Postrider.
Rochester, N.Y.   141,000,000
'75   .11

I. Drummer.
New Orleans, La.   150,000,000
'75   .11

1973 AMERICAN REVOLUTION BICENTENNIAL ISSUES

Communications and the Spirit of Independence

F. 2/16/73

G. 4/27/73

H. 6/22/73

I. 9/28/73

J. 7/4/73

J. Boston Tea Party, 200th anniversary. This "party", a form of retaliation by American colonists against the British Tea Act of 1773, took place on the night of December 16. Colonial citizens disguised as Mohawk Indians boarded English ships in the Boston harbor and dumped 342 chests of tea into the water. The four stamps, usually collected in a block, combine to make a complete design. Shown (clockwise from upper left): a British merchantman, a British three-master, boat and dock, and boats and ship's hull.
Boston, Mass.   200,000,000
'75   .48 (block)   .12 (ea.)

Progress in Electronics, 11th anniversary of the first transatlantic television transmission via Telstar satellite on July 10, 1962. The transmission, a picture of a waving American flag, was relayed from an earth station at Andover, Maine to France and England.

The issue consists of four stamps, one for use on air mail (see p. 196). Each of the designs is related to a milestone in the history of electronic communications. Shown:

A. Spark coil and gap used by Guglielmo Marconi in 1901 to receive the first wireless transmission sent across the Atlantic Ocean. New York, N.Y.   55,000,000
'75   .10

B. Printed electronic circuit board and transistors. Both advances were essential to the development of the computer and space - age technology. New York, N.Y.   150,000,000
'75   .11

C. Early microphone, gooseneck speaker, and vacuum radio tube, with modern television camera tube. New York, N.Y.   40,000,000
'75   .22

Postal People Issue, a salute to the nation's 700,000 postal workers. Usually collected in strips of ten.

The stamps portray various activities performed by postal workers. These activities are described by printed texts which appear underneath the gum on the back side of each stamp. Designs and inscriptions are as follows:

D. Counter clerk — "Nearly 27 billion U.S. stamps are sold yearly to carry your letters to every corner of the world."

E. Collecting mail — "Mail is picked up from nearly a third of a million local collection boxes, as well as your mailbox."

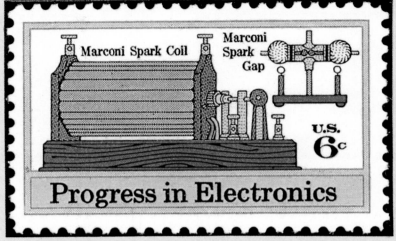
A. *7/10/73*

B. 7/10/73

C. *7/10/73*

F. Letter facing — "More than 87 billion letters and packages are handled yearly — almost 300 million every delivery day."

G. Sorting parcels — "The People in your Postal Service handle and deliver more than 500 million packages yearly."

H. Cancelling mail — "Thousands of machines, buildings, and vehicles must be operated and maintained to keep your mail moving."

D. 4/30/73   E. 4/30/73   F. 4/30/73   G. 4/30/73

H. 4/30/73   I. 4/30/73   J. 4/30/73   K. 4/30/73

L. 4/30/73   M. 4/30/73

Our customers include 54 million urban and 12 million rural families, plus 9 million businesses.

People Serving You

Employees cover 4 million miles each delivery day to bring mail to your home or business.

People Serving You

L. (Gummed Side)   M. (Gummed Side)

I. Manual routing — "The skill of sorting mail manually is still vital to delivery of your mail."

J. Electronic routing —

"Employees use modern, high-speed equipment to sort and process huge volumes of mail in central locations."

K. Loading mail on truck —

"Thirteen billion pounds of mail are handled yearly by postal employees as they speed your letters and packages."

L. City carrier — (text

shown above).

M. Rural delivery — (text shown above).

All post offices
'75 1.15 (strip) .12 (ea.)

A. 2/28/73

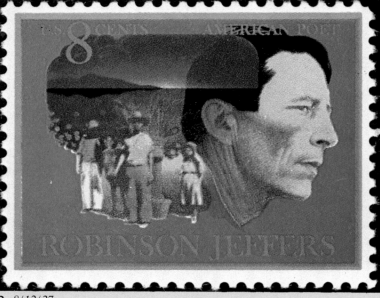

B. *8/13/37*

C. 9/10/73

D. 9/20/73

A. George Gershwin (1898 - 1937), composer who used the elements of jazz to create "Swanee", *Rhapsody in Blue, An American in Paris,* and *Of Thee I Sing.* Shown: portrait of Gershwin with characters from his folk opera, *Porgy and Bess.* The opera, which takes place in Catfish Row, Charleston, South Carolina, was written for black singers. It includes "Summertime", "I Got Plenty o' Nuttin", and other songs.
Beverly Hills, Calif.   '75   .12

B. Robinson Jeffers (1887 - 1962), controversial poet of the post - World War I period whose works include *Tamar and Other Poems, Thurso's Landing,* and a masterful adaptation of Euripides' *Medea.* Shown: portrait of Jeffers with a burro and residents of the Big Sur area in California, where he lived and worked.
Carmel, Calif.   '75   .12

C. Henry Ossawa Tanner (1859 - 1937), 19th century

black artist best remembered for religious works and landscapes. He spent most of his life in France, where he was made a Chevalier of the Legion of Honor. *The Banjo Lesson, Daniel in the Lion's Den,* and *The Raising of Lazarus* are among his most famous paintings. Shown: likeness of Tanner, based upon a portrait by Thomas Eakins, under whom he studied; and an artist's palette.
Pittsburgh, Pa.   '75   .12

D. Willa Cather (1873 - 1947), American novelist who recaptured in her books the spirit of the pioneers. She spent her childhood in Red Cloud, Nebraska, where she saw how people struggled to adapt themselves to prairie life. From her experiences she gathered the material for *O Pioneers!* and *My Antonia.* She received a Pulitzer Prize for *One of Ours* in 1923. Shown: portrait of Miss Cather with pioneers and a covered wagon.
Red Cloud, Nebr.   '75   .12

E. 12/14/73

F. 12/8/73

G. *11/7/73*

H. 11/7/73

I. 10/5/73

J. 1/4/74

K. 4/18/74

E. Jefferson Memorial, with inscription "We hold these truths…" from the Declaration of Independence, and facsimile signature of Thomas Jefferson. Regular issue. Also issued in coils and booklets.
Washington, D.C.   '75 .15

F. Crossed flags, showing the current 50-star flag and the 13-star flag of the revolutionary era. Regular issue. Also issued in coils.
San Francisco, Calif. '75 .15

G. Christmas. Shown: *The Small Cowper Madonna,* painted by Italian master Raphael about 1505, in Florence (National Gallery of Art, Washington, D.C.).
Washington, D.C.   '75 .12

H. Christmas. Shown: an old-fashioned Christmas tree, designed by Dolli Tingle. First U.S. stamp designed in needlepoint.
Washington, D.C.   '75 .12

I. Rural America, 100th anniversary of the introduction of Angus cattle into the United States from Scotland, where the breed was developed. First in a series of three stamps. Shown: angus and longhorn cattle on the prairie.
St. Joseph, Mo.   '75 .12

J. Zip Code, after a multicolor poster by Randall McDougall. The design shows different means of transport used to move the mails. Regular issue.
Washington, D.C.   '75 .15

K. Expo '74, issued for the first world's fair to have an ecology theme, "Preserve the Environment". The fair was held in Spokane, Washington, from May 4 to November 4, 1974. Shown: original design by Peter Max, showing his "Cosmic Jumper" running through the Max Universe. The "Smiling Sage", a profile of a woman's head, appears at the right.
Spokane, Wash.   '75 .15

A. *6/6/74*

B. *6/6/74*

Universal Postal Union Centennial Issue. Founded on October 9, 1874, at Berne, Switzerland, the UPU was organized to bring order to international mail delivery. Before it was formed a host of different, often ineffective, treaties governed mail delivery among the nations of the world. In 1863, due to the efforts of U.S. Postmaster General Montgomery Blair, a conference was held in Paris to discuss the problem. Five years later, Heinrich von Stephan of the North German Postal Confederation offered a plan for a universal postal union. In 1874, delegates from 22 countries signed the document that brought the General Postal Union, now the UPU, into existence. Today, some 140 nations belong to the organization, which has helped to standardize mail delivery throughout the world (see p. 191). The eight U.S. commemoratives, usually collected in a block, stress the theme of letter-writing. All the stamps portray famous works of art; four of them carry the words "Letters mingle souls" from *Verse Letter to Sir Henry Wotton* by the English metaphysical poet, John Donne. The designs portray:

A. *Mrs. John Douglas,* painted by English artist Thomas Gainsborough in 1784 (National Trust of England).

Universal
Postal Union
1874-1974   Liotard
10c US

C. 6/6/74

Letters
mingle souls   Peto
Donne
10c US

D. 6/6/74

Letters
mingle souls   Raphael
Donne
10c US

E. 6/6/74

Universal   Hokusai
Postal Union
1874-1974
10c US

F. 6/6/74

Universal   Chardin
Postal Union
1874-1974
10c US

G. 6/6/74

Letters   Terborch
mingle souls
Donne
10c US

H. 6/6/74

B. *Don Antonio Noriega,* painted by Spanish artist Francisco de Goya in 1801 (National Gallery of Art, Washington, D.C.).

C. *La Belle Liseuse* (The Lovely Reader), painted by Swiss artist Jean Etienne Liotard in 1746 (Rijks Museum, Amsterdam, The Netherlands).

D. *Old Scraps* (Old Letter Rack), painted by American artist John Frederick Peto in 1894 (Museum of Modern Art, New York, New York).

E. Portrait of Michelangelo: a detail from *The School of Athens,* painted in 1509 by Raphael for the Stanza della Segnatura in the Vatican. The painting, a fresco, was commissioned by Pope Julius II.

F. *Five Feminine Virtues,* a hanging scroll executed c. 1811 by Japanese Ukiyo-e artist Katsushika Hokusai (Seattle Art Museum, Washington).

G. *Enfant au Toton* (Young Boy with a Top), painted by French artist Jean-Baptiste-Simeon Chardin in 1738 (Louvre Museum, Paris, France).

H. *Briefschreiberin* (Lady Writing a Letter), painted by Dutch artist Gerard Terborch c. 1654 (Maritshuis, The Hague, The Netherlands).
Washington, D.C.
   '75   1.55 (block)   .15 (ea.)

A. 6/13/74

B. 3/11/74

C. 5/4/74

A. Mineral Heritage. Usually collected in blocks of four, these stamps can be rotated to form a nearly perfect diamond. They were issued at the opening of the National Gem and Mineral Show.
Lincoln, Nebr.
    '75 .65 (block) .15 (ea.)

B. Veterans of Foreign Wars, a tribute to the veterans of the Spanish - American and all other foreign wars. Their official organization has over over 1.8 million members.
Washington, D.C.   '75 .15

C. Horse Racing. Issued in connection with the 100th running of the Kentucky Derby.
Louisville, Ky.   '75 .15

D. Elizabeth Blackwell (1821 - 1910), first woman physician in the United States. She was refused admission to medical school until Geneva College (now Hobart College) accepted her. In 1849 she graduated at the head of her class. During her career, she lectured and wrote in

England and America and established an infirmary in New York which trained women to practice medicine. Regular issue.
Geneva, N.Y.   '75 .24

E. Robert Frost (1874 - 1963), Yankee poet who used down - to - earth, New England language to express universal values. He won four Pulitzer Prizes and was associated with many leading universities, among them, Harvard, Dartmouth, and the University of Michigan.

In the Clearing, West - running Brook, and *New Hampshire* are among his best known books of verse. *American Poet Series.*
Derry, N.H.   '75 .15

F. Skylab, first anniversary of the launch of Skylab 1 on May 14, 1973. The Skylab flights of 1973 and 1974 marked a new phase in the U.S. space program. Orbiting the earth in a huge workshop, astronauts conducted scientific

D. 1/23/74

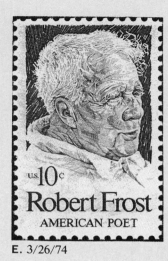

E. 3/26/74

F. 5/14/74

G. 6/15/74

H. 7/4/74

experiments and collected information that added to man's knowledge of his planet. Shown: the two-man space walk of Skylab 2 that freed a jammed solar panel. Houston, Tex. '75 .15

G. Fort Harrod, first permanent settlement in Kentucky. Named for its founder, James Harrod, this stockade was built in 1774. It was the site of the first school, the first physician's office, and the first court in Kentucky. Shown: settlers in ox-drawn wagons approaching the fort. Harrodsburg, Ky. '75 .15

H. Continental Congress, 200th anniversary. Usually collected in blocks of four. On September 5, 1774, 44 delegates from all the colonies save Georgia met for the first time in a unified assembly, the First Continental Congress. The meeting, held in Carpenters' Hall, Philadelphia, was spurred by Britain's passage of the Intolerable Acts and the closing of the Boston port. Meeting in closed session, the delegates condemned taxation without representation and other British acts. They also prepared a petition to the king, which read in part: "Had our Creator been pleased to give us existence in a land of slavery, the sense of our condition might have been mitigated by ignorance and habit. But... we were born the heirs of freedom..." The petition also included the words, "We ask but for peace, liberty, and safety." Negotiation by diplomacy, was, however, almost at an end. Just a few months later, the guns of war were heard at Lexington and Concord, and when the Second Continental Congress met in Philadelphia the colonies declared their independence. *American Revolution Bicentennial Series.* Philadelphia, Pa. '75 .65 (block) .15 (ea.)

AIR MAIL POSTAGE

B. 7/11/18

A. 12/10/18

C. 5/13/18

D. *5/14/18*

E. 8/15/23

F. 8/17/23

G. 8/21/23

When the United States inaugurated air mail service on May 15, 1918, special stamps were issued to indicate the prepayment of mail carried by plane. The initial route used army airplanes and pilots to link Washington, D.C. and New York City, via Philadelphia. The rate was 24c an ounce, including special delivery to the addressee. This rate was reduced to 16c on July 15, and then to 6c, without special delivery, on December 15. Shown:

A. Army Curtiss biplane, called the "Jenny" because the official designation began with the letters JN.

Washington, D.C.   3,395,854
'25	.12	'55	2.25
'35	.60	'65	4.10
'45	1.10	'75	25.00

B. Army Curtiss "Jenny".

Washington, D.C.   3,793,887
'25	.20	'55	5.50
'35	2.15	'65	8.00
'45	4.80	'75	40.00

C. Army Curtiss "Jenny".

Washington, D.C.   2,134,888
'25	.35	'55	3.95
'35	.95	'65	7.25
'45	2.00	'75	38.50

D. Army Curtiss "Jenny", center inverted. William T. Robey experienced the stamp collector's dream when he received a full sheet of these stamps from a window clerk at a Washington, D.C. post office on May 14, 1918. Resisting efforts of postal inspectors to get him to return the sheet, he sold it one week later to Eugene Klein for $15,000.00. Klein then sold it to Colonel E.H.R. Green for $20,000.00. Green broke up the sheet into blocks and singles, which periodically appear at auction. In 1974, a very fine copy sold for $47,000.00.

Washington, D.C.   100
'25	750.00	'55	4,000.00
'35	3,300.00	'65	12,500.00
'45	3,500.00	'75	47,000.00

E-G. When night-flying service was begun between New York and San Francisco,

— 184 —

H. 2/13/26

I. 9/18/26

J. 1/25/27

K. *6/18/27*

new stamps were released. The service had been planned for 1923, but did not start until July 1, 1924. Shown:

E. Propeller on plane radiator.
Washington, D.C.   6,414,576

'25	.12	'55	1.00
'35	.22	'65	1.85
'45	.65	'75	9.75

F. Air mail service insignia.
Washington, D.C.   5,309,275

'25	.20	'55	4.25
'35	1.05	'65	6.75
'45	2.45	'75	37.50

G. De Havilland biplane.
Washington, D.C.   5,285,775

'25	.30	'55	5.50
'35	1.10	'65	8.75
'45	2.65	'75	40.00

H. Mail planes and U.S. map. Issue required by new rates.
Washington, D.C.; Detroit, Mich.; Dearborn, Mich.; Chicago, Ill.; Cleveland, Ohio   42,092,800

'35	.15	'65	.25
'45	.15	'75	1.15
'55	.16		

I. Mail planes and U.S. map.
Washington, D.C.   15,597,307

'35	.20	'65	.40
'45	.22	'75	1.35
'55	.27		

J. Mail planes and U.S. map.
New York, N.Y. and
Washington, D.C.   17,616,350

'35	.25	'65	.70
'45	.27	'75	3.25
'55	.40		

K. Charles A. Lindbergh, a tribute to the former air mail pilot who made the first nonstop solo flight from New York to Paris on May 20 - 21, 1927. Also issued in booklets. Shown: Lindbergh's plane, the *Spirit of St. Louis,* which is on exhibit at the Smithsonian Institution, Washington, D.C. A map of Lindbergh's route is also shown.

Washington, D.C.; Detroit, Mich.; St. Louis, Missouri; Little Falls, Minn.   20,379,179

'35	.16	'65	.55
'45	.20	'75	2.00
'55	.40		

GRAF ZEPPELIN ISSUE

A. 4/19/30

B. 4/19/30

C. 4/19/30

In 1930, three stamps were released for use on mail carried by the *Graf Zeppelin* on its first flight to the Americas (May - June). The huge dirigible went from Germany to Spain, and then to Brazil and the United States. It returned to Germany via Spain.

Completed in 1928, the *Graf Zeppelin* saw nine years of continuous service before it was decommissioned in 1937.

The German airship made 590 flights, including 144 ocean crossings, and covered more than one million miles. It carried over 13,000 passengers and 235,300 pounds of mail and freight.

The *Graf Zeppelin* stamps were sold to the general public at a limited number of post offices from April 21 to June 7, 1930. Their limited availability accounts in part for what were considered

dissatisfying sales. Of the more than one million copies of each denomination that were printed, 90 percent were destroyed after the stamps were withdrawn from sale. Quantities listed below reflect the number of stamps actually sold. Shown:

A. *Graf Zeppelin* crossing the Atlantic Ocean.
Washington, D.C.   93,536
 '35   2.50   '65   30.00
 '45   10.00   '75   130.00
 '55   17.00

B. *Graf Zeppelin* between the eastern and western hemispheres.
Washington, D.C.   72,428
 '35   6.00   '65   61.00
 '45   23.50   '75   225.00
 '55   31.50

C. *Graf Zeppelin* passing in front of globe.
Washington, D.C.   61,296
 '35   9.50   '65   95.00
 '45   30.50   '75   375.00
 '55   54.00

D. 7/25/28

E. 2/10/30

F. 9/26/32

G. 7/1/34

H. 5/16/39

D. Airplane and beacon.
Airplane pilots of the 1920s depended exclusively on visual landmarks to determine their location during the progress of their flights. The beacon light was one of the first navigational aids adapted for night fliers. Shown: beacon light on Sherman Hill, Wyoming, a guide to pilots flying the night mail across the Rocky Mountains.
Washington, D.C.   106,887,675

'35	.08	'65	.32
'45	.12	'75	1.35
'55	.22		

E. Winged globe, insignia of the air mail pilot. Two types of this stamp were issued. The first, printed on flatbed presses, was perforated 11. The second, printed on the rotary press, was perforated 10½ by 11 and was a full millimeter wider than the flat press version. The value of the earlier, flat press type (shown) is about double that of the later, rotary press type.
Washington, D.C.   97,641,200

'35	.10	'65	.90
'45	.15	'75	4.75
'55	.40		

F. Winged globe, increased rate.
Washington, D.C.   76,648,803

'35	.12	'65	.25
'45	.12	'75	.65
'55	.18		

G. Winged globe, reduced rate.

Baltimore, Md. and
New York, N.Y.   302,205,100

'35	.08	'65	.25
'45	.12	'75	.60
'55	.24		

H. Winged globe, inauguration of transatlantic air mail service. The first regularly scheduled flight for Europe left Port Washington, Long Island, on May 20, 1939.
New York, N.Y.   19,768,150

| '45 | .45 | '65 | 1.30 |
| '55 | 1.15 | '75 | 4.75 |

A. Century of Progress Exposition, for use on mail carried by the *Graf Zeppelin* on its flight to the Chicago World's Fair in October 1933. The German dirigible stopped at Miami, Florida, and Akron, Ohio, before completing its journey to Chicago. The stamp was sold only in these cities and in New York City. Although it remained on sale at the Philatelic Sales Agency until 1935, more than 90 percent of the 3,260,000 stamps printed were eventually destroyed. Shown: the *Graf Zeppelin* over the Atlantic; its hangar at Friedrichshafen, Germany; and the Federal Building at the Chicago fair.

New York, N.Y. 324,070

'35	.70	'65	9.00
'45	3.25	'75	45.00
'55	6.40		

B. National Air Mail Week, May 15-21, 1938, marked the 20th anniversary of government air mail service in the United States. Official cachets were prepared for use at Dayton, Ohio, home of the Wright brothers, and St. Petersburg, Florida, origin of the first passenger flight. In addition, the Post Office Department authorized special commemorative cachets for any town from which any aviator carried mail to the nearest regular air mail stop. Shown: eagle design inspired by President F.D. Roosevelt's suggestion and sketch proposing issuance of a new air mail stamp on the occasion.

Washington, D.C.;
Dayton, Ohio;
St. Petersburg, Fla. 349,946,500

| '45 | .10 | '65 | .19 |
| '55 | .16 | '75 | .30 |

C-E. Trans-Pacific air mail, for service to Hawaii, Guam, the Philippines, and eventually to China. The first contract flight across the Pacific took place in November 1935. Shown:

C. The *China Clipper.*
Washington, D.C. 10,205,400

| '45 | .30 | '65 | .50 |
| '55 | .36 | '75 | 1.00 |

A. 10/2/33

B. 5/14/38

C. 11/22/35

D. 2/15/37

E. 2/15/37

D. The *China Clipper.*
Washington, D.C. 12,794,600

| '45 | .25 | '65 | .64 |
| '55 | .50 | '75 | 3.00 |

E. The *China Clipper.*
Washington, D.C. 9,285,300

| '45 | .60 | '65 | 1.10 |
| '55 | .77 | '75 | 4.50 |

F. Twin-motored transport. Also issued in booklets.
Washington, D.C. 4,746,527,700

| '45 | .08 | '65 | .09 |
| '55 | .09 | '75 | .12 |

G. Twin-motored transport.
Washington, D.C. 1,744,876,650

| '45 | .10 | '65 | .12 |
| '55 | .12 | '75 | .20 |

F. 6/25/41

G. 3/21/44

H. 8/15/41

I. 8/19/41

J. 8/27/41

K. 9/25/41

L. 10/29/41

H. Twin - motored transport.
Atlantic City, N.J. 67,117,400

'45	.12	'65	.22
'55	.16	'75	.45

I. Twin - motored transport.

Baltimore, Md. 78,434,800

'45	.18	'65	.44
'55	.30	'75	.90

J. Twin - motored transport.
Philadelphia, Pa. 42,359,850

'45	.24	'65	.40
'55	.35	'75	.85

K. Twin - motored transport.
Kansas City, Mo. 59,880,850

'45	.35	'65	.55
'55	.45	'75	1.10

L. Twin - motored transport.
St. Louis, Mo. 11,160,600

'45	.58	'65	1.10
'55	.75	'75	3.50

Note: the design of **F-L** was influenced by a model airplane owned by the post office.

A. 9/25/46

B. 8/30/47

C. 8/20/47

D. 7/30/47

E. 3/26/47

F. 7/31/48

G. 5/11/49

A. DC-4 Skymaster. Issued in conjunction with the inauguration of the first "flying mail car", an airborne postal sorting facility.
Washington, D.C. 864,753,100
'55 .08 '65 .08 '75 .10

B. Pan American Union Building. Primarily for use on mail to South and Central America.
Washington, D.C. 207,976,550
'55 .13 '65 .16 '75 .30

C. New York Harbor and Skyline. For use on mail to Western Europe and North Africa.
New York, N.Y. 756,186,350
'55 .20 '65 .20 '75 .35

D. San Francisco-Oakland Bay Bridge. For use on mail to the Pacific Islands, Asia, and Central and South Africa.
San Francisco, Calif.
132,956,100
'55 .32 '65 .35 '75 .80

E. DC-4 Skymaster. Also issued in coils, which are about ten times more valuable than the ordinary stamp.
Washington, D.C. 971,903,700
'55 .08 '65 .08 '75 .10

F. City of New York, 50th anniversary. The five boroughs were consolidated in 1898.
New York, N.Y. 38,449,100
'55 .10 '65 .10 '75 .15

G. Alexandria, Virginia, 200th anniversary. The city of Alexandria was founded in 1749. Shown: seal of the city; Carlyle House, home of John Carlyle, one of the city's founders; and Gadsby's Tavern, frequented by such notables as John Paul Jones and George Washington.
Alexandria, Va. 75,085,000
'55 .09 '65 .09 '75 .13

H. *12/17/49*

I. 1/18/49

J. 11/18/49

K. 11/30/49

L. 10/7/49

H. Wright brothers, 46th anniversary of the first successful sustained flight in a motor-powered airplane. On December 17, 1903, Orville Wright (1871-1948) took the *Kitty Hawk* up for 12 seconds and covered 120 feet. On the same day, his brother Wilbur Wright (1867-1912) kept the plane aloft for 59 seconds and flew 852 feet. The flights took place at Kill Devil Hill, near Kitty Hawk, North Carolina.
Kitty Hawk, N.C. 80,405,000
'55 .09   '65 .09   '75 .12

I. DC-4 Skymaster, increased rate. Also issued in coils and booklets. The value of the coils is more than ten times that of the ordinary stamp.
Washington, D.C. 5,070,095,200
'55 .08   '65 .08   '75 .14

J-L. Universal Postal Union, 75th anniversary. Almost every member of the UPU issued one or more stamps to mark this anniversary. The three United States commemoratives were air mail stamps. It was felt that this type of postage best portrayed the advance in world communications for which the UPU stands. Shown:

J. UPU monument in Berne, Switzerland, and U.S. Post Office Department Building, Washington, D.C.
New Orleans, La. 21,061,300
'55 .15   '65 .18   '75 .30

K. World encircled by doves carrying messages.
Chicago, Ill. 36,613,100
'55 .22   '65 .27   '75 .40

L. Globe with Boeing Stratoliner.
Seattle, Wash. 16,217,000
'55 .37   '65 .40   '75 .70

A. 3/26/52

B. 5/29/53

C. 8/1/57

D. 9/3/54

E. 7/31/58

F. 1/3/59

G. 8/17/59

H. 8/27/59

A. Diamond Head, Hawaii, air parcel post rate per lb. from Hawaii to the mainland.
Honolulu, Hawaii 18,876,800
   '55 1.00   '75 3.25
   '65 1.40

B. Powered Flight, 50th anniversary, a tribute to progress in American aviation from the time of the Wright brothers.
Dayton, Ohio 78,415,000
   '55 .09   '75 .12
   '65 .10

C. United States Air Force, 50th anniversary. The Air Force dates its history from August 1, 1907, when the Aeronautical Division of the U.S. Army Signal Corps was established. Shown: B-52 Stratofortress and three F-104 Starfighters.
Washington, D.C. 63,185,000
   '65 .10   '75 .12

D. Eagle in flight, intended for use on air mail post cards.
Philadelphia, Pa. 50,483,977
   '55 .06   '75 .10
   '65 .07

E. Eagle in flight, increased rate.
Colorado Springs, Colo.
72,480,000
       '65 .08   '75 .20

F. Alaska Statehood, honoring the admission of Alaska as the 49th state. Capital, Juneau. Leading industries include: fisheries, petroleum, wood products, and tourism.
Juneau, Alaska 90,055,200
       '65 .12   '75 .18

G. Balloon Jupiter, 100th anniversary of mail-carrying flight from Lafayette to Crawfordsville, Indiana, on August 17, 1859.
Lafayette, Ind. 79,290,000
       '65 .12   '75 .18

H. Pan American Games, opening. The Third Pan American Games were held in Chicago from August 27 to September 7, 1959.
Chicago, Ill. 38,770,000
       '65 .16   '75 .35

I. 7/31/58   **J.** 8/21/59   **K.** 8/12/60

L. 11/20/59

M. 1/13/61

N. 4/22/60

O. 6/10/60

I. Jet airliner, also issued in coils and booklets. Shown: composite silhouette of elements from contemporary jet airliners.
Philadelphia, Pa. 1,326,960,000
'65   .11   '75   .16

J. Hawaii Statehood. 50th state, admitted 1959. Capital, Honolulu, on the island of Oahu. Leading industries are tourism, sugar, and pineapples. The Hawaiian islands are of volcanic origin.

Hawaii, the Big Island, has three active volcanoes: Mauna Loa, Mauna Kea, and Kilauea. Shown: Alii Warrior and map of the islands.
Honolulu, Hawaii   84,815,000
'65   .12   '75   .18

K. Jet airliner, new color. Also issued in coils and booklets. The coil varieties of **I** and **K** are valued at more than 20 times the ordinary stamps.
Arlington, Va.   1,289,460,000
'65   .09   '75   .20

L. Statue of Liberty, international air mail rate for Europe and North Africa.
New York, N.Y.   98,160,000
'65   .23   '75   .60

M. Statue of Liberty, modified design to reduce color seepage from the tablet portion to the pictorial portion of the stamp during printing.
New York, N.Y.
'65   .23   '75   .30

N. Abraham Lincoln, international air mail rate for Asia, Australia, and most of Africa. Shown: portrait and quotation from the Gettysburg Address.
San Francisco, Calif.
'65   .35   '75   .40

O. Liberty Bell, international air mail rate for the West Indies and Central and South America.
Miami, Fla.   39,960,000
'65   .16   '75 1.15

A. 6/28/61

B. 12/5/62

C. 7/12/63

D. 7/24/63

E. 5/3/63

F. 10/5/64

G. 3/30/67

H. 4/26/67

A. Liberty Bell, for use on mail to Central America and the Caribbean.
New York, N.Y.
'65 .20 '75 .30

B. Jet over Capitol. Also issued in coils and booklets. The regular stamp, overprinted with luminescent ink, was released August 1, 1963, at Dayton, Ohio, for experimental use with equipment that could sort and face mail automatically. All U.S. stamps are now overprinted or "tagged" in this manner.
Washington, D.C.
'65 .12 '75 .15

C. Bald Eagle, post card rate.
Boston, Mass.
'65 .09 '75 .15

D. Amelia Earhart (1898 - 1937), honoring the first woman to fly across the Atlantic Ocean.
Atchison, Kans. 63,890,000
'65 .12 '75 .25

E. Montgomery Blair (1813 - 83), U.S. postmaster general (1861 - 64) whose efforts led to the first International Postal conference in 1863. The meeting, held in Paris, laid the foundations for the Universal Postal Union.
Silver Spring, Md. 42,245,000
'65 .23 '75 1.10

F. Robert H. Goddard (1882 - 1945), physicist and pioneer researcher whose step - rocket theory led to the United States' successful space probes.
Roswell, N.M. 62,255,000
'65 .13 '75 .75

G. Alaska Purchase, 100th anniversary. Secretary of State William H. Seward negotiated the purchase of Alaska from Russia for $7,200,000 (about 2c an acre) in 1867.
Sitka, Alaska 64,710,000
'75 .35

H. International air mail, rate to Europe and North

I. *9/9/69*

J. *1/5/68*

K. *5/7/71*

"It has a stark beauty all its own. It's like much of the high desert of the United States. It's different, but it's very pretty out here."

The date was July 20, 1969. An astronaut named Neil A. Armstrong descended to the moon and spoke these words to his companion, Edwin Aldrin, Jr. "This is history," exclaimed Apollo 11 pilot Michael Collins from the command module *Columbia*. And it was. Two men from the planet earth had set foot on the moon for the first time.

L. 5/15/68

M. 11/22/68

N. *5/15/71*

Africa. Shown: Audubon's *Columbia Jays* (see p. 136). New York, N.Y.   165,430,000   '75   .50

I. First Man on the Moon, a tribute to man's first landing on the moon, July 20, 1969. First jumbo-size United States commemorative. The engraved master die for the stamp was carried to the lunar surface by the Apollo 11 astronauts, who also cancelled an envelope

bearing a die proof of the stamp in their space capsule. Shown: painting by Paul Calle based upon his observations of the astronauts' preparations for their journey. Washington, D.C.   146,073,600   '75   .22

J. Fifty-star runway. Also issued in coils and booklets. San Francisco, Calif.   '75   .22

K. Jet airliner. Also issued

in coils and booklets. Spokane, Wash.   '75   .15

L. Air mail, 50th anniversary. President Woodrow Wilson was among the dignitaries who watched the takeoff of one of the first regularly scheduled air mail flights on May 15, 1918. This flight, which was bound from the nation's capital to New York via Philadelphia, was never completed due to mechanical difficulties. A second flight,

which went from New York to Washington (also via Philadelphia), was successful. Shown: Army Curtiss Jenny (see p. 184). Washington, D.C.   74,180,000   '75   .30

M. International air mail, rate for Europe and North Africa. New York, N.Y.   '75   .40

N. Delta-winged jet, post card rate. Kitty Hawk, N.C.   '75   .14

A. 5/3/72

B. 5/21/71

C. 7/13/71

D. 8/17/72

E. 11/16/73

F. 7/10/73

A. National Parks Centennial Issue, a set of eight commemoratives released in 1973 (see p. 170 for the other seven). This stamp, the only air mail value in the set, honors the City of Refuge National Historical Park on the island of Hawaii. The park, an ancient sanctuary for taboo breakers and victims of war, was set aside in 1961. It is the site of the mausoleum of King Kamehameha the Great, who united the islands of Hawaii around 1800. Shown: wooden statue of one of the Ki'i, or old gods of Hawaii, in the park.
Honolulu, Hawaii   78,210,000
                    '75   .18

B. International air mail, rate for all foreign countries except Canada, Central and South America, and the Caribbean.
Washington, D.C.   49,815,000
                   '75   .30

C. Statue of Liberty, international air mail rate to Central and South America and the Caribbean.
Lakehurst, N.J.   '75   .24

D. Olympic Games Issue, a salute to the 1972 competitions (see p. 171 for the other stamps in this issue). Shown: skiing.
Washington, D.C.   92,710,000
                   '75   .16

E. Flying envelope, for use on domestic air mail. The rate also applies to Canada and Mexico. Also issued in coils and booklets.
New York, N.Y.   '75   .18

F. Progress in Electronics, a salute to technical advancements in communications (see p. 176 for the other stamps in this issue). Shown: Lee De Forest's audion and audion tube, which made radio broadcasting as we know it possible. De Forest also made significant contributions to the

G. 1/11/74

H. 1/2/74

CERTIFIED MAIL

J. 6/6/55

REGISTRY

I. 12/1/11

SPECIAL DELIVERY AIR MAIL

K. 8/30/34

L. 2/10/36

---

development of sound motion pictures, television, and facsimile transmission.
New York, N.Y.   56,000,000
'75   .16

G. Statue of Liberty, for use on mail to Latin America.
Hempstead, N.Y.   '75 .26

H. Mt. Rushmore Memorial, for use on mail to all countries other than Canada, Central and South America, and the Caribbean.
Rapid City, S.D.   '75   .36

I. Registry, the only U.S. stamp ever issued specifically to prepay the fee for registered mail. Production of the stamp was halted in 1913. Postal patrons still pay for this service, but ordinary stamps are used.
Any post office
'25 .20   '45 1.50   '65 3.60
'35 .40   '55 2.25   '75 25.00

J. Certified Mail, a special service that gives the sender a record of the mailing and delivery of first-class mail.

Unlike registered mail it does not insure against loss or damage. This was the only special stamp ever issued for this service, which is now prepaid with ordinary postage.
Washington, D.C.   54,460,300
'65 .24   '75 .33

K. Special Delivery Air Mail, a single stamp for the prepayment of both the special delivery fee and air mail postage. Shown: the

Great Seal of the United States, in a design proposed by President Franklin D. Roosevelt.
Chicago, Ill.   9,215,750
'35 .22   '55 .23   '75 .40
'45 .20   '65 .28
Note: One of the Farley special printings (see note on p. 69).

L. Special Delivery Air Mail, new color.
Washington, D.C.   72,517,850
'45 .18   '65 .22
'55 .20   '75 .30

While ordinary stamps may be used to pay for special delivery service, special stamps have been available for this purpose since 1885. Shown:

A. Mail messenger on foot. Inscription reads "Secures immediate delivery at a special delivery office."

Any post office
| '25 | 1.00 | '45 | 2.50 | '65 | 10.25 |
| '35 | 1.25 | '55 | 5.25 | '75 | 31.00 |

B. Mail messenger on foot. Inscription concludes "at any post office."

Any post office
| '25 | .30 | '45 | 1.20 | '65 | 2.80 |
| '35 | .50 | '55 | 1.25 | '75 | 9.00 |

Note: This stamp was first issued in blue on September 6, 1888. The color was changed to orange (shown) in 1893‑94 to provide more color contrast with the Columbian Exposition Issue of 1893 (see pp. 38‑40). In 1894, when the Bureau of Engraving and Printing began to produce all U.S. stamps, a decorative line was added under "ten cents". In 1895 the stamp was printed on paper that was watermarked double‑line USPS. Earlier printings by the American Bank Note Company and the Bureau were on unwatermarked paper.

C. Messenger on bicycle.
Any post office
| '25 | .30 | '45 | .75 | '65 | 2.00 |
| '35 | .60 | '55 | 1.00 | '75 | 6.50 |

Note: This stamp was first printed perf. 12 on paper that was watermarked double‑line USPS (shown). It was later issued in the following varieties: perf. 12, watermarked single‑line USPS; perf. 10, watermarked single‑line USPS; perf. 11, unwatermarked; and perf. 10, unwatermarked. The latter is slightly lighter in color than the others and is worth about $40.00.

D. Olive branch and Mercury's helmet.
Any post office   3,876,551
| '25 | .40 | '45 | 1.50 | '65 | 3.20 |
| '35 | .70 | '55 | 2.40 | '75 | 6.25 |

A. *10/1/1885*

Special delivery service was inaugurated by the postal service on October 1, 1885. It was limited at first to letters sent to towns with a population of 4,000 or more, but in 1886 it was extended to all mailable matter and all post offices. Modern special delivery service, while limited to reasonable hours of the day, is normally available every day, including Sundays and holidays.

B. 1/24/1893

C. 12/9/02

D. 12/12/08

E. 7/12/22

E. Messenger and motorcycle, perf. 11. Also issued perf. 11 by 10½.
Washington, D.C.
| '25 | .15 | '45 | .24 | '65 | 1.20 |
| '35 | .20 | '55 | .50 | '75 | 3.75 |

F. Messenger and motorcycle, perf. 11. Also issued perf. 11 by 10½.
Washington, D.C.
| '35 | .20 | '55 | .40 | '75 | 2.70 |
| '45 | .21 | '65 | .85 | | |

G. Post office truck, perf. 11. Also issued perf. 11 by 10½.
Washington, D.C.
| '35 | .30 | '55 | .30 | '75 | .85 |
| '45 | .25 | '65 | .40 | | |

F. 4/11/25

G. 4/25/25

H. 10/30/44

I. 10/30/44

J. 10/13/54

K. 9/3/57

L. 11/21/69

M. 5/10/71

H. Messenger and
motorcycle.
Washington, D.C.

'45	.16	'65	.20
'55	.18	'75	.30

I. Messenger and
motorcycle.
Washington, D.C.

'45	.20	'65	.40
'55	.25	'75	.90

J. Hand - to - hand delivery.
Boston, Mass.

'55	.25	'65	.32	'75	.40

K. Hand - to - hand delivery.
Indianapolis, Ind.

'65	.40	'75	.40

L. Arrow design.
New York, N.Y.   '75   .90

M. Arrow design,
increased rate.
Phoenix, Ariz.   '75   .85

The 1912 Act of Congress that established rates for fourth-class mail, the parcel category, also prescribed distinctive stamps for such matter. Twelve large stamps, all printed in the same color, were issued in 1912 and 1913. The designs portrayed postal employees at work, different methods of transporting mail, and economic activities. Issued in panes of 45 instead of the customary 100, the stamps were unpopular with the public and with postal employees because of their size and color uniformity. As of July 1, 1913, ordinary stamps were declared valid for use on fourth-class mail and parcel post stamps were declared valid for use on letters. After the original supplies of parcel post stamps were exhausted, no more were produced. Shown:

G. *12/16/12*

A. Post office clerk sorting mail.

Any post office	209,691,094				
'25	.03	'45	.07	'65	.22
'35	.04	'55	.12	'75	.75

B. City letter carrier.

Any post office	206,417,253				
'25	.05	'45	.12	'65	.22
'35	.08	'55	.13	'75	.80

C. Railway postal clerk.

Any post office	29,027,433				
'25	.10	'45	.25	'65	.75
'35	.20	'55	.36	'75	2.10

D. Rural carrier.

Any post office	76,743,813				
'25	.15	'45	.60	'65	1.50
'35	.25	'55	.95	'75	4.40

E. Mail train.

Any post office	108,153,993				
'25	.15	'45	.38	'65	1.25
'35	.25	'55	.90	'75	3.60

F. Steamship and mail tender.

Any post office	56,896,653				
'25	.30	'45	.95	'65	2.10
'35	.60	'55	1.40	'75	5.75

G. Automobile service.

Any post office	21,147,033				
'25	.60	'45	1.90	'65	4.00
'35	1.00	'55	2.75	'75	8.50

H. "Aeroplane" carrying mail. First appearance of an

A. 11/27/12

B. 11/27/12

C. 4/5/13

D. 12/12/12

airplane on a U.S. stamp.

Any post office	17,142,393				
'25	.70	'45	1.75	'65	4.25
'35	1.40	'55	2.95	'75	13.50

I. Manufacturing.

Any post office	21,940,653				
'25	1.00	'45	1.35	'65	3.00
'35	.90	'55	2.10	'75	6.25

J. Dairying.

Any post office	2,117,793				
'25	2.00	'45	6.50	'65	15.00
'35	2.75	'55	11.00	'75	37.50

E. 11/27/12

F. 12/9/12

H. 12/16/12

I. 11/27/12

J. 3/15/13

K. 12/18/12

L. 1/3/13

SPECIAL HANDLING

M. 4/11/25

K. Harvesting.
Any post office   2,772,615

| '25 1.75 | '45 1.60 | '65 3.00 |
| '35 1.40 | '55 2.25 | '75 7.00 |

L. Fruit growing.
Any post office   1,053,273

| '25 2.25 | '45 10.50 | '65 21.00 |
| '35 6.00 | '55 14.50 | '75 52.50 |

M. Special Handling, for prepayment of a fee to expedite the delivery of fourth - class mail. Also issued in 10c, 15c, and 20c denominations in 1928.
Washington, D.C.

| '35 .50 | '55 .63 | '75 2.85 |
| '45 .50 | '65 1.25 | |

POSTAGE DUE

A. 5/9/1879

B. 1889

C. 1891

D. 1894

E. 9/24/1894

F. 1914-15

G. 7/1/30

H. 7/1/30

I. 6/19/59

J. 6/19/59

PARCEL POST POSTAGE DUE

K. 12/9/12

Postage due stamps have been in use since May, 1879. They indicate the amount of postage that was not prepaid for mail. This amount is due from the addressee at the time the mail is delivered. At least one example of every postage due stamp design is shown on this page. Additional denominations as well as varieties in watermarks, perforations, and color exist. Shown:

A. Issue of 1879, printed by the American Bank Note Company.

'25	.10	'45	.10	'65	.70
'35	.20	'55	.38	'75	1.65

B. Issue of 1889, new color.

'25	.10	'45	.15	'65	.30
'35	.10	'55	.15	'75	.80

C. Issue of 1891, new color.

'25	.75	'45	2.75	'65	5.00
'35	.90	'55	3.20	'75	16.50

D. Issue of 1894, new design. First postage due stamps produced by the Bureau of Engraving and Printing.

'25	1.00	'45	4.50	'65	10.00
'35	3.00	'55	4.50	'75	30.00

E. Issue of 1894, new color.

'25	.50	'45	.50	'65	.85
'35	.35	'55	.45	'75	2.85

F. Issue of 1914-15, new color.

'25	.20	'45	.40	'65	.40
'35	.35	'55	.28	'75	.80

G. Issue of 1930, new design.

'35	.85	'55	.90	'75	3.35
'45	.85	'65	1.50		

H. Issue of 1930, design for dollar denominations.

'35	7.00	'55	2.25	'75	7.00
'45	7.00	'65	6.00		

I. Issue of 1959, new design.

'65	.03	'75	.35

J. Issue of 1959, design for dollar denominations.

'65	1.50	'75	1.50

K. Parcel Post Postage Due, indicates insufficient prepayment of postage on parcel post matter. The stamps were subject to the same usage as parcel post stamps and postage dues.

'25	.15	'45	.45	'65	1.30
'35	.35	'55	.60	'75	7.00

OFFICIAL POSTAGE

When the franking privilege was abolished in 1873 special stamps were issued for use on government mail. Nine sets of these stamps were produced, one set for each department. The department names were inscribed on the stamps instead of U.S. postage and each set was printed in a different color. Otherwise the stamps are basically the same, with the same portrait appearing on the same denomination in each set. Exceptions were the numeral designs on all the stamps used by the Post Office Department.

A. 1873

B. 1873

C. 1873

D. 1873

E. 1873

F. 1873

G. 1873

H. 1873

I. 1873

J. 1873

The first issue of official stamps was produced in 1873 by the Continental Bank Note Company. In 1879 certain denominations were reprinted by the American Bank Note Company on a different type of paper. Most of the designs were adapted from the regular stamps then in use (see pp. 34-35). Benjamin Franklin (not shown) appeared on the 1c stamps; Henry Clay (also not shown) on the 12c stamps. Other denominations used the following portraits and designs:

A. Daniel Webster (15c).

| '25 | 2.35 | '45 | 4.15 | '65 | 5.75 |
| '35 | 2.95 | '55 | 4.75 | '75 | 8.75 |

B. George Washington (3c).

| '25 | 5.65 | '45 | 9.40 | '65 | 11.00 |
| '35 | 7.10 | '55 | 8.25 | '75 | 21.00 |

C. William H. Seward ($2, $5, $10, $20). Only the State Department stamps included denominations higher than 90c.

'25	82.00	'55	125.00
'35	125.00	'65	137.50
'45	125.00	'75	325.00

D. Abraham Lincoln (6c).

| '25 | .25 | '45 | .80 | '65 | 1.10 |
| '35 | .70 | '55 | .60 | '75 | 1.85 |

E. General Winfield Scott (24c).

| '25 | 8.25 | '45 | 10.75 | '65 | 18.00 |
| '35 | 10.75 | '55 | 10.75 | '75 | 30.00 |

F. Edwin Stanton (7c).

| '25 | 8.35 | '45 | 10.75 | '65 | 15.00 |
| '35 | 9.50 | '55 | 10.75 | '75 | 23.50 |

G. Andrew Jackson (2c).

| '25 | 4.25 | '45 | 3.30 | '65 | 3.65 |
| '35 | 4.00 | '55 | 2.95 | '75 | 4.95 |

H. Post Office Department. These were the only stamps that used numerals instead of portraits.

| '25 | .75 | '45 | .95 | '65 | 1.20 |
| '35 | .75 | '55 | .95 | '75 | 1.75 |

I. Alexander Hamilton (30c).

| '25 | .20 | '45 | 1.40 | '65 | 3.00 |
| '35 | .60 | '55 | 1.25 | '75 | 4.50 |

J. Commodore Oliver Perry (90c).

| '25 | .65 | '45 | 1.35 | '65 | 1.75 |
| '35 | .75 | '55 | 1.35 | '75 | 2.50 |

In 1884 official stamps were replaced by envelopes with a printed warning of a penalty for private use.

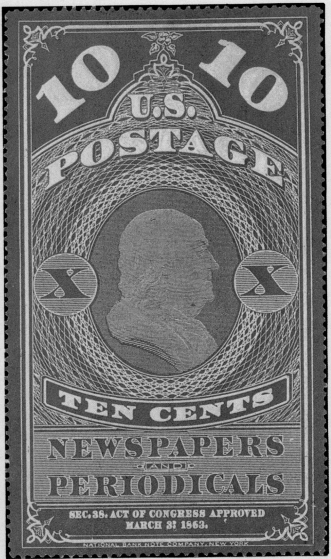

A. 10/1/1865

B. 1/1/1875

C. 1/1/1875

E. 1879

D. 1/1/1875

The belief that an informed citizenry is essential to democracy has been traditional since the earliest days of the American republic. For this reason printed materials have almost always enjoyed preferential postage rates. From 1865 to 1898, special stamps were issued to prepay postage on bulk shipments of newspapers and periodicals. The first of these, issued in 1865, were used on large packages that were sent by news agents and publishers directly to the postal handlers on mail cars and ships. Because the packages did not pass through the post office, used copies are very scarce. The three stamps, the largest postage stamps ever issued, portray George Washington (on the 5c), Abraham Lincoln (on the 25c), and Benjamin Franklin (shown).

A. Benjamin Franklin.

'25 6.00	'45 6.00	'65 9.00
'35 6.00	'55 7.50	'75 16.50

Starting in 1875, newspaper and periodical stamps were used to prepay all bulk shipments by publishers and news agents, including those mailed at post offices. The stamps were not attached to the packages, but were affixed to memorandums of mailing which were retained by the post office. Shown:

B. Ceres, goddess of agriculture.

'25 5.00	'45 9.00	'65 9.00
'35 6.00	'55 7.50	'75 17.50

C. Minerva, goddess of wisdom.

'25 12.00	'45 22.50	'65 35.00
'35 20.00	'55 27.50	'75 75.00

D. Vesta, goddess of the fireside.

'25 25.00	'45 30.00	'65 27.50
'35 25.00	'55 22.50	'75 75.00

E. Hebe, goddess of youth.

'25 35.00	'45 35.00	'65 30.00
'35 35.00	'55 23.50	'75 62.50

F. 2/1/1895

G. 2/1/1895

H. 7/31/1897

I. 1/23/1896

J. 2/1/1895

K. *9/19/1895*

L. 1/27/1896

F. Freedom, allegorical model of Thomas Crawford's statue atop the Capitol dome in Washington, D.C.

| '25 1.50 | '45 1.50 | '65 1.35 |
| '35 1.50 | '55 1.10 | '75 3.00 |

G. Clio, muse of history.

| '25 12.00 | '45 12.00 | '65 18.00 |
| '35 12.00 | '55 14.00 | '75 40.00 |

H. Commerce, allegorical figure.

| '25 3.00 | '45 3.00 | '65 3.00 |
| '35 3.00 | '55 2.25 | '75 4.00 |

I. Indian maiden.

| '35 .75 | '55 1.75 | '75 5.00 |
| '45 1.00 | '65 2.75 | |

J. Goddess of Victory.

| '25 10.00 | '45 12.00 | '65 9.00 |
| '35 12.00 | '55 8.00 | '75 18.50 |

K. Astraea, or Justice.

| '25 1.00 | '45 1.25 | '65 .90 |
| '35 1.25 | '55 .75 | '75 1.75 |

L. Goddess of Peace.

| '25 1.50 | '45 1.50 | '65 2.00 |
| '35 1.50 | '55 1.50 | '75 3.00 |

The illustrations shown on B-L were used on newspaper and periodical stamps from 1875 to 1898. During that time the stamps were printed separately by the Continental Bank Note Company, the American Bank Note Company, and the Bureau of Engraving and Printing. There were also reprintings and special printings of the stamps.

In 1898 newspaper and periodical stamps were declared invalid for postal use. At that time 50,000 sets of the stamps were placed on sale at first - class post offices for $5.00 per set. This is the only time that the postal service has sold stamps at less than face value. Before their final withdrawal in January 1899, some 26,989 sets of stamps were sold.

The astronomical costs of the Civil War forced the federal government to impose a broad schedule of internal taxes to raise revenue. Legislation of July 1, 1862, set out items to be taxed and led to the creation of the Internal Revenue Service and the Bureau of Engraving and Printing. The legislation also authorized the use of stamps to indicate the payment of prescribed taxes. Known as revenues, these stamps exist in three general categories — documentary and proprietary, tax paid, and special tax. Documentary stamps were used on certain legal documents. Proprietary stamps were used on specific consumer products such as patent medicines that were made by firms which held exclusive (or proprietary) rights to their manufacture. Tax paid stamps indicated the payment of excises on bulk quantities of certain manufactured goods. Special tax stamps were permits for business operations. Hundreds of these stamps exist; highly selective examples are shown here.

A-B. First general revenue issue, 1862. These designs, current for eight years, were used on stamps for the payment of taxes on playing cards, telegrams (shown), entry of goods (shown), proprietary items, etc. Their usage was at first limited to the specific purpose inscribed on them, but after December, 1862, all but proprietary stamps were permitted indiscriminate use.

A.

'25 1.40	'45 1.50	'65 1.65
'35 1.40	'55 1.40	'75 2.35

B.

'25 .20	'45 1.10	'65 1.40
'35 .20	'55 1.10	'75 2.35

C. Second general revenue issue, 1871. The stamps were inscribed "proprietary" (shown) or "internal revenue" (for payment of all other prescribed taxes).

'25 175.00	'55 245.00
'35 210.00	'65 375.00
'45 210.00	'75 525.00

A. 1862, green

B. 1862, red brown

C. 1871, green and black
(Shown at actual size.)

D. 1898, deep blue

E. 1894, lake

F. 1933, rose

G. 1934, blue

H. 1954, carmine

I. 1914, black

J. 1925, blue

K. 1942, bright green

L. 1947, bright green

M. 1935, orange

D. Revenue stamps issued during the Spanish-American War were inscribed "proprietary" (shown) or "documentary" (for payment of all other prescribed taxes).

| '25 | .03 | '45 | .04 | '65 | .05 |
| '35 | .03 | '55 | .05 | '75 | .07 |

E. Playing cards, 1894.

| '55 | .15 | '65 | .20 | '75 | .20 |

F. Paid the tax on paper used to make cigarettes.

| '55 | .10 | '65 | .15 | '75 | .15 |

G. Hunting permit stamps were introduced in 1934 to license waterfowl hunters. A new design is issued yearly.

| '35 | 1.25 | '55 | 8.15 | '75 | 26.50 |
| '45 | 5.00 | '65 | 8.85 | | |

H. This documentary stamp shows Lyman J. Gage, who was secretary of the treasury under Presidents McKinley and Theodore Roosevelt.

| '55 | 2.40 | '65 | 3.55 | '75 | 4.35 |

I. The proprietary stamps of 1914 feature numeral designs.

| '25 | .04 | '45 | .05 | '65 | .05 |
| '35 | .04 | '55 | .05 | '75 | .05 |

J. From 1906 to 1955 stamps were used to pay the fee charged for documents by the Consular Service of the Department of State.

| '55 | .02 | '65 | .04 | '75 | .08 |

K. Many revenue stamps were used for long periods of time, the year of current use being designated by an overprint. The example shown was used through 1952. It depicts Roger B. Taney, President Jackson's secretary of the treasury in 1833.

| '45 | .95 | '65 | 2.30 |
| '55 | 2.30 | '75 | 2.30 |

L. The highest denomination of any U.S. stamp, this revenue shows President Arthur's secretary of the treasury, Walter Q. Gresham.

| '55 | 165.00 | '65 | 85.00 | '75 | 45.00 |

M. Under the Agricultural Adjustment Act of 1935 potato growers who exceeded their allotments were required to pay a tax for the excess. In 1936 the act was declared unconstitutional.

| '55 | .40 | '65 | .55 | '75 | .55 |

Civil War hostilities erupted at Fort Sumter, South Carolina on April 12, 1861. On June 1 of that year the United States suspended postal service to the South. Also on that date U.S. stamps were demonetized and redesigned to prevent the South from using them. The action put still another strain on the South, which lacked the economic resources and the manpower of the North. Mail delivery was crucial so the local postmasters in various southern towns issued provisional stamps or used appropriate hand markings until hastily designed and produced Confederate stamps were issued in October, 1861. These general issues were valid for use anywhere in the South. Typographed stamps and plates were supposed to be supplied by a London firm but shipment was delayed, so the first stamps placed on sale were lithographed at Richmond. The stamps portray the leader of the Confederate government, Jefferson Davis, as well as many prominent Americans who lived in the South. Dates given are those of earliest known use. Shown:

A. Jefferson Davis (1808 - 89), president of the Confederate States of America (1861 - 65). Davis was a graduate of the U.S. Military Academy. Prior to the Civil War he represented Mississippi in the Senate and the House of Representatives and served as secretary of war under Franklin Pierce. He resigned his Senate seat 12 days after Mississippi left the Union. As president of the Confederacy he was an iron-willed executive. "Without him," wrote a northerner in 1864, "the rebellion would crumble in a day." In 1865, shortly after Lee's surrender, he was captured by the North and imprisoned for two years. An indictment against him for treason was dropped in 1868.

| '25 | 7.00 | '45 | 5.00 | '65 | 11.00 |
| '35 | 7.00 | '55 | 5.50 | '75 | 17.50 |

CONFEDERATE STATES OF AMERICA

In 1860 and 1861 eleven southern states left the Union and formed the Confederate States of America. This action precipitated the Civil War between the North and the South. The North held that the states could not secede from the Union, the South that they could. During the war the Confederate government at Richmond, Virginia assumed political, military, and economic control over the South.

A. 10/23/1861

B. 11/8/1861

E. *4/16/1862*

D. 4/10/1862

C. 3/21/1862

F. 3/10/1862

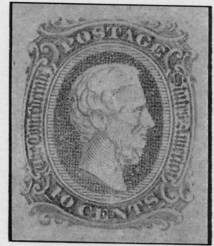

G. *4/23/1863*

H. 1862

I. 4/23/1863

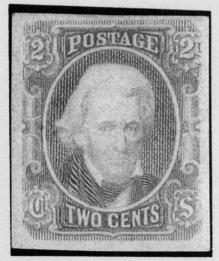

J. *4/8/1863*

K. 6/1/1863

B. Thomas Jefferson. The stamp exists in various shades of color, as do most Confederate issues.

| '25 | 8.00 | '45 | 7.50 | '65 | 12.00 |
| '35 | 8.10 | '55 | 6.80 | '75 | 17.50 |

C. Andrew Jackson, rate for local drop letters and printed matter.

| '25 | 6.00 | '45 | 8.40 | '65 | 25.00 |
| '35 | 7.20 | '55 | 13.75 | '75 | 65.00 |

D. Jefferson Davis.

| '25 | 3.00 | '45 | 3.00 | '65 | 5.00 |
| '35 | 3.00 | '55 | 3.00 | '75 | 10.50 |

E. Jefferson Davis. This stamp was produced by De La Rue & Company, London, and delivered by blockade runners. Previous Confederate stamps had been produced by Hoyer & Ludwig and by J. T. Paterson & Company, both of Richmond.

| '25 | .20 | '45 | .24 | '65 | 1.00 |
| '35 | .24 | '55 | .70 | '75 | 1.50 |

F. Thomas Jefferson, new color.

| '25 | 30.00 | '45 | 28.00 | '65 | 37.50 |
| '35 | 30.00 | '55 | 26.25 | '75 | 90.00 |

G. Jefferson Davis. Two varieties of this stamp were produced by Archer & Daley of Richmond in April 1863. One had a frame line around the design, the other (shown) did not.

| '25 | .12 | '45 | .12 | '65 | 1.00 |
| '35 | .12 | '55 | .50 | '75 | 1.75 |

H. John C. Calhoun (1782-1850), vice president under Andrew Jackson and John Quincy Adams and an ardent supporter of states' rights. Prepared by De La Rue & Company of London this stamp was never put in use.

| '25 | 1.20 | '45 | 1.50 | '65 | 12.00 |
| '35 | 1.35 | '55 | 5.00 | '75 | 70.00 |

I. Jefferson Davis.

| '25 | 16.00 | '45 | 17.50 | '65 | 35.00 |
| '35 | 17.50 | '55 | 18.50 | '75 | 70.00 |

J. Andrew Jackson.

| '25 | .60 | '45 | .60 | '65 | 4.00 |
| '35 | .60 | '55 | 1.75 | '75 | 6.00 |

K. George Washington, rate for mail carried across the Mississippi by blockade runners. Also used as currency.

| '25 | .90 | '45 | .75 | '65 | 3.25 |
| '35 | .90 | '55 | 1.20 | '75 | 4.75 |

U.S. OVERSEAS ADMINISTRATION AND HAWAII

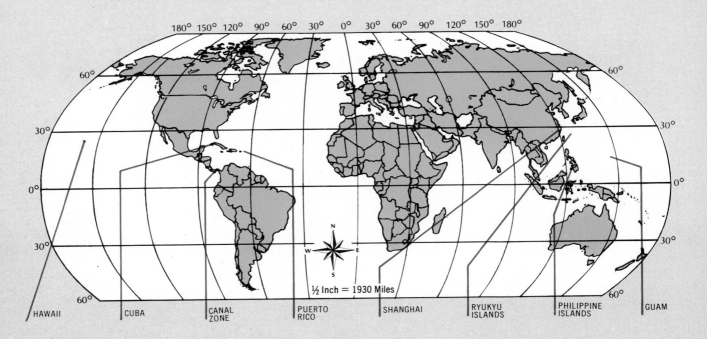

The next eight pages show a limited selection of examples of postage stamps used in U.S. territories overseas, including Cuba, Puerto Rico, Guam, the Canal Zone, the Philippine Islands, and the Ryukyu Islands. Also included are some of the stamps issued for use at the postal agency in Shanghai, China, and a few of those of the Kingdom of Hawaii.

Offices in China

A. 7/1/19

B. 7/1/19

C. 7/3/22

The Spanish-American War of 1898 and its settlement marked the emergence of the United States as a world power. Acquisition of the Philippines on the threshold of Asia, Guam in the western Pacific, Cuba and Puerto Rico in the Caribbean, assured access to world markets which had been but tentatively probed during the preceding half century. The war also accelerated the peaceful annexation of Hawaii, in which Americans had developed strong economic interests. At the turn of the century far-sighted U.S. leaders became profoundly aware of the need for greater interocean maneuverability, which led directly to the construction and administration of the Panama Canal. U.S. presence in these overseas territories occasioned the production of special postage stamps as described on the following pages.

Offices in China. The development of commercial relations with China resulted in the growth of a large American community at Shanghai. Treaty arrangements that permitted foreign nations to trade with China also allowed them to administer their foreign settlements. In 1919, regular U.S. stamps overprinted for use at Shanghai were issued for the first time. Their denominations were in local currency, whose nominal value was double U.S. currency. The use of special stamps ended when the postal facilities in Shanghai were closed in 1922.

A. 12c on 6c Washington.

| '25 | .14 | '45 | .85 | '65 | 2.00 |
| '35 | .25 | '55 | 1.50 | '75 | 3.85 |

B. $2 on $1 Franklin.

| '25 | 2.25 | '45 | 4.75 | '65 | 7.75 |
| '35 | 3.30 | '55 | 5.75 | '75 | 15.50 |

C. 4c on 2c Washington.

| '25 | .80 | '45 | 3.00 | '65 | 3.75 |
| '35 | 1.25 | '55 | 3.50 | '75 | 8.00 |

Cuba

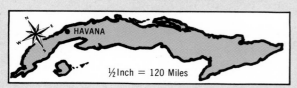

½ Inch = 120 Miles

Puerto Rico

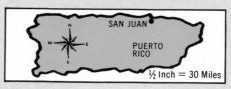

½ Inch = 30 Miles

D. 1899

E. 1899

I. 1898

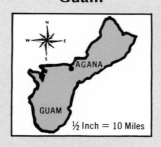

J. 8/ - /98

Guam

F. 1899

G. 1899

½ Inch = 10 Miles

K. 1899

H. 1902

L. 8/10/30

M. 4/8/30

Cuba. Occupied in the summer of 1898, Cuba remained under U.S. Army administration until 1902. Indigenous stamps were used provisionally until overprinted U.S. stamps were supplied in 1899.

D. 10c on 10c Webster.
'55 400.00 '75 1150.00
'65 400.00

E. 5c on 5c postage due.
'25 .10 '45 .32 '65 .55
'35 .16 '55 .48 '75 1.50

The first stamps of the republic, still under U.S. administration, appeared also in 1899.

F. Coconut palm trees.
'25 .04 '45 .07 '65 .16
'35 .05 '55 .10 '75 .48

G. Ocean steamship.
'25 .10 '45 .14 '65 .40
'35 .10 '55 .20 '75 .80

H. Special delivery stamp.
'25 .03 '45 .03 '65 .07
'35 .03 '55 .06 '75 .15

Puerto Rico. Provisional issues of 1898 gave way to

overprinted U.S. stamps in 1899 and 1900. Ordinary U.S. stamps are now used.

I. La Playa de Ponce, handstamped provisional.
'65 200.00 '75 950.00

J. Coamo, type set provisional.
'25 17.50 '45 42.00 '65 55.00
'35 42.00 '55 45.00 '75 90.00

Guam. Overprinted U.S. stamps were used from 1899 to 1901; regular U.S. stamps since then.

K. "Guam" on $1 Oliver Perry.
'25 5.50 '45 11.00 '65 13.50
'35 10.00 '55 12.00 '75 47.50

L. Philippines stamp overprinted "Guam Guard Mail". Shown: José Rizal (see p. 215).
'35 .18 '55 .42 '75 1.94
'45 .28 '65 .88

M. U.S. stamp overprinted "Guam Guard Mail". Shown: President McKinley.
'35 1.75 '55 21.00 '75 87.50
'45 8.75 '65 22.75

The U.S. Canal Zone postal service began operating in June 1904 when the United States assumed responsibility for constructing the Panama Canal. The advantages of cutting a canal through the isthmus to reduce the sailing time between the Atlantic and the Pacific had been apparent for a long time.

Practical efforts to accomplish the task were initiated by the French in 1882. But it was the drive of vigorous Americans such as President Theodore Roosevelt and army engineer Colonel George Goethals that brought the immense project to fruition in 1914.

The stamps issued for use in the Canal Zone reflect the complex yet unique circumstances surrounding U.S. administration of the Zone, which extends five miles on either side of the the canal for its roughly 50-mile length. Pending the preparation of overprinted U.S. stamps, which were used intermittently until 1928, stamps of the Republic of Panama were procured and overprinted for use in the Zone. For the first two years, many of these Panamanian stamps were provisional overprints on the stamps of Colombia, from which Panama had won its independence in 1903. Since 1928, distinctive stamps have been issued for use in the Canal Zone.

A. Map of Isthmus of Panama, Colombian stamp overprinted first for use in Panama and then for the Canal Zone.

| '25 | .14 | '45 | .25 | '65 | .32 |
| '35 | .20 | '55 | .28 | '75 | 1.25 |

B. Balboa Taking Possession of the Pacific Ocean in 1513, Panama commemorative overprinted "Canal Zone".

| '25 | .08 | '45 | .45 | '65 | .60 |
| '35 | .20 | '55 | .50 | '75 | 1.80 |

C-F. California Gold Rush Centennial. Four stamps were issued to recall the many gold seekers who elected to sail to Panama, cross the isthmus, and sail on

Canal Zone

A. 12/12/04

B. 3/1/15

C. 6/1/49

D. 6/1/49

E. 6/1/49

G. 1/28/55

F. 6/1/49

H. *8/15/39*

I. 8/15/39

J. 8/15/64

K. *10/27/49*

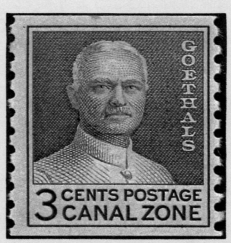

L. *11/1/60*

to California in their quest for gold in 1849. Shown:

C. Arriving at Chagres on the Atlantic side.
'55 .06   '65 .16   '75 .20

D. Up the Chagres River to Las Cruces.
'55 .10   '65 .19   '75 .23

E. Las Cruces Trail to Panama.
'55 .23   '65 .30   '75 .45

F. Leaving Panama for San Francisco.
'55 .32   '65 .43   '75 .65

G. Panama Railroad, 100th anniversary. The railway, whose route was followed much of the way by the canal, was completed in 1855.
'65 .15   '75 .25

H-I. Sixteen stamps were issued in 1939 to mark the 25th anniversary of the opening of the canal. They depict eight parts of the canal before and after U.S. construction operations. Shown:

H. Canal channel during construction.
'45 .35   '65 2.20
'55 1.75   '75 2.20

I. Canal channel after construction.
'45 .35   '65 2.00
'55 1.20   '75 2.20

J. Air mail stamp issued for the 50th anniversary of the completion of the canal. Shown: jet over Cristobal.
'65 .12   '75 .30

K. Theodore Roosevelt (1858 - 1919), blunt diplomat, advocate of a strong navy, and energetic leader under whose presidency the the construction of the Panama Canal was begun.
'55 .03   '65 .03   '75 .05

L. George Goethals (1858 - 1928), army engineer selected by Roosevelt to oversee the construction of the canal after two other engineers had given up. His authority over the workers and their operations was virtually absolute.
'65 .05   '75 .10

Hawaii

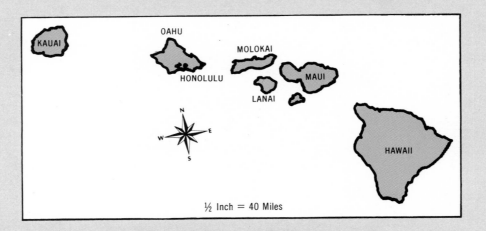

½ Inch = 40 Miles

A. 1851

B. 1864

C. 1853

D. 1883

E. 1894

F. 1884

G. 1883

H. 1883

Discovered in 1778 by Captain Cook, the Hawaiian Islands preserved their independence until their voluntary union with the United States in 1898. From 1851 to 1899 Hawaii used its own distinctive stamps, many of which portrayed members of the ruling family. Regular U.S. stamps have been used since 1900, when Hawaii was given U.S. territorial status. It became the 50th state in 1959.

A. Numeral of denomination (used prices).

'25	8,000.00	'55	15,000.00
'35	10,000.00	'65	18,000.00
'45	15,000.00	'75	50,000.00

B. Numeral of denomination, without filigree design. Various printings of this stamp were on different types of paper.

'25	140.00	'55	200.00
'35	175.00	'65	300.00
'45	200.00	'75	1,400.00

C. Kauikeaouli (1813-54), who reigned as Kamehameha III. Different printings of this stamp were on different paper types, and official imitations made in 1889 show slight engraving modifications.

'25	12.00	'45	14.00	'65	40.00
'35	14.00	'55	19.00	'75	150.00

D. Princess Likelike, who became Mrs. Archibald Cleghorn.

'25	.07	'45	.15	'65	.45
'35	.15	'55	.15	'75	1.30

E. Star and palm trees.

'25	.20	'45	.35	'65	.66
'35	.35	'55	.35	'75	1.40

F. King David Kalakaua (1836-91), who was elected to the throne by the legislature in 1874.

'25	.65	'45	.80	'65	1.30
'35	.80	'55	.85	'75	4.25

G. Queen Emma Kaleleonalani, widow of King Kamehameha IV.

'25	4.00	'45	6.00	'65	10.75
'35	6.00	'55	6.00	'75	32.50

H. Prince William Pitt Leleiohoku.

'25	1.15	'45	1.50	'65	2.80
'35	1.50	'55	1.50	'75	10.00

Philippine Islands

I. 2/15/35

J. 2/15/35

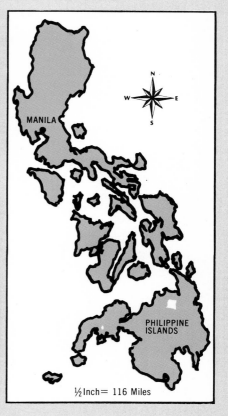

MANILA

PHILIPPINE ISLANDS

½ Inch= 116 Miles

K. 1925

L. 2/15/35

M. 11/15/39

N. 11/15/35

O. 1/23/43

The Philippines were under U.S. administration from the close of the Spanish - American War until independence was achieved in 1946. Before overprinted U.S. stamps were introduced in 1899, Philippine stamps issued under Spanish auspices and regular U.S. stamps without overprints were used. Distinctive stamps were issued beginning in 1906.

I. Battle of Manila Bay, May 1, 1898, in which Commodore George Dewey crushed the Spanish fleet.

| '45 | 1.70 | '65 | 2.40 |
| '55 | 1.70 | '75 | 2.60 |

J. Magellan's Landing in the Philippines, 1521.

| '45 | .10 | '65 | .10 |
| '55 | .10 | '75 | .12 |

K. Ferdinand Magellan (1480 - 1521), Portuguese navigator in the service of Spain who headed the first expedition to sail around the world. He never completed the voyage because he was killed on the Philippine island of Mactán.

| '35 | .40 | '55 | 1.00 | '75 | 1.20 |
| '45 | 1.30 | '65 | 1.20 | | |

L. José Rizal (1861 - 96), Filipino nationalist hero who sought to expose the evils of Spanish rule.

| '45 | .03 | '65 | .04 |
| '55 | .02 | '75 | .04 |

M. Commonwealth Triumphal Arch, hailing the fourth anniversary of the Commonwealth.

| '45 | .03 | '65 | .07 |
| '55 | .04 | '75 | .07 |

N. *The Temples of Human Progress,* honoring the November 15, 1935 inauguration of the Philippine Commonwealth.

| '45 | .12 | '65 | .15 |
| '55 | .12 | '75 | .15 |

O. Philippine Executive Commission, first anniversary of the executive organ of Japanese occupation during World War II.

| '55 | .08 | '65 | .10 | '75 | .14 |

Ryukyu Islands

Commodore Matthew Perry visited the Ryukyu Islands in 1853 and concluded a friendship treaty with them in 1854. Yet many Americans were unaware of their existence until the Pacific campaigns of World War II, when U.S. forces captured the main island of Okinawa from Japan in 1945. Postal services under U.S. military administration, for both U.S. forces and local civilians, dated from that time. A free local mail system gave way to a civilian service that utilized handstamps and provisionally overprinted Japanese stamps until 1948. In that year the semi-autonomous Ryukyu postal administration introduced its own issues, which were also valid on international mail. Ryukyu stamps continued in use until U.S. military administration of the islands ended with their reversion to Japan in 1972.

A. Shuri Castle, 100 yen overprinted on 2 yen.
'55 60.00 '65 160.00 '75 675.00

B. New Year 1959. Shown: the Lion Dance.
'65 .12 '75 .20

C. Air mail. Shown: goddess or heavenly maiden.
'65 .15 '75 .25

D. Air mail. Shown: goddess or heavenly maiden.
'65 .22 '75 .35

E. Philatelic Week 1963. Shown: lacquer ware bowl.
'65 .15 '75 2.25

F. Opening of Shioya Bridge, linking Okinawa and Miyagi Island in Shioya Bay.
'65 .15 '75 .95

G. Gooseneck cactus, issued for the "Make Ryukyus Green" campaign.
'65 .04 '75 .06

H. New Year 1966. In the Oriental cycle of years 1966 was the Year of the Horse (shown).
'75 .60

I. Turtle (geomyda spengleri japonica).
'75 .18

A. 1952

B. 12/10/58

½ Inch = 8 Miles

C. 9/21/61

D. 9/21/61

E. 7/1/63

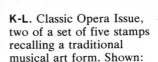

F. 6/5/63

J. New Year 1971. The year 1971 was the Oriental Year of the Boar (shown).
'75 .12

K-L. Classic Opera Issue, two of a set of five stamps recalling a traditional musical art form. Shown:

K. "The Bell" (shushin-kaneiri).
'75 .35

G. 4/5/63

I. 4/20/66

J. 12/10/70

H. 12/10/65

L. 6/30/70

M. 4/20/72

K. 4/28/70

N. 3/30/72

O. 4/14/72

L. "Robe of Feathers" (mekarushi).
    '75 .42

M. Philatelic Week 1972. Shown: antique sake pot (yushibin), the receptacle for Ryukyu rice wine.
    '75 .55

Note: This was the final issue by the Ryukyu government under U.S. administration. Stamps of Japan have been in use since May 15, 1972.

N. Coral reef, representative of formations that virtually surround the islands.
    '75 .28

O. Sunlight bathing islands.
    '75 .28

SUGGESTIONS FOR FURTHER READING

By Wm. W. Wylie

Editor, Scott Monthly Journal

"Knowledge is of two kinds. We know a subject ourselves, or we know where we can find information on it. When we inquire into any subject, the first thing we have to do is to know what books have treated of it."
— Dr. Samuel Johnson (1775)

While there is no dearth of literature relating to United States stamps and their use, the student may find it difficult to locate many of the sources of information he would like to use to augment his understanding of this country's postal paper. Most philatelic books, monographs and pamphlets were published in limited editions and are out of print. They must be sought in libraries or purchased from stamp dealers who handle philatelic literature or in the shops of antiquarian booksellers.

The picture really isn't as frustrating as it may appear to be. Many stamp dealers realize the value of philatelic literature and are anxious to help their clients locate useful reference material. Many stamp clubs have libraries which contain at least a few of the books the student of U.S. stamps will find enlightening. Public libraries shouldn't be overlooked. Many of them have impressive holdings of reference material on stamp collecting. Even those in small communities are likely to have a few philatelic titles on their shelves.

The country's most comprehensive philatelic reference library, of course, is the one maintained by the Collectors Club at 22 East 35th Street in New York City. In Los Angeles, the Philatelic Club has a superlative library. There's an impressive holding of philatelic literature at the Smithsonian Institution in the national capital. Currently, the American Philatelic Research Library, functioning under sponsorship of the American Philatelic Society, is building a comprehensive collection of reference material in State College, Pennsylvania.

Of particular value to the newcomer in U.S. collecting is Barbara R. Mueller's *United States Postage Stamps, How to Collect, Understand and Enjoy Them,* published by the D. Van Nostrand Co. in 1958. Based on articles published in *Western Stamp Collector,* this title explains the more recondite aspects of U.S. collecting adequately and without undue emphasis on philately's more technical aspects.

John N. Luff's *Postage Stamps of the United States,* a scholarly work published in 1902 by the Scott Stamp & Coin Co., is the standard reference work on 19th century U.S. material. A revised edition was planned by the late Hugh M. Clark, but he was able to bring out only a single volume in 1941 covering the Postmaster's Provisionals. During the 1950s the original Luff book was reprinted as a serial by *Philatelic Gossip* and bound copies of this reprint enjoyed good circulation.

Lester G. Brookman's *19th Century Stamps of the United States,* an updating of the Luff book by a distinguished philatelic scholar of our era, was published in two volumes in 1947 by H. L. Lindquist, New York City. A revised edition, in three volumes, appeared in 1971.

A landmark reference book for a specific 19th century U.S. adhesive is *The 3c Stamp of the U.S. 1851-1857,* by Dr. Carroll Chase. Dealing in depth with the production and use of a single letter rate adhesive current in the years before the Civil War, Doctor Chase's book is the classic exposition of what specialized study of a stamp can involve. It was reprinted in the 1940s by the Tatham Stamp Co. and copies of the reprint appear on the market as frequently as examples of the edition published in 1929.

The by-line of the late Stanley B. Ashbrook appears on a number of books and monographs on 19th century U.S. stamps which are invaluable to students.

The landmark Ashbrook title is the two-volume *The United States One Cent Stamp of 1851-1857,* published in 1938 by H. L. Lindquist. While much of its text is highly technical, since it deals at length with the plating of stamps, the serious student of U.S. stamps ignores it at his peril since it provides data on stamp production and use, basic in all philatelic studies.

In recent years Mortimer Neinken has been working in areas where Ashbrook pioneered and a result has been publication of scholarly studies of the 10c and 12c U.S. stamps of 1851-1857 by the Theodore E. Steinway Memorial Publications Fund of the Collectors Club.

The U.S. Postage Stamps of the 20th Century is the title of a series of books by the late Max Johl which are to modern U.S. what Luff is to classic material. The four books in the series were published by H. L. Lindquist after the text had appeared serially in the *Collectors Club Philatelist.*

Vol. I of Johl (written in collaboration with the late Beverly S. King) covers U.S. issues from the Pan American Exposition commemoratives of 1901 through the 1908-22 Washington-Franklin portrait definitives. A revised edition of Vol. I appeared after federal regulations restricting illustration of U.S. stamps were liberalized and this revised edition is the one most useful to the student.

Vol. II of the Johl series covers the commemorative issues of the 1920s. Vol. III deals with the 1922-38 regular postage stamps, the 1912 Parcel Post issue, and the air mails, including the Zeppelins; Vol. IV covers commemoratives from 1932 through 1937.

Johl also produced a two-volume work, *United States Commemorative Issues of the 20th Century,* which Lindquist published in 1947.

Later U.S. commemoratives are treated rather adequately by Sol Glass in *U.S. Postage Stamps, 1945-1952,* published in 1954 by the Bureau Issues Association.

Ralph Kimble's *Commemorative Stamps of the United States,* published in 1933 by Grosset & Dunlap, is a readable discussion of U.S. special issues antedating the Washington Bicentennial series of 1932.

In the field of air post issues, the value of the four volumes of the American Air Mail Society's *American Air Mail Catalog* isn't to be discounted. Useful monographs by Henry M. Goodkind, *The First Air Mail Stamps of the U.S., The U.S. 24c Inverted Center of 1918,* and *The 5c Beacon Air Mail of 1928* have been published by the Collectors Club.

There's a wealth of information invaluable to the student of U.S. stamps in philately's periodical literature, but good "runs" of stamp papers aren't too readily available and indexes are likely to be inadequate if they exist at all. However, the student willing to spend time scanning the pages of philatelic periodicals will run across an impressive amount of valuable information.

A hard-bound book titled *Sloane's Column,* published in 1961 by the Bureau Issues Association, demonstrates the value of periodical literature as a source of information. It's a reprinting of columns on U.S. stamps which the late George B. Sloane, a ranking Nassau Street professional, published in *Stamps* from 1933 until his death in 1959. They're grouped by subject in the book and the result is an invaluable reference work, providing information available in no other single source.

The monthly journal of the Bureau Issues Association, now known as the *United States Specialist,* but formerly titled *The Bureau Specialist,* is one periodical where the student will find much information on U.S. stamps. However, every stamp paper published in this country is likely to contain articles and notes of interest and value so any "run" of a stamp paper or accumulation of odd copies merits attention.

Not to be overlooked as reference material are the so-called *Congress Books* which the American Philatelic Congress has published annually since 1935. A lot of the original papers published in these volumes deal with U.S. stamps and postal history. Cumulative indexes appear in a number of the volumes. Carl H. Scheele's *A Short History of the Mail Service,* published in 1970 by the Smithsonian Institution Press, is a succinct and readable introduction to postal history. *Ten Decades Ago,* by Winthrop S. Boggs, published by the Collectors Club, covers a significant era in U.S. postal history. Information on U.S. postal history as well as postal markings will also be found in the *American Stampless Cover Catalog,* edited by E. N. Sampson. The Herst-Zarelski *19th Century Fancy Cancellations of the U.S.* is a well-illustrated study of postal markings.

Equally useful are the 20 volumes of the *Stamp Specialist* series of hard-cover monographs published quarterly by H. L. Lindquist from 1939 through 1948. Most of them contain useful U.S. articles, and the so-called *Forest Green* book of the series contains a cumulative index.

For a real understanding of philately the collector will need to understand how stamps are made. He will find classic line engraving discussed in many of the titles mentioned, notably in the first volume of Ashbrook's study of the *1c U.S. 1851-57.* Further information on the subject may be found in James H. Baxter's *Printing Postage Stamps by Line Engraving,* and in *Fundamentals of Philately* by L. N. and M. Williams, published in 1971 by the A.P.S. George W. Brett's monograph, *The Giori Press,* published by the Bureau Issues Association, deals in depth with the production of recent multicolor issues of the U.S. *The History of the Bureau of Engraving and Printing,* published when it celebrated its centennial in 1962, gives useful information on stamp-making there.

While books such as Richard Cabeen's *Standard Handbook of Stamp Collecting,* Ernest A. Kehr's *Romance of Stamp Collecting,* and *Nassau Street,* by Herman Herst, Jr., don't deal specifically with U.S. stamps, they contain useful information which the student will be well-advised to seek out.

Since the listings in the *Scott Specialized Catalogue of United States Stamps* delineate the existing patterns in U.S. collecting, the student will undoubtedly make constant use of its annual editions. He'll find it to his advantage to be familiar with the treatment of U.S. material in the *Minkus New American Stamp Catalog.* Retail price lists published by stamp dealers such as H. E. Harris & Co. of Boston aren't to be ignored for information on current market values, and quite often the student will find them useful in other ways.

In the 1930s the U.S. Post Office Department released the first of several editions of monographs titled *United States Postage Stamps* and the U.S. Postal Service now publishes this title in a loose-leaf form which is supplemented annually.

U.S. adhesives are shown in color in *United States Stamps & Stories,* a pocket-size study of U.S. postal paper sold in post offices.

While information on stamps and stamp collecting may not always be easy to find, there is no lack of sources of philatelic information which will reward the student with the determination to locate them. Patience and a good memory are keys to the treasure house of philatelic understanding.

INDEX